Macroscale and Microscale Organic Experiments

Special Sixth Edition

Kenneth L Williamson| Katherine M. Masters

VICTOR ONYEKWERE

CENGAGE Learning

Australia • Brazil • Japan • Korea • Mexico • Singapore • Spain • United Kingdom • United States

**Macroscale and Microscale Organic
Experiments: Special Sixth Edition**

Macroscale and Microscale Organic Experiments, 6th Edition
Kenneth L Williamson| Katherine M. Masters

© 2011 Cengage Learning. All rights reserved.

Executive Editors:
 Maureen Staudt
 Michael Stranz

Senior Project Development Manager:
 Linda deStefano

Marketing Specialist:
 Courtney Sheldon

Senior Production/Manufacturing Manager:
 Donna M. Brown

Production Editorial Manager:
 Kim Fry

Sr. Rights Acquisition Account Manager:
 Todd Osborne

For product information and technology assistance, contact us at
Cengage Learning Customer & Sales Support, 1-800-354-9706

For permission to use material from this text or product,
submit all requests online at **cengage.com/permissions**
Further permissions questions can be emailed to
permissionrequest@cengage.com

This book contains select works from existing Cengage Learning resources and
was produced by Cengage Learning Custom Solutions for collegiate use. As such,
those adopting and/or contributing to this work are responsible for editorial
content accuracy, continuity and completeness.

Compilation © 2012 Cengage Learning
ISBN-13: 978-1-285-13577-9

ISBN-10: 1-285-13577-6

Cengage Learning
5191 Natorp Boulevard
Mason, Ohio 45040
USA
Cengage Learning is a leading provider of customized learning solutions with
office locations around the globe, including Singapore, the United Kingdom,
Australia, Mexico, Brazil, and Japan. Locate your local office at:
international.cengage.com/region.

Cengage Learning products are represented in Canada by Nelson Education, Ltd.
For your lifelong learning solutions, visit **www.cengage.com/custom.**
Visit our corporate website at **www.cengage.com.**

Printed in the United States of America

Table of Contents

Introduction

PRELAB EXERCISE: Study the glassware diagrams presented in this chapter and be prepared to identify the reaction tube, the fractionating column, the distilling head, the filter adapter, and the Hirsch funnel.

Welcome to the organic chemistry laboratory! Here, the reactions that you learned in your organic lectures and studied in your textbook will come to life. The main goal of the laboratory course is for you to learn and carry out techniques for the synthesis, isolation, purification, and analysis of organic compounds, thus experiencing the experimental nature of organic chemistry. We want you to enjoy your laboratory experience and ask you to remember that safety always comes first.

EXPERIMENTAL ORGANIC CHEMISTRY

You are probably not a chemistry major. The vast majority of students in this laboratory course are majoring in the life sciences. Although you may never use the exact same techniques taught in this course, you will undoubtedly apply the skills taught here to whatever problem or question your ultimate career may present. Application of the scientific method involves the following steps:

1. Designing an experiment, therapy, or approach to solve a problem.
2. Executing the plan or experiment.
3. Observing the outcome to verify that you obtained the desired results.
4. Recording the findings to communicate them both orally and in writing.

The teaching lab is more controlled than the real world. In this laboratory environment, you will be guided more than you would be on the job. Nevertheless, the experiments in this text are designed to be sufficiently challenging to give you a taste of experimental problem-solving methods practiced by professional scientists. We earnestly hope that you will find the techniques, the apparatus, and the experiments to be of just the right complexity, not too easy but not too hard, so that you can learn at a satisfying pace.

Macroscale and Microscale Experiments

This laboratory text presents a unique approach for carrying out organic experiments; they can be conducted on either a *macroscale* or a *microscale*. Macroscale was the traditional way of teaching the principles of experimental organic chemistry and is the basis for all the experiments in this book, a book that traces its history to

1

1934 when the late Louis Fieser, an outstanding organic chemist and professor at Harvard University, was its author. Macroscale experiments typically involve the use of a few grams of *starting material,* the chief reagent used in the reaction. Most teaching institutions are equipped to carry out traditional macroscale experiments. Instructors are familiar with these techniques and experiments, and much research in industry and academe is carried out on this scale. For these reasons, this book has macroscale versions of most experiments.

For reasons primarily related to safety and cost, there is a growing trend toward carrying out microscale laboratory work, on a scale one-tenth to one-thousandth of that previously used. Using smaller quantities of chemicals exposes the laboratory worker to smaller amounts of toxic, flammable, explosive, carcinogenic, and teratogenic material. Microscale experiments can be carried out more rapidly than macroscale experiments because of rapid heat transfer, filtration, and drying. Because the apparatus advocated by the authors is inexpensive, more than one reaction may be set up at once. The cost of chemicals is, of course, greatly reduced. A principal advantage of microscale experimentation is that the quantity of waste is one-tenth to one-thousandth of that formerly produced. To allow maximum flexibility in the conduct of organic experiments, this book presents both macroscale and microscale procedures for the vast majority of the experiments. As will be seen, some of the equipment and techniques differ. A careful reading of both the microscale and macroscale procedures will reveal which changes and precautions must be employed in going from one scale to the other.

Synthesis and Analysis

The typical sequence of activity in synthetic organic chemistry involves the following steps:

1. Designing the experiment based on knowledge of chemical reactivity, the equipment and techniques available, and full awareness of all safety issues.
2. Setting up and running the reaction.
3. Isolating the reaction product.
4. Purifying the crude product, if necessary.
5. Analyzing the product using chromatography or spectroscopy to verify purity and structure.
6. Disposing of unwanted chemicals in a safe manner.

1. Designing the Experiment

Because the first step of experimental design often requires considerable experience, this part has already been done for you for most of the experiments in this introductory level book. Synthetic experimental design becomes increasingly important in an advanced course and in graduate research programs. Safety is paramount, and therefore it is important to be aware of all possible personal and environmental hazards before running any reaction.

2. Running the Reaction

The rational synthesis of an organic compound, whether it involves the transformation of one functional group into another or a carbon-carbon bond-forming reaction, starts with a *reaction*. Organic reactions usually take place in the liquid phase and are *homogeneous*—the reactants are entirely in one phase. The reactants can be solids and/or liquids dissolved in an appropriate solvent to mediate the reaction. Some reactions are *heterogeneous*—that is, one of the reactants is a solid and requires stirring or shaking to bring it in contact with another reactant. A few heterogeneous reactions involve the reaction of a gas, such as oxygen, carbon dioxide, or hydrogen, with material in solution.

An *exothermic* reaction evolves heat. If it is highly exothermic with a low activation energy, one reactant is added slowly to the other, and heat is removed by external cooling. Most organic reactions are, however, mildly *endothermic*, which means the reaction mixture must be heated to overcome the activation barrier and to increase the rate of the reaction. A very useful rule of thumb is that *the rate of an organic reaction doubles with a 10°C rise in temperature.* Louis Fieser introduced the idea of changing the traditional solvents of many reactions to high-boiling solvents to reduce reaction times. Throughout this book we will use solvents such as triethylene glycol, with a boiling point (bp) of 290°C, to replace ethanol (bp 78°C), and triethylene glycol dimethyl ether (bp 222°C) to replace dimethoxyethane (bp 85°C). Using these high-boiling solvents can greatly increase the rates of many reactions.

Effect of temperature

The progress of a reaction can be followed by observing: a change in color or pH, the evolution of a gas, or the separation of a solid product or a liquid layer. Quite often, the extent of the reaction can be determined by withdrawing tiny samples at certain time intervals and analyzing them by *thin-layer chromatography* or *gas chromatography* to measure the amount of starting material remaining and/or the amount of product formed.

Chapters 8–10: Chromatography

The next step, product isolation, should not be carried out until one is confident that the desired amount of product has been formed.

3. Product Isolation: Workup of the Reaction

Running an organic reaction is usually the easiest part of a synthesis. The real challenge lies in isolating and purifying the product from the reaction because organic reactions seldom give quantitative yields of a single pure substance.

In some cases the solvent and concentrations of reactants are chosen so that after the reaction mixture has been cooled, the product will *crystallize* or *precipitate* if it is a solid. The product is then collected by *filtration*, and the crystals are washed with an appropriate solvent. If sufficiently pure at that point, the product is dried and collected; otherwise, it is purified by the process of *recrystallization* or, less commonly, by *sublimation*.

Chapter 4: Recrystallization

More typically, the product of a reaction does not crystallize from the reaction mixture and is often isolated by the process of *liquid/liquid extraction*.

Chapter 7: Liquid/Liquid Extraction

This process involves two liquids, a water-insoluble organic liquid such as dichloromethane and a neutral, acidic, or basic aqueous solution. The two liquids do not mix, but when shaken together, the organic materials and inorganic byproducts go into the liquid layer that they are the most soluble in, either organic or aqueous. After shaking, two layers again form and can be separated. Most organic products remain in the organic liquid and can be isolated by evaporation of the organic solvent.

Chapter 5: Distillation

If the product is a liquid, it is isolated by *distillation*, usually after extraction. Occasionally, an extraction is not necessary and the product can be isolated by the process of *steam distillation* from the reaction mixture.

Chapter 6: Steam Distillation and Vacuum Distillation

4. Purification

When an organic product is first isolated, it will often contain significant impurities. This impure or crude product will need to be further purified or cleaned up before it can be analyzed or used in other reactions. Solids may be purified by recrystallization or sublimation, and liquids by distillation or steam distillation. Small amounts of solids and liquids can also be purified by *chromatography*.

Chapters 11–14: Structure Analysis

5. Analysis to Verify Purity and Structure

The purity of the product can be determined by melting point analysis for solids, boiling point analysis or, less often, refractive index for liquids, and chromatographic analysis for either solids or liquids. Once the purity of the product has been verified, structure determination can be accomplished by using one of the various spectroscopic methods, such as ^1H and ^{13}C nuclear magnetic resonance (NMR), infrared (IR), and ultraviolet/visible (UV/Vis) spectroscopies. Mass spectrometry (MS) is another tool that can aid in the identification of a structure.

⚠ Never smell chemicals in an attempt to identify them.

6. Chemical Waste Disposal

All waste chemicals must be disposed of in their proper waste containers. Instructions on chemical disposal will appear at the end of each experiment. It is recommended that nothing be disposed of until you are sure of your product identity and purity; you do not want to accidentally throw out your product before the analysis is complete. Proper disposal of chemicals is essential for protecting the environment in accordance with local, state, and federal regulations.

EQUIPMENT FOR EXPERIMENTAL ORGANIC CHEMISTRY

A. Equipment for Running Reactions

Organic reactions are usually carried out by dissolving the reactants in a solvent and then heating the mixture to its boiling point, thus maintaining the reaction at that elevated temperature for as long as is necessary to complete the reaction. To keep the solvent from boiling away, the vapor is condensed to a liquid, which is allowed to run back into the boiling solvent.

Microscale reactions with volumes up to 4 mL can be carried out in a *reaction tube* (Fig. 1.1a). The mass of the reaction tube is so small and heat transfer is so rapid that 1 mL of nitrobenzene (bp 210°C) will boil in 10 seconds, and 1 mL of benzene (mp 5°C) will crystallize in the same period of time. Cooling is effected by simply agitating the tube in a small beaker of ice water, and heating is effected by immersing the reaction tube to an appropriate depth in an electrically heated sand bath. This sand bath usually consists of an electric 100-mL flask heater or heating mantle half filled with sand. The temperature is controlled by the setting on a variable voltage controller, but it heats slowly and changes temperature slowly.

Turn on the sand bath about 20 minutes before you intend to use it. The sand heats slowly and changes temperature slowly.

The air above the heater is not hot. It is possible to hold a reaction tube containing refluxing solvents between the thumb and forefinger without the need for forceps or other protective devices. Because sand is a fairly poor conductor of heat, there can be a very large variation in temperature in the sand bath depending on its depth. The temperature of a 5-mL flask can be regulated by using a spatula to pile up or remove sand from near the flask's base. The heater is easily capable of producing temperatures in excess of 300°C; therefore, never leave the controller at its maximum setting. Ordinarily, it is set at 20%–40% of maximum.

⚠ Never put a mercury thermometer in a sand bath! It will break, releasing highly toxic mercury vapor.

FIG. 1.1

(a) A reaction tube being heated on a hot sand bath in a flask heater. The area of the tube exposed to the heat is small. The liquid boils and condenses on the cool upper portion of the tube, which functions as an air condenser. (b) A variable voltage controller used to control the temperature of the sand bath. (c) The condensing area can be increased by adding a distilling column as an air condenser.

Photos: Williamson Microscale Kit, Refluxing a Liquid in a Reaction Tube on a Sand Bath; Video: The Reaction Tube in Use

Because the area of the tube exposed to heat is fairly small, it is difficult to transfer enough heat to the contents of the tube to cause the solvents to boil away. The reaction tube is 100 mm long, so the upper part of the tube can function as an efficient *air condenser* (Fig. 1.1a) because the area of glass is large and the volume of vapor is comparatively small. The air condenser can be made even longer by attaching the empty *distilling column* (Fig. 1.1c and 1.13o) to the reaction tube using the *connector with support rod* (Fig. 1.1c and Fig. 1.13m). The black connector is made of Viton, which is resistant to high-boiling aromatic solvents. The cream-colored connector is made of Santoprene, which is resistant to all but high-boiling aromatic solvents. As solvents such as water and ethanol boil, the hot vapor ascends to the upper part of the tube. These condense and run back down the tube. This process is called *refluxing* and is the most common method for conducting a reaction at a constant temperature, the boiling point of the solvent. For very low-boiling solvents such as diethyl ether (bp 35°C), a pipe cleaner dampened with water makes an efficient cooling device. A water-cooled condenser is also available (Fig. 1.2) but is seldom needed for microscale experiments.

FIG. 1.2
Refluxing solvent in a 5-mL round-bottomed flask fitted with a water-cooled condenser.

Video: *How to Assemble Apparatus*

Organic reactions should be conducted in a fume hood with the sash lowered.

A Petri dish containing sand and heated on a hot plate is not recommended for microscale experiments. It is too easy to burn oneself on the hot plate; too much heat wells up from the sand, so air condensers do not function well; the glass dishes will break from thermal shock; and the ceramic coating on some hot plates will chip and come off.

Larger scale (macroscale) reactions involving volumes of tens to thousands of milliliters are usually carried out in large, round-bottom flasks that fit snugly (without sand!) into the appropriately sized flask heater or heating mantle (Figure 16.2). The round shape can be heated more evenly than a flat-bottom flask or beaker. Heat transfer is slower than in microscale because of the smaller ratio of surface area to volume in a round-bottomed flask. Cooling is again conducted using an ice bath, but heating is sometimes done in a steam bath or hot water bath for low-boiling liquids. The narrow neck is necessary for connection via a *standard-taper ground glass joint* to a water-cooled *reflux condenser*, where the water flows in a jacket around the central tube.

The high heat capacity of water makes it possible to remove a large amount of heat in the larger volume of refluxing vapor (Fig. 1.2).

Heating and Stirring

In modern organic laboratories, electric flask heaters (heating mantles), used alone or as sand baths, are used exclusively for heating. Bunsen burners are almost never used because of the danger of igniting flammable organic vapors. For solvents that boil below 90°C, the most common method for heating macroscale flasks is the *steam bath* or *hot water bath*.

Reactions are often stirred using a *magnetic stirrer* to help mix reagents and to promote smooth boiling. A Teflon-coated bar magnet (*stirring bar*) is placed in the reaction flask, and a magnetic stirrer is placed under the flask and flask heater. The stirrer contains a large, horizontally rotating bar magnet just underneath its metal surface that attracts the Teflon-coated stirring bar magnet through the glass of the flask and causes it to turn. The speed of stirring can be adjusted on the front of the magnetic stirrer.

B. Equipment for the Isolation of Products

Filtration

If the product of a reaction crystallizes from the reaction mixture on cooling, the solid crystals are isolated by *filtration*. This can be done in several ways when using microscale techniques. If the crystals are large enough and in a reaction tube, expel the air from a *Pasteur pipette*, insert it to the bottom of the tube and withdraw the solvent (Fig. 1.3). Highly effective filtration occurs between the square, flat tip of the pipette and the bottom of the tube. This method of filtration has several advantages over the alternatives. The mixture of crystals and solvent can be kept on ice during the entire process. This minimizes the solubility of the crystals in the solvent. There are no transfer losses of material because an external filtration device is not used. This technique allows several recrystallizations to be carried out in the same tube with final drying of the product under vacuum. If you know the *tare* (the weight of the empty tube), the weight of the product can be determined without removing it from the tube. In this manner a compound can be synthesized, purified by crystallization, and dried all in the same reaction tube. After removal of material for analysis, the compound in the tube can then be used for the next

FIG. 1.3

Filtration using a Pasteur pipette and a reaction tube.

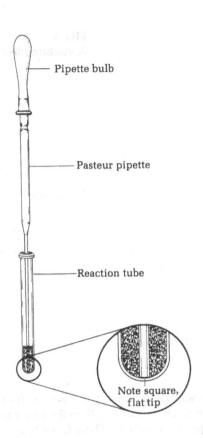

Pipette bulb

Pasteur pipette

Reaction tube

Note square, flat tip

FIG. 1.4

A Hirsch funnel with an integral adapter, a polyethylene frit, and a 25-mL filter flask.

Filter paper, 12 mm dia.

Polyethylene filter disk (frit), 10 mm dia.

Hirsch funnel

To aspirator

25-mL Filter flask

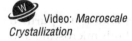

Videos: *The Reaction Tube in Use; Filtration of Crystals Using the Pasteur Pipette*

Video: *Macroscale Crystallization*

Chapter 7: Extraction

reaction. This technique is used in many of this book's microscale experiments. When the crystals are dry, they are easily removed from the reaction tube. When they are wet, it is difficult to scrape them out. If the crystals are in more than about 2 mL of solvent, they can be isolated by filtration with a *Hirsch funnel*. The one that is in the microscale apparatus kit is particularly easy to use because the funnel fits into the *filter flask* with no adapter and is equipped with a *polyethylene frit* for the capture of the filtered crystals (Fig. 1.4). The Wilfilter is especially good for collecting small quantities of crystals (Fig. 1.5).

Macroscale quantities of material can be recrystallized in conical *Erlenmeyer flasks* of the appropriate size. The crystals are collected in porcelain or plastic *Büchner funnels* fit with pieces of filter paper covering the holes in the bottom of the funnel (Fig. 1.6). A rubber *filter adapter* (*Filtervac*) is used to form a vacuum tight seal between the flask and the funnel.

Extraction

The product of a reaction will often not crystallize. It may be a liquid or a viscous oil, it may be a mixture of compounds, or it may be too soluble in the reaction solvent being used. In this case, an immiscible solvent is added, the two layers are shaken to effect *extraction*, and after the layers separate, one layer is removed. On a microscale, this can be done with a Pasteur pipette. The extraction process is repeated if necessary. A tall, thin column of liquid, such as that produced in a reaction tube, makes it easy to selectively remove one layer by pipette. This is more difficult to do in the usual test tube because the height/diameter ratio is small.

FIG. 1.5
A Wilfilter is placed upside down in a centrifuge tube and spun in a centrifuge.

Crystals

Wilfilter

Filtrate

FIG. 1.6
A suction filter assembly.

Büchner funnel

Filtervac

To aspirator

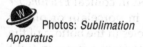
On a larger scale, a *separatory funnel* is used for extraction (Fig. 1.7a). The mixture can be shaken in the funnel and then the lower layer removed through the stopcock after the stopper is removed. These funnels are available in sizes from 10 mL to 5000 mL. The chromatography column in the apparatus kit is also a *micro separatory funnel* (Fig. 1.7b). Remember to remove the frit at the column base of the micro Büchner funnel and to close the valve before adding liquid.

C. Equipment for Purification

Many solids can be purified by the process of *sublimation*. The solid is heated, and the vapor of the solid condenses on a cold surface to form crystals in an apparatus constructed from a *centrifuge tube* fitted with a rubber adapter and pushed into a *filter flask* (Fig. 1.8). Caffeine can be purified in this manner. This is primarily a microscale technique, although sublimers holding several grams of solid are available.

Mixtures of solids and, occasionally, of liquids can be separated and purified by *column chromatography*. The *chromatography column* for both microscale and macroscale work is very similar (Fig. 1.9).

Some of the compounds to be synthesized in these experiments are liquids. On a very small scale, the best way to separate and purify a mixture of liquids is by *gas chromatography,* but this technique is limited to less than 100 mg of material for the usual gas chromatograph. For larger quantities of material, *distillation* is used. For this purpose, small distilling flasks are used. These flasks have a large surface area to allow sufficient heat input to cause the liquid to vaporize rapidly so that it can be distilled and then condensed for collection in a *receiver*. The complete apparatus (Fig. 1.10) consists of a *distilling flask*, a *distilling adapter* (which also functions as an air condenser on a microscale), a *thermometer adapter*, and a *thermometer*; for macroscale, a water-cooled *condenser* and *distilling adapter* are added to the

FIG. 1.7
(a) A separatory funnel with a Teflon stopcock.
(b) A microscale separatory funnel. Remove the
polyethylene frit from the micro Büchner funnel
before using.

FIG. 1.8
A small-scale sublimation
apparatus.

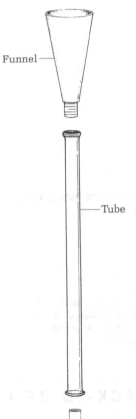

15-mL Centrifuge
tube, to be filled
with ice

Rubber
adapter

To
vacuum

25-mL Filter flask

Material to
be sublimed

Sublimate

Heat source

Polyethylene
cap

Glass
column

Teflon
stopcock

Micro
Büchner
funnel

(b)

(a)

FIG. 1.9
A chromatography
column consisting
of a funnel, a tube,
a base fitted with a
polyethylene frit,
and a Leur valve.

Funnel

Tube

Polyethylene
frit

Leur
valve

FIG. 1.10
A small-scale simple distillation apparatus. Note that the entire thermometer bulb is below the side arm of the distilling adapter.

Thermometer

Thermometer adapter

Distilling adapter and air condenser

Vial (receiver)

30-mL Beaker

Ice (if needed)

Distilling flask

Hot sand bath

Boiling chip

⚠ Use mercury-free thermometers whenever possible.

🪐 Photos: *Simple and Fractional Distillation Apparatus*; Video: *How to Assemble the Apparatus*

apparatus (Fig. 1.11). *Fractional distillation* is carried out using a small, packed *fractionating column* (Fig. 1.12). The apparatus for fractional distillation is very similar for both microscale and macroscale. On a microscale, 2 mL to 4 mL of a liquid can be fractionally distilled, and 1 mL or more can be simply distilled. The usual scale in these experiments for macroscale distillation is about 25 mL.

Some liquids with a relatively high vapor pressure can be isolated and purified by *steam distillation*, a process in which the organic compound codistills with water at the boiling point of water and is then further purified and concentrated. The microscale and macroscale apparatus for this process are shown in Chapter 6.

The collection of typical equipment used for microscale experimentation is shown in Figure 1.13 and for macroscale experimentation in Figure 1.14. Other equipment commonly used in the organic laboratory is shown in Figure 1.15.

CHECK-IN OF LAB EQUIPMENT

Your first duty will be to check in to your assigned lab desk. The identity of much of the apparatus should already be apparent from the preceding outline of the experimental processes used in the organic laboratory.

Check to see that your thermometer reads about 22–25°C (71.6–77°F), which is normal room temperature. Examine the fluid column to see that it is unbroken and continuous from the bulb up. Replace any flasks that have star-shaped cracks.

FIG. 1.11
An apparatus for simple distillation.

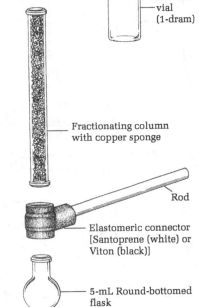

FIG. 1.12
A microscale fractional distillation apparatus. The thermometer adapter is to be fitted with a thermometer.

Remember that apparatus with graduations, stopcocks, or ground glass joints and anything porcelain are expensive. Erlenmeyer flasks, beakers, and test tubes are, by comparison, fairly cheap.

TRANSFER OF LIQUIDS AND SOLIDS

Borosilicate Pasteur pipettes (Fig. 1.16) are very useful for transferring small quantities of liquid, adding reagents dropwise, and carrying out recrystallizations. Discard used Pasteur pipettes in the special disposal container for waste glass. Surprisingly, the acetone used to wash out a dirty Pasteur pipette usually costs more than the pipette itself.

A plastic funnel that fits on the top of the reaction tube is very convenient for the transfer of solids to reaction tubes or small Erlenmeyer flasks for

FIG. 1.13

Microscale apparatus kit.

(a) Pipette (1 mL), graduated in 1/1000ths.
(b) Chromatography column (glass) with a polypropylene funnel and 20-μm polyethylene frit in the base, which doubles as a micro Büchner funnel. The column, base, and stopcock can also be used as a separatory funnel.
(c) Thermometer adapter.
(d) Connector only (Viton).
(e) Magnetic stirring bars (4 × 12 mm) in a distillation receiver vial.
(f) Hirsch funnel (polypropylene) with a 20-μm fritted polyethylene disk.
(g) Stopcock for a chromatography column or separatory funnel.
(h) Claisen adapter/distillation head with an air condenser.

(i) Filter flask, 25 mL.
(j) Distillation head with a 105° connecting adapter.
(k) Rubber septa/sleeve stoppers, 8 mm.
(l) Syringe (polypropylene).
(m) Connector with a support rod.
(n) Centrifuge tube (15 mL)/sublimation receiver, with cap.
(o) Distillation column/air condenser.
(p) Reaction tube, calibrated, 10 × 100 mm.
(q) Erlenmeyer flasks, 10 mL.
(r) Long-necked flask, 5 mL.
(s) Short-necked flask, 5 mL.
(t) Rubber adapter for sublimation apparatus.
(u) Tubing (polyethylene), 1/16-in. diameter.
(v) Spatula (stainless steel) with scoop end.

FIG. 1.14

Macroscale apparatus kit with 14/20 standard-taper ground-glass joints.

(a) Polyacetal Keck clamps, size 14.
(b) Hex-head glass stopper, 14/20 standard taper.
(c) Hirsch funnel (polypropylene) with a 20-μm fritted polyethylene disk.
(d) Filter adapter for use with sublimation apparatus.
(e) Distilling head with O-ring thermometer adapter.
(f) Vacuum adapter.
(g) Centrifuge tube (15 mL)/sublimation receiver.
(h) Filter flask, 25 mL.
(i) Claisen adapter.

(j) Water-jacketed condenser.
(k) Chromatography column (glass) with a polypropylene funnel and 20-μm polyethylene frit in the base, which doubles as a micro Büchner funnel.
(l) Stopcock for a chromatography column.
(m) Separatory funnel, 125 mL.
(n) Pear-shaped flask, 100 mL.
(o) Pear-shaped flask, 50 mL.
(p) Conical flask (15 mL) with a side arm for an inlet tube.
(q) Distilling column/air condenser.
(r) Conical reaction vial (5 mL)/distillation receiver.

FIG. 1.15

Miscellaneous apparatus.

(a) 1.0 ± 0.01 mL graduated pipette.
(b) Septum.
(c) 1.0-mL syringe with a blunt needle.
(d) Calibrated Pasteur pipette.
(e) Pipette pump.
(f) Glass scorer.
(g) Filtervac.
(h) Set of neoprene filter adapters.
(i) Hirsch funnel with a perforated plate in place.
(j) Rubber thermometer adapter.
(k) Powder funnel.

(l) Polyethylene wash bottle.
(m) Single-pan electronic balance with automatic zeroing and 0.001 g digital readout; 100 g capacity.
(n) Electric flask heater.
(o) Solid-state control for electric flask heater.
(p) Stainless steel spatula.
(q) Stirring bar.
(r) Keck clamp.
(s) Wilfilter.

microscale experiments (Fig. 1.17). It can also function as the top of a chromatography column (Fig. 1.9). A special spatula with a scoop end (Fig. 1.13v) is used to remove solid material from the reaction tube. On a large scale, a powder funnel is useful for adding solids to a flask (Fig. 1.15k). A funnel can also be fashioned from a sheet of weighing paper for transferring lightweight solids.

WEIGHING AND MEASURING

The single-pan electronic balance (Fig. 1.15m), which is capable of weighing to ±0.001 g and having a capacity of at least 100 g, is the single most important instrument that makes microscale organic experiments possible. Most of the weighing measurements made in microscale experiments will use this type of balance. Weighing is fast and accurate with these balances as compared to mechanical balances. There should be one electronic balance for every 12 students. For macroscale experiments, a balance of such high accuracy is not necessary. Here, a balance with ±0.01 g accuracy would be satisfactory.

A container such as a reaction tube standing in a beaker or flask is placed on the balance pan. Set the digital readout to register zero and then add the desired quantity of the reagent to the reaction tube as the weight is measured periodically to the nearest milligram. Even liquids are weighed when accuracy is needed. It is much easier to weigh a liquid to 0.001 g than it is to measure it volumetrically to 0.001 mL.

It is often convenient to weigh reagents on glossy weighing paper and then transfer the chemical to the reaction container. The success of an experiment often depends on using just the right amount of starting materials and reagents. Inexperienced workers might think that if 1 mL of a reagent will do the job, then 2 mL will do the job twice as well. Such assumptions are usually erroneous.

Liquids can be measured by either volume or weight according to the following relationship:

$$\text{Volume (mL)} = \frac{\text{Weight (g)}}{\text{Density (g/mL)}}$$

Modern Erlenmeyer flasks and beakers have approximate volume calibrations fused into the glass, but these are *very* approximate. Better graduations are found on the microscale *reaction tube*. Somewhat more accurate volumetric measurements are made in 10-mL graduated cylinders. For volumes less than 4 mL, use a graduated pipette. **Never** apply suction to a pipette by mouth. Use a rubber bulb, a pipette pump, or fit the pipette with a small plastic syringe using appropriately sized rubber tubing. A Pasteur pipette can be converted into a calibrated pipette with the addition of a plastic syringe (Fig. 1.15d). Figure 1.16 also shows the calibration marks for a 9-in. Pasteur pipette. You will find among your equipment a 1-mL pipette, calibrated in hundredths of a milliliter (Fig. 1.15a). Determine whether it is designed to *deliver* 1 mL or *contain* 1 mL between the top and bottom calibration marks. For our purposes, the latter is the better pipette.

Because the viscosity, surface tension, vapor pressure, and wetting characteristics of organic liquids are different from those of water, the so-called automatic pipette (designed for aqueous solutions) gives poor accuracy in measuring organic

FIG. 1.16
The approximate calibration of a Kimble 9" Pasteur pipette.

2.0 mL

1.5 mL

1.0 mL

0.75 mL

0.50 mL

0.25 mL

0.10 mL

0.05 mL

FIG. 1.17
A funnel for adding solids and liquids to a reaction tube.

FIG. 1.18
Using a pipette pump to measure liquids to ±0.01 mL.

2-mL Pipette pump

1-mL Pipette graduated to ± 0.01 mL

Reaction tube

Never pipette by mouth!

liquids. Syringes (Fig. 1.15c and Fig. 1.15d) and pipette pumps (Fig. 1.18), on the other hand, are quite useful, and these will be used frequently. Do not use a syringe that is equipped with a metal needle to measure corrosive reagents because these reagents will dissolve the metal in the needle. Because many reactions are "killed" by traces of moisture, many students' experiments are ruined by damp or wet apparatus. Several reactions that require especially dry or oxygen-free atmospheres will be run in systems sealed with a rubber septum (Fig. 1.15b). Reagents can be added to the system via syringe through this septum to minimize exposure to oxygen or atmospheric moisture.

Careful measurements of weights and volumes take more time than less accurate measurements. Think carefully about which measurements need to be made with accuracy and which do not.

TARES

Tare = weight of empty container

The tare of a container is its weight when empty. Throughout this laboratory course, it will be necessary to know the tares of containers so that the weights of the compounds within can be calculated. If identifying marks can be placed on the containers (e.g., with a diamond stylus for glassware), you may want to record tares for frequently used containers in your laboratory notebook.

To be strictly correct, we should use the word *mass* instead of *weight* because gravitational acceleration is not constant at all places on earth. But electronic balances record weights, unlike two-pan or triple-beam balances, which record masses.

WASHING AND DRYING LABORATORY EQUIPMENT

Washing

Clean apparatus immediately.

Both ethanol and acetone are very flammable.

Wash acetone is disposed in an organic solvents waste container; halogenated solvents go in the halogenated solvents waste container.

Considerable time may be saved by cleaning each piece of equipment soon after use, for you will know at that point which contaminant is present and be able to select the proper method for its removal. A residue is easier to remove before it has dried and hardened. A small amount of organic residue can usually be dissolved with a few milliliters of an appropriate organic solvent. Acetone (bp 56.1°C) has great solvent power and is often effective, but it is extremely flammable and somewhat expensive. Because it is miscible with water and vaporizes readily, it is easy to remove. Detergent and water can also be used to clean dirty glassware if an appropriate solvent cannot be found. Cleaning after an operation may often be carried out while another experiment is in process.

A *polyethylene bottle* (Fig. 1.15l) is a convenient wash bottle for acetone. Be careful not to store solvent bottles in the vicinity of a reaction where they can provide additional fuel for an accidental fire. The name, symbol, and formula of a solvent should be written on a bottle with a marker or a wax pencil. For macroscale crystallizations, extractions, and quick cleaning of apparatus, it is convenient to have a bottle of each frequently used solvent—95% ethanol, ligroin or hexanes, dichloromethane, ether, and ethyl acetate. A pinhole opposite the spout, which is covered with the finger when in use, will prevent the spout from dribbling the solvent. For microscale work, these solvents are best dispensed from 25-mL or 50-mL bottles with an attached test tube containing a graduated (1-mL) polypropylene pipette (Fig. 1.19). Be aware of any potential hazards stemming from the reactivity of these wash solvents with chemical residues in flasks. Also, be sure to dispose of wash solvents in the proper container. Acetone and most other organic solvents do not contain halogens and can therefore go in the regular organic solvents waste container. However, if dichloromethane or another halogen-containing solvent is used, it must be disposed of in the halogenated solvents waste container.

Sometimes a flask will not be clean after a washing with detergent and acetone. At that point, try an abrasive household cleaner. If still no success, try adding dilute acid or base to the dirty glassware, let it soak for a few minutes, and rinse with plenty of water and acetone.

Drying

To dry a piece of apparatus rapidly, rinse with a few milliliters of acetone and invert over a beaker to drain. **Do not use compressed air**, which contains droplets of oil, water, and particles of rust. Instead, draw a slow stream of air through the apparatus using the suction of your water aspirator or house vacuum line.

FIG. 1.19
A recrystallization solvent bottle and dispenser.

MISCELLANEOUS CLEANUP

If a glass tube or thermometer becomes stuck to a rubber connector, it can be removed by painting on glycerol and forcing the pointed tip of a small spatula between the rubber and the glass. Another method is to select a cork borer that fits snugly over the glass tube, moisten it with glycerol, and slowly work it through the connector. If the stuck object is valuable, such as a thermometer, the best policy is to cut the rubber with a sharp knife. Care should be taken to avoid force that could potentially cause a thermometer to break, causing injury and the release of mercury.

THE LABORATORY NOTEBOOK

The Laboratory Notebook
What you did.
How you did it.
What you observed.
Your conclusions.

A complete, accurate record is an essential part of laboratory work. Failure to keep such a record means laboratory labor lost. An adequate record includes the procedure (what was done), observations (what happened), and conclusions (what the results mean).

Never record anything on scraps of paper. Use a lined, 8.5" × 11" paperbound notebook, and record all data in ink. Allow space at the front for a table of contents, number the pages throughout, and date each day's work. Reserve the left-hand page for calculations and numerical data, and use the right-hand page for notes. Never record **anything** on scraps of paper to be recorded later in the notebook. Do not erase, remove, or obliterate notes; simply draw a single line through incorrect entries.

The notebook should contain a statement or title for each experiment and its purpose, followed by balanced equations for all principal and side reactions and, where relevant, mechanisms of the reactions. Consult your textbook for supplementary information on the class of compounds or type of reaction involved. Give a reference to the procedure used; do not copy verbatim the procedure in the laboratory manual. Make particular note of safety precautions and the procedures for cleaning up at the end of the experiment.

Before coming to the lab to do preparative experiments, prepare a table (in your notebook) of reagents to be used and the products expected, with their physical properties. Use the molar ratios of reactions from your table to determine the limiting reagent, and then calculate the theoretical yield (in grams) of the desired product. Begin each experiment on a new page.

Include an outline of the procedure and the method of purification of the product in a flow sheet if this is the best way to organize the experiment (for example, an extraction; *see* Chapter 8). The flow sheet should list all possible products, by-products, unused reagents, solvents, and so on that are expected to appear in the crude reaction mixture. On the flow sheet diagram indicate how each of these is removed (e.g., by extraction, various washing procedures, distillation, or crystallization). With this information entered in your notebook before coming to the laboratory, you will be ready to carry out the experiments with the utmost efficiency. Plan your time before the laboratory period. Often two or three experiments can be run simultaneously.

When working in the laboratory, record everything you do and everything you observe **as it happens.** The recorded observations constitute the most important part of the laboratory record, since they form the basis for the conclusions you will draw at the end of each experiment. One way to do this is in a narrative form.

Alternatively, the procedure can be written in outline form on the left-hand side of the page and the observations recorded on the right-hand side.

In some colleges and universities, you will be expected to have all the relevant information about the running of an experiment entered in your notebook *before coming to the laboratory* so that your textbook will not be needed when you are conducting experiments. In industrial laboratories, your notebook may be designed so that carbon copies of all entries are kept. These are signed and dated by your supervisor and removed from your notebook each day. Your notebook becomes a legal document in case you make a discovery worth hundreds of millions of dollars!

Record the physical properties of the product from your experiment, the yield in grams, and the percent yield. Analyze your results. When things did not turn out as expected, explain why. When your record of an experiment is complete, another chemist should be able to understand your account and determine what you did, how you did it, and what conclusions you reached. That is, from the information in your notebook, a chemist should be able to repeat your work.

Preparing a Laboratory Record

Use the following steps to prepare your laboratory record. The letters correspond to the completed laboratory records that appear at the end of this chapter. Because your laboratory notebook is so important, two examples, written in alternative forms, are presented.
A. Number each page. Allow space at the front of the notebook for a table of contents. Use a hardbound, lined notebook, and keep all notes in ink.
B. Date each entry.
C. Give a short title to the experiment, and enter it in the table of contents.
D. State the purpose of the experiment.
E. Write balanced equation(s) for the reaction(s).
F. Give a reference to the source of the experimental procedure.
G. Prepare a table of quantities and physical constants. Look up the needed data in the *Handbook of Chemistry and Physics*.
H. Write equation(s) for the principal side reaction(s).
I. Write out the procedure with just enough information so that you can follow it easily. Do not merely copy the procedure from the text. Note any hazards and safety precautions. A highly experienced chemist might write a procedure in a formal report as follows: "Dibenzalacetone was prepared by condensing at room temperature 1 mmol acetone with 2 mmol benzaldehyde in 1.6 mL of 95% ethanol to which was added 2 mL of aqueous 3 *M* sodium hydroxide solution. After 30 min the product was collected and crystallized from 70% ethanol to give 0.17 g (73%) of flat yellow plates of dibenzalacetone, mp 110.5–111.5°C." Note that in this formal report, no jargon (e.g., EtOH for 95% ethanol, FCHO for benzaldehyde) is used and that the names of reagents are written out (sodium hydroxide, not NaOH). In this report the details of measuring, washing, drying, crystallizing, collecting the product, and so on are assumed to be understood by the reader.
J. Don't forget to note how to dispose of the byproducts from the experiment using the "Cleaning Up" section of the experimental procedure.
K. Record what you do as you do it. These observations are the most important part of the experiment. Note that conclusions do not appear among these observations.
L. Calculate the theoretical yield in grams. The experiment calls for exactly 2 mmol fluorobenzaldehyde and 1 mmol acetone, which will produce 1 mmol

of product. The equation for the experiment also indicates that the product will be formed from exactly a 2:1 ratio of the reactants. Experiments are often designed to have one reactant in great excess. In this experiment, a very slight excess of fluorobenzaldehyde was used inadvertently, so acetone becomes the limiting reagent.

M. Once the product is obtained, dried, and weighed, calculate the ratio of product actually isolated to the amount theoretically possible. Express this ratio as the percent yield.

N. Write out the mechanism of the reaction. If it is not given in the text of the experiment, look it up in your lecture text.

O. Draw conclusions from the observations. Write this part of the report in narrative form in complete English sentences. This part of the report can, of course, be written after leaving the laboratory.

P. Analyze TLC, IR, and NMR spectra if they are a part of the experiments. Rationalize observed versus reported melting points.

Q. Answer assigned questions from the end of the experiment.

R. This page presents an alternative method for entering the experimental procedure and observations in the notebook. Before coming to the laboratory, enter the procedure in outline form on the left side of the page. Then enter observations in brief form on the right side of the page as the experiment is carried out. Draw a single line through any words incorrectly entered. Do not erase or obliterate entries in the notebook, and never remove pages from the notebook.

Two samples of completed laboratory records follow. An alternative method for recording procedure, cleaning up, and observations is given on p. 25. The other parts of the report are the same.

(A) p. 35

(B) Sept. 23, 2010

DIFLUORODIBENZALACETONE

(D) *Purpose:* To observe and carry out an aldol condensation reaction.

(E) 2 [4-Fluorobenzaldehyde, CHO with F] + CH$_3$CCH$_3$ →[3 N NaOH] F—CH=CH—C—CH=CH—F [4,4'-Difluorodibenzalacetone]

4-Fluorobenzaldehyde Acetone   **4,4'-Difluorodibenzalacetone**

(F) *Reference:* Williamson and Masters, *Macroscale and Microscale Organic Experiments*, p. 792.

Table of Quantities and Physical Constants (G)

Substance	Mol wt	G/mol Used or Produced	Mol Needed (from eq.)	Density	mp	bp	Solubility
4-Fluorobenzaldehyde	124.11	0.248/0.002	0.002	1.157		181°C	Slightly soluble in H$_2$O; soluble in ethanol, diethyl ether, acetone
Acetone	58.08	0.058/0.001	0.001	0.790		56°C	Soluble in H$_2$O, ethanol, diethyl ether, acetone
4,4'-Difluoro-dibenzalacetone	270.34	0.270/0.001			167°C		Insoluble in H$_2$O; slightly soluble in ethanol, diethyl ether, acetone
4-Fluorobenzalacetone	164.19				54°C		Insoluble in H$_2$O; slightly soluble in ethanol, diethyl ether, acetone
Sodium hydroxide	40.01						Soluble in H$_2$O; insoluble in ethanol, diethyl ether, acetone

(H) *Side Reactions:* No important side reactions, but if excess acetone is used, product will be contaminated with 4-fluorobenzalacetone.

Ⓘ   *Procedure:*   To a reaction tube, add 0.248 g (0.002 mole) of 4-fluorobenzalde-hyde and then 1.6 mL of an ethanol solution that contains 58 mg of acetone. Mix the solution and observe it for 1 min. Remove sample for TLC. Then add 2 mL of 3 *M* NaOH(*aq*). Cap the tube with a septum and shake it at intervals over a 30-min period. Collect product on Hirsch funnel, wash crystals thoroughly with water, press as dry as possible, determine crude weight, and save sample for mp. Recrystallize product from 70% ethanol in a 10-mL Erlenmeyer flask. Cool solution slowly, scratch or add seed crystal, cool in ice, and collect product on Hirsch. Wash crystals with a few drops of ice-cold ethanol. Run TLC on silica gel plates using hexane to elute, develop in iodine chamber. Run NMR spectrum in deuterochloroform and IR spectrum as a mull.

Ⓙ   *Cleaning Up:*   Neutralize filtrate with HCl and flush solution down the drain. Put recrystallization filtrate in organic solvents container.

Ⓚ   *Observations:*   Into a reaction tube, 0.250 g of 4-fluorobenzaldehyde was weighed (0.248 called for). Using the 1.00-mL graduated pipette and pipette pump, 1.61 mL of the stock ethanol solution containing 58 mg of acetone was added (1.6 mL called for). The contents of the tube were mixed by flicking the tube, and then a drop of the reaction mixture was removed and diluted with 1 mL of hexane for later TLC. The water-clear solution did not change in appearance during 1 min.

Then about 2 mL of 3 *M* NaOH(*aq*) was added using graduations on side of reaction tube. The tube was capped with a septum and shaken. The clear solution changed to a light yellow color immediately and got slightly warm. Then after about 50 sec, the entire solution became opaque. Then yellow oily drops collected on sides and bottom of tube. Shaken every 5 min for 1/2 hr. The oily drops crystallized, and more crystals formed. At the end of 30 min, the opaque solution became clear, and yellow crystals had formed. Tube filled with crystals.

Product was collected on 12-mm filter paper on a Hirsch funnel; transfer of material to funnel was completed using the filtrate to wash out the tube. Crystals were washed with about 15 mL of water. The filtrate was slightly cloudy and yellow. It was poured into a beaker for later disposal. The crude product was pressed as dry as possible with a cork. Wt (damp) 270 mg. Sample saved for mp.

Recrystallized from about 50 mL of 70% ethanol on sand bath. Almost forgot to add boiling stick! Clear, yellow solution cooled slowly by wrapping tube in cotton. A seed crystal from Julie added to start crystallization. After about 25 min, flask was placed in ice bath for 15 min, then product was collected on Hirsch funnel (filter paper), washed with a few drops of ice-cold solvent, pressed dry and then spread out on paper to dry. Wt 190 mg. Very nice flat, yellow crystals, mp 179.5–180.5°C. The crude material before recrystallization had mp 177.5–179°C.

TLC on silica gel using hexane to elute gave only one spot, R_f 0.23, for the starting material and only one spot for the product, R_f 0.66. See attached plate.

p. 37

The NMR spectrum that was run on the Bruker in deuterochloroform containing TMS showed a complex group of peaks centered at about 7 ppm with an integrated value of 17.19 and a sharp, clear quartet of peaks centered at 6.5 ppm with an integral of 8.62. The coupling constant of the AB quartet was 7.2 Hz. See attached spectrum.

The IR spectrum, run as a Nujol mull on the Mattson FT IR, showed intense peaks at 1590 and 1655 cm^{-1} as well as small peaks at 3050, 3060, and 3072 cm^{-1}. See attached spectrum.

Cleaning Up: Recrystallization filtrate put in organic solvents container. First filtrate neutralized with HCl and poured down the drain.

Ⓛ   *Theoretical Yield Calculations:*

$$0.250 \text{ g 4-fluorobenzaldehyde used } \frac{0.250 \text{ g}}{124.11 \text{ g/mole}} = 0.00201 \text{ mole}$$

$$0.058 \text{ g of acetone used } \frac{0.058 \text{ g}}{58.08 \text{ g/mole}} = 0.001 \text{ mole}$$

The moles needed (from equation) are 2 mmol of the 4-fluorobenzaldehyde and 1 mmol of acetone. Therefore, acetone is the limiting reagent, and 1.00 mmol of product should result. The MW of the product is 270.34 g/mol.

$$0.001 \text{ mol} \times 270.34 \text{ g/mol}$$
$$= 0.270 \text{ g, theoretical yield of difluorodibenzalacetone}$$

Ⓜ   *Percent Yield of Product:*

$$\frac{0.19 \text{ g}}{0.270 \text{ g}} \times 100 = 70\%$$

Ⓝ   *The Mechanism of the Reaction:*

p. 38

$$CH_3C-\overset{\overset{\displaystyle O}{\|}}{\underset{\underset{\displaystyle H}{|}}{\overset{\overset{\displaystyle H}{|}}{C}}}-\overset{\overset{\displaystyle H}{|}}{\underset{\underset{\displaystyle OH}{|}}{C}}-\bigcirc\!\!-F \longrightarrow CH_3\overset{\overset{\displaystyle O}{\|}}{C}-C=\overset{\overset{\displaystyle H}{|}}{\underset{\underset{\displaystyle H}{|}}{C}}-\bigcirc\!\!-F + H_2O + OH^-$$

⊚ *Discussion and Conclusions:* Mixing the 4-fluorobenzaldehyde, acetone, and ethanol gave no apparent reaction because the solution did not change in appearance, but less than a minute after adding the NaOH, a yellow oil appeared and the reaction mixture got slightly warm, indicating that a reaction was taking place. The mechanism given in the text (above) indicates that hydroxide ion is a catalyst for the reaction, confirmed by this observation. The reaction takes place spontaneously at room temperature. The reaction was judged to be complete when the liquid surrounding the crystals became clear (it was opaque) and the amount of crystals in the tube did not appear to change. This took 30 min. The crude product was collected and washed with water. Forgot to cool it in ice before filtering it off. The crude product weighed more than the theoretical because it must still have been damp. However, this amount of crude material indicates that the reaction probably went pretty well to completion. The crude product was recrystallized from 5 mL of 70% ethanol. This was probably too much, since it dissolved very rapidly in that amount. This and the fact that the reaction mixture was not cooled in ice probably accounts for the relatively low 70% yield. Probably could have obtained second crop of crystals by concentrating filtrate. It turned very cloudy when water was added to it.

Theoretically, it is possible for this reaction to give three different products (*cis, cis-; cis, trans-;* and *trans, trans*-isomers). Because the mp of the crude and recrystallized products were close to each other and rather sharp, and because the TLC of the product gave only one spot, it is presumed that the product is just one of these three possible isomers. The NMR spectrum shows a sharp quartet of peaks from the vinyl protons, which also indicates only one isomer. Since the coupling constant observed is 7.2 Hz, the protons must be *cis* to each other. Therefore, the product is the *cis, cis*-isomer.

ⓟ The infrared spectrum shows two strong peaks at 1590 and 1655 cm^{-1}, indicative of an α-β-unsaturated ketone. The small peaks at 3050, 3060, and 3072 cm^{-1} are consistent with aromatic and vinyl protons. The yellow color indicates that the molecule must have a long conjugated system.

The fact that the TLC of the starting material showed only one peak is probably due to the evaporation of the acetone from the TLC plate. The spot with R_f 0.23 must be from the 4-fluorobenzaldehyde.

ⓠ Answers to assigned questions are written at the end of the report.

p. 39

ⓡ	*Sept. 23, 2010 Procedure*	*Sept. 24, 2010 Observations*
	Weigh 0.248 g of 4-fluorobenz-aldehyde into reaction tube.	Actually used 0.250 g.
	Add 1.6 mL of ethanol stock soln that contains 0.058 g of acetone.	Actually used 1.61 mL.
	Mix, observe for 1 min.	Nothing seems to happen. Water clear soln.
	Add 2 mL of 3 M NaOH(aq).	Clear, then faintly yellow but clear, then after about 50 sec, the entire soln very suddenly turned opaque. Got slightly warm. Light yellow color.
	Cap tube with septum; shake at 5-min intervals for 30 min.	Oily drops separate on sides and bottom of tube. These crystallized; more crystals formed. Tube became filled with crystals. Liquid around crystals became clear.
	Filter on Hirsch funnel.	Filtered (filter paper) on Hirsch.
	Wash crystals with much water.	Washed with about 150 mL of H_2O. Transfer of crystals done using filtrate.
	Press dry.	Crystals pressed dry with cork.
	Weigh crude.	Crude (damp) wt 0.27 g.
	Save sample for mp.	Crude mp 177.5–179°C.
	Recrystallize from 70% ethanol; . wash with a few drops of ice-cold solvent.	Used about 50 mL of 70% EtOH. Too much. Dissolved very rapidly.
	Dry product.	Dried on paper for 30 min.
	Weigh.	Wt 0.19 g.
	Take mp.	Mp 179.5–180.5°C.
	Run IR as mull.	Done.
	Run NMR in $CDCl_3$.	Done.
	Neutralize first filtrate with HCl, pour down drain.	Done.
	Org. filtrate in waste organic bottle.	Done.

2 CHAPTER

Laboratory Safety, Courtesy, and Waste Disposal

PRELAB EXERCISE: Read this chapter carefully. Locate the emergency eyewash station, the safety shower, the fire extinguisher, and the emergency exits in your laboratory. Check your safety glasses or goggles for size and transparency. Learn which reactions must be carried out in the hood. Learn to use your laboratory fire extinguisher; learn how to summon help and how to put out a clothing fire. Learn first aid procedures for acid and alkali spills on the skin. Learn how to tell if your laboratory hood is working properly. Learn which operations under reduced pressure require special precautions. Check to see that compressed gas cylinders in your lab are firmly fastened to benches or walls. Learn the procedures for properly disposing of solid and liquid waste in your laboratory.

Small-scale (microscale) organic experiments are much safer to conduct than their macroscale counterparts that are run on a scale up to 100 times larger. However, for either microscale or macroscale experiments, the organic chemistry laboratory is an excellent place to learn and practice safety. The commonsense procedures practiced here also apply to other laboratories as well as to the shop, kitchen, and studio.

General laboratory safety information—particularly applicable to this organic chemistry laboratory course—is presented in this chapter. But it is not comprehensive. Throughout this text you will find specific cautions and safety information presented as margin notes printed in red. For a brief and thorough discussion of the topics in this chapter, you should read *Safety in Academic Chemistry Laboratories*.[1] There are also some specific admonitions regarding contact lenses (see "Eye Safety").

IMPORTANT GENERAL RULES

- Know the safety rules of your particular laboratory.
- Know the locations of emergency eyewashes, fire extinguishers, safety showers, and emergency exits.
- Never eat, drink, smoke, or apply cosmetics while in the laboratory.

[1]American Chemical Society Joint Board-Council Committee on Chemical Safety. *Safety in Academic Chemistry Laboratories, Vol. 1: Accident Prevention for College and University Students*, 7th ed.; American Chemical Society: Washington, DC, 2003 (0-8412-3864-2).

26

- Wear gloves and aprons when handling corrosive materials.
- Never work alone.
- Perform no unauthorized experiments and do not distract your fellow workers; horseplay has no place in the laboratory.

Dress sensibly.

- Dress properly for lab work. Do not wear open-toed shoes; your feet must be completely covered; wear shoes that have rubber soles and no heels or sneakers.
- Confine long hair and loose clothes. Do not wear shorts.
- Immediately report any accident to your instructor.
- If the fire extinguisher is used, report this to your instructor.
- Never use mouth suction to fill a pipette.
- Always wash your hands before leaving the laboratory.
- Do not use a solvent to remove a chemical from your skin. This will only hasten the absorption of the chemical through the skin.
- Do not use cell phones or tape, CD, MP3, iPods, or similar music players while working in the laboratory.
- Refer to the chemical supplier's hazard warning information or Material Safety Data Sheet (MSDS) when handling a new chemical for the first time.

Information on Eye Protection

Eye protection

Eye protection is extremely important. The requirement that you wear approved eye protection in the laboratory is mandatory and is most effective in preventing the largest number of potential accidents of serious consequence. Safety glasses or goggles of some type must be worn at all times that you are in the laboratory, whether engaged in experimental work or not. Ordinary prescription eyeglasses do not offer adequate protection.

There are three types of eye protection acceptable for use in the organic chemistry laboratory; they are described below. Laboratory safety glasses should be constructed of plastic or tempered glass. If you do not have such glasses, wear goggles that afford protection from splashes and objects coming from the side as well as from the front. Chemical splash goggles are the preferred eye protection. One of the most important features of safety glasses/goggles is the brow bar. It is critical to have proper eye protection above the eyes; a brow bar satisfies this requirement for adequate splash protection. If plastic safety glasses are permitted in your laboratory, they should have side shields (Fig. 2.1). Eye safety cannot be overemphasized in the chemistry laboratory.

1. **Goggles** are pliable, form a complete cup around the eyes, and are held in place by a strap that wraps around the head. Goggles offer the highest level of splash protection compared to other types of protective eyewear. The disadvantages are that they may fog up and limit peripheral vision. Most goggles will fit over prescription eyeglasses.

2. **Safety Glasses** look similar to prescription glasses but have side shields and a browbar to provide extra splash protection. They are generally considered to be more comfortable and to offer better peripheral vision compared to goggles. The disadvantages are that they do not fit well, if at all, over prescription eyeglasses and they offer less protection than goggles since they do not completely cover the eye.

FIG. 2.1
(a) Chemical splash goggles
(b) Safety glasses

Brow bar   Brow bar

Side Shield

(a)   (b)

3. **Visor Goggles** are a type of "half goggle"; the upper half is similar to a goggle and the lower half is similar to safety glasses. As such, they have some of the advantages and disadvantages of both safety glasses and goggles. They are reasonably comfortable, afford good splash protection, have better peripheral vision, and show less tendency to fog than goggles. They fit over many types of prescription eyeglasses.

Contact Lens Users

In 1994, the Occupational Safety and Health Administration (OSHA) concluded that "contact lenses do not pose additional hazards to the wearer, and has determined that additional regulation addressing the use of contact lenses is unnecessary."[2] Other reports support this position.[3,4] It has been determined "that contact lenses can be worn in most work environments provided the same approved eye protection is worn as required of other workers in the area. Approved eye protection refers to safety glasses or goggles."[5]

LABORATORY COURTESY

Please show up on time and be prepared for the day's work. Clean up and leave promptly at the end of the lab period. Clean your desktop and sink before you leave the lab. Be certain that no items such as litmus paper, used filter papers, used cotton, or stir bars collect in the sink. Dispose of all trash properly. Please keep the balances clean. Always replace the caps on reagent bottles after use.

WORKING WITH FLAMMABLE SUBSTANCES

Relative flammability of organic solvents.

Flammable substances are the most common hazard in the organic laboratory. Two factors can make today's organic laboratory much safer than its predecessor: (1) making the scale of the experiments as small as possible and (2) not using flames. Diethyl ether (bp 35°C), the most flammable substance you will usually work with in this course, has an ignition temperature of 160°C, which means that a hot plate at that temperature will set it afire. For comparison, n-hexane (bp 69°C), a constituent of gasoline, has an ignition temperature of 225°C. The flash points of these organic liquids— that is, the temperatures at which they will catch fire if exposed to a flame or spark—are below 220°C. These are very flammable liquids; however, if you are

[2]OSHA Personal Protective Equipment for General Industry Standard, 29 CFR 1910; final rule, April 6, 1994, p. 16343.
[3]*Chemical Health and Safety* **1995**, 16.
[4]*Chemical Health and Safety* **1997**, 33.
[5]Ramsey, H.; and Breazeale, W. H. Jr. *Chem. Eng. News* **1998**, *76* (22), 6.

careful to eliminate all possible sources of ignition, they are not difficult to work with. Except for water, almost all of the liquids you will use in the laboratory are flammable.

Bulk solvents should be stored in and dispensed from appropriate safety containers (Fig. 2.2). These and other liquids will burn in the presence of the proper amount of their flammable vapors, oxygen, and a source of ignition (most commonly a flame or spark). It is usually difficult to remove oxygen from a fire, although it is possible to put out a fire in a beaker or a flask by simply covering the vessel with a flat object, thus cutting off the supply of air. Your lab notebook might do in an emergency. The best prevention is to pay close attention to sources of ignition—open flames, sparks, and hot surfaces. Remember, the vapors of flammable liquids are **always** heavier than air and thus will travel along bench tops, down drain troughs, and remain in sinks. For this reason all flames within the vicinity of a flammable liquid must be extinguished. Adequate ventilation is one of the best ways to prevent flammable vapors from accumulating. Work in an exhaust hood when manipulating large quantities of flammable liquids.

If a person's clothing catches fire and there is a safety shower close at hand, then shove the person under it and turn the shower on. Otherwise, push the person down and roll him or her over to extinguish the flames (stop, drop, and roll!). It is extremely important to prevent the victim from running or standing because the greatest harm comes from breathing the hot vapors that rise past the mouth. The safety shower might then be used to extinguish glowing cloth that is no longer aflame. A so-called fire blanket should not be used because it tends to funnel flames past the victim's mouth, and clothing continues to char beneath it. It is, however, useful for retaining warmth to ward off shock after the flames are extinguished.

An organic chemistry laboratory should be equipped with a carbon dioxide or dry chemical (monoammonium phosphate) *fire extinguisher* (Fig. 2.3). To use this type of extinguisher, lift it from its support, pull the ring to break the seal, raise the horn, aim it at the base of the fire, and squeeze the handle. Do not hold on to the horn because it will become extremely cold. Do not replace the extinguisher; report the incident so the extinguisher can be refilled.

When disposing of certain chemicals, be alert for the possibility of *spontaneous combustion*. This may occur in oily rags; organic materials exposed to strong oxidizing agents such as nitric acid, permanganate ions, and peroxides; alkali metals such as sodium; or very finely divided metals such as zinc dust and platinum catalysts. Fires sometimes start when these chemicals are left in contact with filter paper.

FIG. 2.2
Solvent safety can.

⚠ Flammable vapors travel along bench tops.

⚠ Keep ignition sources away from flammable liquids.

FIG. 2.3
Carbon dioxide fire extinguisher.

⚠ Flammable vapors plus air in a confined space are explosive.

WORKING WITH HAZARDOUS CHEMICALS

If you do not know the properties of a chemical you will be working with, it is wise to regard the chemical as hazardous. The flammability of organic substances poses the most serious hazard in the organic laboratory. There is a possibility that storage containers in the laboratory may contribute to a fire. Large quantities of organic solvents should not be stored in glass bottles; they should be stored in solvent safety cans. Do not store chemicals on the floor.

A flammable liquid can often be vaporized to form, with air, a mixture that is explosive in a confined space. The beginning chemist is sometimes surprised to learn that diethyl ether is more likely to cause a laboratory fire or explosion than a worker's accidental anesthesia. The chances of being confined in a laboratory with a concentration of ether high enough to cause a loss of consciousness are extremely small, but a spark in such a room would probably destroy the building.

FIG. 2.4
Functional groups that can be explosive in some compounds.

R—O—O—R   R—C≡C—Metal
Peroxide   **Acetylide**

R—N=N=N   R—NO₂
Azide   **Nitro**

R—N=O   R—Ṅ≡N   Ozonide (ring structure)
Nitroso   **Diazonium salts**   **Ozonide**

Safety glasses or goggles must be worn at all times.

The probability of forming an explosive mixture of volatile organic liquids with air is far greater than that of producing an explosive solid or liquid. The chief functional groups that render compounds explosive are the *peroxide, acetylide, azide, diazonium, nitroso, nitro, and ozonide groups* (Fig. 2.4). Not all members of these groups are equally sensitive to shock or heat. You would find it difficult to detonate trinitrotoluene (TNT) in the laboratory, but nitroglycerine is treacherously explosive. Peroxides present special problems that are discussed in the next section.

You will need to contend with the corrosiveness of many of the reagents you will handle. The principal danger here is to the eyes. Proper eye protection is mandatory, and even small-scale experiments can be hazardous to the eyes. It takes only a single drop of a corrosive reagent to do permanent damage. Handling concentrated acids and alkalis, dehydrating agents, and oxidizing agents calls for commonsense care to avoid spills and splashes and to avoid breathing the often corrosive vapors.

Certain organic chemicals present acute toxicity problems from short-duration exposure and chronic toxicity problems from long-term or repeated exposure. Exposure can result from ingestion, contact with the skin, or, most commonly, inhalation. Currently, great attention is being focused on chemicals that are teratogens (chemicals that often have no effect on a pregnant woman but cause abnormalities in a fetus), mutagens (chemicals causing changes in the structure of the DNA, which can lead to mutations in offspring), and carcinogens (cancer-causing chemicals). Small-scale experiments significantly reduce these hazards but do not completely eliminate them.

WORKING WITH EXPLOSIVE HAZARDS

1. Peroxides

Ethers form explosive peroxides.

Certain functional groups can make an organic molecule become sensitive to heat and shock, such that it will explode. Chemists work with these functional groups only when there are no good alternatives. One of these functional groups, the peroxide group (R—O—O—R), is particularly insidious because it can form spontaneously when oxygen and light are present (Fig. 2.5). Ethers, especially cyclic ethers and those made from primary or secondary alcohols (such as tetrahydrofuran, diethyl ether, and diisopropyl ether), form peroxides. Other compounds that form peroxides are aldehydes, alkenes that have allylic hydrogen atoms (such as

FIG. 2.5
Some compounds that form peroxides.

Tetrahydrofuran   Diisopropyl ether   Dioxane   Benzylic compounds   Ketones

Cyclohexene   Vinyl acetate   Allylic compounds   Aldehydes

Never distill to dryness.

cyclohexene), compounds having benzylic hydrogens on a tertiary carbon atom (such as isopropyl benzene), and vinyl compounds (such as vinyl acetate). Peroxides are low-power explosives but are extremely sensitive to shock, sparks, light, heat, friction, and impact. The greatest danger from peroxide impurities comes when the peroxide-forming compound is distilled. The peroxide has a higher boiling point than the parent compound and remains in the distilling flask as a residue that can become overheated and explode. For this reason, one should never distill a liquid for too long a period of time so that the distilling flask completely dries out, and the distillation of a peroxide-containing liquid should be run in a hood with the sash down to help contain a possible explosion.

The Detection of Peroxides	The Removal of Peroxides
To a solution of 0.01 g of sodium iodide in 0.1 mL of glacial acetic acid, add 0.1 mL of the liquid suspected of containing a peroxide. If the mixture turns brown, a high concentration of peroxide is present; if it turns yellow, a low concentration of peroxide is present.	Pouring the solvent through a column of activated alumina will remove peroxides and simultaneously dry the solvent. Do not allow the column to dry out while in use. When the alumina column is no longer effective, wash the column with 5% aqueous ferrous sulfate and discard the column as nonhazardous waste.

Problems with peroxide formation are especially critical for ethers. Ethers (R-O-R) form peroxides readily. Because ethers are frequently used as solvents, they are often used in quantity and then removed to leave reaction products. Cans of diethyl ether should be dated when opened. If opened cans are not used within one month, they should be treated for peroxides and disposed of.

t-Butyl methyl ether, $(CH_3)_3C$-O-CH_3, with a primary carbon on one side of the oxygen and a tertiary carbon on the other, does not form peroxides easily. It is highly desirable to use this in place of diethyl ether for extraction. Refer to the discussion in Chapter 7.

You may have occasion to use 30% *hydrogen peroxide*. This material causes severe burns if it contacts the skin and decomposes violently if contaminated with metals or their salts. Be particularly careful not to contaminate the reagent bottle.

Richard Reid, the Shoe Bomber, was arrested in 2001 for attempting to set off a peroxide explosion on a trans-Atlantic air flight. He had packed 240 g of the peroxide-initiated explosive in the heel of his shoe, a highly hazardous undertaking considering the sensitivity of peroxides to any type of friction. Theoretically, he could have made his peroxide in the airplane lavatory by mixing 30% hydrogen peroxide (not easily obtained) with another common organic liquid and an acid catalyst at 0°C, allowing the mixture to react with thorough stirring and cooling for a number of hours, preferably overnight, and then isolating the crystalline peroxide by filtration. To prevent the possibility of anyone doing this in the future, no liquids can be carried on to passenger airplanes.

2. Closed Systems

A closed system is defined as not being open to the atmosphere. Any sealed system is a closed system. If a closed system is not properly prepared, an explosion may result from the system being under pressure, caused from gas or heat evolution from the reaction or from applied heat to the system. One way to prevent an explosion of a closed system is to use glassware that can withstand the pressure, and to evacuate the system under vacuum before it is closed to the atmosphere.

Most reactions are run in open systems; that is, they are run in apparatus that are open to atmosphere, either directly or through a nitrogen line hooked up to a bubbler, which is open to atmosphere.

WORKING WITH CORROSIVE SUBSTANCES

Handle strong acids, alkalis, dehydrating agents, and oxidizing agents carefully so as to avoid contact with the skin and eyes, and to avoid breathing the corrosive vapors that attack the respiratory tract. All strong, concentrated acids attack the skin and eyes. Concentrated *sulfuric acid* is both a dehydrating agent and a strong acid and will cause very severe burns. *Nitric acid and chromic acid* (used in cleaning solutions) also cause bad burns. *Hydrofluoric* acid is especially harmful and causes deep, painful, and slow-healing wounds. It should be used only after thorough instruction. Do not add water to concentrated sulphuric acid. The heat of solution is so large that the acid may boil and spatter. It can best be diluted by pouring the acid into water, with stirring. You should wear approved safety glasses or goggles, protective gloves, and an apron when handling these materials.

Sodium, potassium, and ammonium *hydroxides* are common bases that you will encounter. Sodium and potassium hydroxides are extremely damaging to the eyes, and ammonium hydroxide is a severe bronchial irritant. Like sulfuric acid, sodium hydroxide, *phosphorous pentoxide*, and *calcium oxide* are powerful dehydrating agents. Their great affinity for water will cause burns to the skin. Because they release a great deal of heat when they react with water, to avoid spattering they should always be added to water rather than water being added to them. That is, the heavier substance should always be added to the lighter one so that layers don't form where one liquid floats on another; the desired result is a rapid mixing that occurs as a consequence of the law of gravity.

You will receive special instructions when it comes time to handle metallic sodium, lithium aluminum hydride, and sodium hydride, three substances that can react explosively with water.

⚠️

Add H_2SO_4, P_2O_5, CaO, and NaOH to water, not the reverse.

Wipe up spilled hydroxide pellets *rapidly.*

FIG. 2.6
Emergency shower and eyewash station.

Among the strong oxidizing agents, *perchloric acid* ($HClO_4$) is probably the most hazardous. It can form heavy metal and organic *perchlorates* that are *explosive*, and it can react explosively if it comes in contact with organic compounds.

If one of these substances gets on the skin or in the eyes, wash the affected area with very large quantities of water, using the safety shower and/or eyewash station (Fig. 2.6) until medical assistance arrives. Do not attempt to neutralize the reagent chemically. Remove contaminated clothing so that thorough washing can take place. Take care to wash the reagent from under the fingernails.

Take care not to let the reagents, such as sulfuric acid, run down the outside of a bottle or flask and come in contact with your fingers. Wipe up spills immediately with a very damp sponge, especially in the area around the balances. Pellets of sodium and potassium hydroxide are very hygroscopic and will dissolve in the water they pick up from the air; they should therefore be wiped up very quickly. When handling large quantities of corrosive chemicals, wear protective gloves, a face mask, and a neoprene apron. The corrosive vapors can be avoided by carrying out work in a good exhaust hood.

Do not use a plastic syringe with a metal needle to dispense corrosive inorganic reagents, such as concentrated acids or bases.

WORKING WITH TOXIC SUBSTANCES

Many chemicals have very specific toxic effects. They interfere with the body's metabolism in a known way. For example, the cyanide ion combines irreversibly with hemoglobin to form cyanometmyoglobin, which can no longer carry oxygen. Aniline acts in the same way. Carbon tetrachloride and other halogenated compounds can cause liver and kidney failure. Carcinogenic and mutagenic substances deserve special attention because of their long-term insidious effects. The ability of certain carcinogens to cause cancer is very great; for example, special precautions are needed when handling aflatoxin B_1. In other cases, such as with dioxane, the hazard is so low that no special precautions are needed beyond reasonable, normal care in the laboratory.

Women of childbearing age should be careful when handling any substance of unknown properties. Certain substances are highly suspected as teratogens and will cause abnormalities in an embryo or fetus. Among these are benzene, toluene, xylene, aniline, nitrobenzene, phenol, formaldehyde, dimethylformamide (DMF), dimethyl sulfoxide (DMSO), polychlorinated biphenyls (PCBs), estradiol, hydrogen sulfide, carbon disulfide, carbon monoxide, nitrites, nitrous oxide, organolead and mercury compounds, and the notorious sedative thalidomide. Some of these substances will be used in subsequent experiments. Use care when working with these (and all) substances. One of the leading known causes of embryotoxic effects is ethyl alcohol in the form of maternal alcoholism, but the amount of ethanol vapor inhaled in the laboratory or absorbed through the skin is so minute that it is unlikely to have morbid effects.

It is impossible to avoid handling every known or suspected toxic substance, so it is wise to know what measures should be taken. Because the eating of food or the consumption of beverages in the laboratory is strictly forbidden and because one should never taste material in the laboratory, the possibility of poisoning by mouth is remote. Be more careful than your predecessors—the hallucinogenic properties of LSD and **all** artificial sweeteners were discovered by accident. The two most important measures to be taken, then, are (1) avoiding skin contact by wearing the *proper* type of protective gloves (*see* "Gloves") and (2) avoiding inhalation by working in a good exhaust hood.

Many of the chemicals used in this course will be unfamiliar to you. Their properties can be looked up in reference books, a very useful one being the *Aldrich Handbook of Fine Chemicals*.[6] Note that 1,4-dichlorobenzene is listed as a "toxic irritant" and naphthalene is listed as an "irritant." Both are used as mothballs. Camphor, used in vaporizers, is classified as a "flammable solid irritant." Salicylic acid, which we will use to synthesize aspirin (Chapter 41), is listed as a "moisture-sensitive toxic." Aspirin (acetylsalicylic acid) is classified as an "irritant." Caffeine, which we will isolate from tea or cola syrup (Chapter 7), is classified as "toxic." Substances not so familiar to you, for example, 1-naphthol and benzoic acid, are classified, respectively, as "toxic irritant" and "irritant." To put things in perspective, nicotine is classified as "highly toxic." Pay attention to these health warnings. In laboratory quantities, common chemicals can be hazardous. Wash your hands carefully after coming in contact with laboratory chemicals. Consult the *Hazardous Laboratory Chemicals Disposal Guide*[7] for information on truly hazardous chemicals.

Because you have not had previous experience working with organic chemicals, most of the experiments you will carry out in this course will not involve the use of known carcinogens, although you will work routinely with flammable, corrosive, and toxic substances. A few experiments involve the use of substances that are suspected of being carcinogenic, such as hydrazine. If you pay proper attention to the rules of safety, you should find working with these substances no more hazardous than working with ammonia or nitric acid. The single, short-duration exposure you might receive from a suspected carcinogen, should an accident occur, would probably have no long-term consequences. The reason for taking the precautions noted in each experiment is to learn, from the beginning, good safety habits.

GLOVES

Be aware that protective gloves in the organic laboratory may not offer much protection. Polyethylene and latex rubber gloves are very permeable to many organic liquids. An undetected pinhole may bring with it long-term contact with reagents. Disposable polyvinyl chloride (PVC) gloves offer reasonable protection from contact with aqueous solutions of acids, bases, and dyes, but no one type of glove is useful as a protection against all reagents. It is for this reason that no less than 25 different types of chemically resistant gloves are available from laboratory supply houses. Some gloves are quite expensive and will last for years.

If disposable gloves are available, fresh nitrile gloves can be worn whenever handling a corrosive substance and disposed of once the transfer is complete. When not wearing gloves, it is advised that you wash your hands every 15 minutes to remove any traces of chemicals that might be on them.

USING THE LABORATORY HOOD

Modern practice dictates that in laboratories where workers spend most of their time working with chemicals, there should be one exhaust hood for every two people. However, this precaution is often not possible in the beginning organic chemistry laboratory. In this course you will find that for some experiments, the hood

[6]Free copies of this catalog can be obtained from http://www.sigmaaldrich.com/Brands/Aldrich.html.
[7]Armour, M-A. *Hazardous Laboratory Chemicals Disposal Guide*, 3rd ed.; CRC Press LLC: Boca Raton, FL, 2003. This extremely useful book is now available without charge on Google Books.

must be used and for others it is advisable; in these instances, it may be necessary to schedule experimental work around access to the hoods. Many experiments formerly carried out in the hood can now be carried out at the lab desk because the concentration of vapors is significantly minimized when working at a microscale.

The hood offers a number of advantages when working with toxic and flammable substances. Not only does it draw off the toxic and flammable fumes, but it also affords an excellent physical barrier on all four sides of a reacting system when the sash is pulled down. If a chemical spill occurs, it may be contained within the hood.

Keep the hood sash closed.

It is your responsibility each time you use a hood to see that it is working properly. You should find some type of indicating device that will give you this information on the hood itself. A simple propeller on a cork works well. Note that the hood is a backup device. Never use it alone to dispose of chemicals by evaporation; use an aspirator tube or carry out a distillation. Toxic and flammable fumes should be trapped or condensed in some way and disposed of in the prescribed manner. The sash should be pulled down unless you are actually carrying out manipulations with the experimental apparatus. The water, gas, and electrical controls should be on the outside of the hood, so it is not necessary to open the hood to make adjustments. The ability of the hood to remove vapors is greatly enhanced if the apparatus is kept as close to the back of the hood as possible, where the air movement is the strongest. Everything should be at least 15 cm back from the hood sash. Chemicals should not be permanently stored in the hood, but should be removed to ventilated storage areas. If the hood is cluttered with chemicals, you will not achieve a good, smooth airflow or have adequate room for experiments.

WORKING AT REDUCED PRESSURE

Whenever a vessel or system is evacuated, an implosion could result from atmospheric pressure on the empty vessel. It makes little difference whether it's a total vacuum or just 10 mm Hg; the pressure difference is almost the same (760 versus 750 mm Hg). An implosion may occur if there is a star crack in the flask or if the flask is scratched or etched. Only with heavy-walled flasks specifically designed for vacuum filtration is the use of a safety shield (Fig. 2.7) ordinarily unnecessary. Although caution should still be observed, the chances of implosion of the apparatus used for microscale experiments are remote.

Implosion

Dewar flasks (thermos bottles) are often found in the laboratory without shielding. These should be wrapped with friction tape or covered with a plastic net to prevent the glass from flying about in case of an implosion (Fig. 2.8). Similarly, vacuum desiccators should be wrapped with tape before being evacuated.

FIG. 2.7
Safety shield.

FIG. 2.8
Dewar flask with safety net in place.

WORKING WITH COMPRESSED GAS CYLINDERS

Many reactions are carried out under an inert atmosphere so that the reactants and/or products will not react with oxygen or moisture in the air. Nitrogen and argon are the inert gases most frequently used. Oxygen is widely used both as a reactant and to provide a hot flame for glassblowing and welding. It is used in the oxidative coupling of alkynes (Chapter 24). Helium is the carrier gas used in gas chromatography. Other gases commonly used in the laboratory are ammonia, which is often used as a solvent; chlorine, used for chlorination reactions; acetylene, used in combination with oxygen for welding; and hydrogen, used for high- and low-pressure hydrogenation reactions.

⚠ **Always clamp gas cylinders**

The following rule applies to all compressed gases: Compressed gas cylinders should be firmly secured at all times. For temporary use, a clamp that attaches to the laboratory bench top and has a belt for the cylinder will suffice (Fig. 2.9). Eyebolts and chains should be used to secure cylinders in permanent installations. Flammable gases should be stored 20 feet from oxidizing gases.

A variety of outlet threads are used on gas cylinders to prevent incompatible gases from being mixed because of an interchange of connections. Both right- and left-handed external and internal threads are used. Left-handed nuts are notched to differentiate them from right-handed nuts. Right-handed threads are used on nonfuel and oxidizing gases, and left-handed threads are used on fuel gases, such as hydrogen. Never grease the threads on tank or regulator valves because there is the possibility that the grease could ignite under certain conditions.

Cylinders come equipped with caps that should be left in place during storage and transportation. These caps can be removed by hand. Under these caps is a cylinder valve. It can be opened by turning the valve counterclockwise. However, because most compressed gases in full cylinders are under very high pressure (commonly up to 3000 lb/in.^{2}), a pressure regulator must be attached to the cylinder. This pressure regulator is almost always of the diaphragm type and has two gauges—one indicating the pressure in the cylinder, the other the outlet pressure (Fig. 2.10). On the outlet, low-pressure side of the regulator is a small needle valve and then the outlet connector. After connecting the regulator to the cylinder, unscrew the diaphragm valve (turn it counterclockwise) before

***Clockwise* movement of the diaphragm valve handle *increases* pressure.**

FIG. 2.9
Gas cylinder clamp.

— Cylinder valve

FIG. 2.10
Gas pressure regulator. Turn the two-flanged diaphragm valve clockwise to increase outlet pressure.

Outlet pressure gauge

Cylinder pressure gauge

Notches indicating left-hand thread

Needle valve

Outlet

Diaphragm valve

This is page 41.

FIG. 2.11
Gas cylinder cart.

Cap

opening the cylinder valve on the top of the cylinder. This valve should be opened only as far as necessary. For most gas flow rates in the laboratory, this will be a very small amount. The gas flow or pressure is increased by turning the two-flanged diaphragm valve **clockwise**. When the gas is not being used, turn off the cylinder valve (clockwise) on the top of the cylinder (Fig. 2.9). Before removing the regulator from the cylinder, reduce the flow or pressure to zero. Cylinders should never be emptied to zero pressure and left with the valve open because the residual contents will become contaminated with air. Empty cylinders should be labeled "empty." Their valves should be closed and capped, and the cylinders should be returned to the storage area and separated from full cylinders. Gas cylinders should never be dragged or rolled from place to place, but should be fastened onto and moved in a cart designed for that purpose (Fig. 2.11). The cap should be in place whenever the cylinder is moved. If you detect even a small leak from any valve or connection, immediately seek the help of an instructor to remedy the problem. If there is a major leak of a corrosive or flammable gas, notify those around you to leave the area and seek help immediately.

ODORIFEROUS CHEMICALS

⚠
Never attempt to identify an unknown organic compound by smelling it.

Some organic chemicals just smell bad. Among these are the thiols (organic derivatives of hydrogen sulfide, also called mercaptans), isonitriles, many amines (e.g., cadaverine), and butyric acid. Washing apparatus and, if necessary, hands in a solution of a quaternary ammonium salt may solve the problem. These compounds apparently complex with many odoriferous substances, allowing them to be rinsed away. Commercial products (e.g., Zephiran, Roccal, San-O-Fec, and others) are available at pet and farm supply stores.

Clean up spills rapidly.

WASTE DISPOSAL—CLEANING UP

Spilled solids should simply be swept up and placed in the appropriate solid waste container. This should be done promptly because many solids are hygroscopic and become difficult if not impossible to sweep up in a short time. This is particularly true of sodium hydroxide and potassium hydroxide; these strong bases should be dissolved in water and neutralized with sodium bisulfate before disposal.

The method used to clean up spills depends on the type and amount of chemical spilled. If more than 1 or 2 g or mL of any chemical, particularly a corrosive or volatile one, is spilled, you should consult your instructor for the best way to clean up the spill. If a large amount of volatile or noxious liquid is spilled as might happen if a reagent bottle is dropped and broken, advise those in the area to leave the laboratory and contact your instructor immediately. If a spill involves a large amount of flammable liquid, be aware of any potential ignition sources and try to eliminate them. Large amounts of spilled acid can be neutralized with granular limestone or cement; large amounts of bases can be neutralized with solid sodium bisulfate, $NaHSO_4$. Large amounts of volatile liquids can be absorbed into materials such as vermiculite, diatomaceous earth, dry sand, kitty litter, or paper towels and these materials swept up and placed in a separate disposal container.

⚠
Mercury requires special measures— see your instructor

For spills of amounts less than 2 g of chemical, proceed as follows. Acid spills should be neutralized by dropping solid sodium carbonate onto them, testing the pH, wiping up the neutralized material with a sponge, and rinsing the neutral salt solution down the drain. Bases should be neutralized by sprinkling solid sodium bisulfate onto them, checking the pH, and wiping up with a sponge or towel. Do not use paper towels to wipe up spills of strong oxidizers such as dichromates or nitrates; the towels can ignite. Bits of sodium metal will also cause paper towels to ignite. Sodium metal is best destroyed with n-butyl alcohol. Always wear gloves when cleaning up a spill.

Cleaning Up. In the not-too-distant past, it was common practice to wash all unwanted liquids from the organic laboratory down the drain and to place all solid waste in the trash basket. For environmental reasons, this is never a wise practice and is no longer allowed by law.

Organic reactions usually employ a solvent and often involve the use of a strong acid, a strong base, an oxidant, a reductant, or a catalyst. None of these should be washed down the drain or placed in the wastebasket. Place the material, classified as waste, in containers labeled for nonhazardous solid waste, organic solvents, halogenated organic solvents, or hazardous wastes of various types.

Waste containers:
Nonhazardous solid waste
Organic solvents
Halogenated organic solvents
Hazardous waste (various types)

Nonhazardous waste encompasses such solids as paper, corks, TLC plates, solid chromatographic absorbents such as alumina or silica that are dry and free of residual *organic solvents*, and solid drying agents such as calcium chloride or sodium sulfate that are also dry and free of residual organic solvents. These will ultimately end up in a sanitary landfill (the local dump). Any chemicals that are leached by rainwater from this landfill must not be harmful to the environment. In the organic solvents container are placed the solvents that are used for recrystallization and for running reactions, cleaning apparatus, and so forth. These solvents can contain dissolved, solid, nonhazardous organic solids. This solution will go to an incinerator where it will be burned. If the solvent is halogenated (e.g., dichloromethane) or contains halogenated material, it must go in the *halogenated organic solvents* container. Ultimately, this will go to a special incinerator equipped with a scrubber to remove HCl from the combustion gases. The organic laboratory should also have several other waste disposal containers for special hazardous, reactive, and noncombustible wastes that would be incompatible with waste organic solvents and other materials. For example, it would be dangerous to place oxidants in lysts with many organics. In particular, separate waste containers should be provided for toxic heavy metal wastes containing mercury, chromium, or lead salts, and so forth. The cleaning up sections throughout this text will call your attention to these special hazards.

Hazardous wastes such as sodium hydrosulfite (a reducing agent), platinum catalysts, and Cr^{6+} an oxidizing agent) cannot be burned and must be shipped to a secure landfill. To dispose of small quantities of a hazardous waste (e.g., solid mercury hydroxide), the material must be carefully packed in bottles and placed in a 55-gal ($\approx$-208-L) drum called a lab pack, to which an inert material has been added. The lab pack is carefully documented and hauled off to a site where such waste is disposed of by a bonded, licensed, and heavily regulated waste disposal company. Formerly, many hazardous wastes were disposed of by burial in a secure landfill. The kinds of hazardous waste that can be thus disposed of have become extremely limited in recent years, and much of the waste undergoes various kinds of treatment at the disposal site (e.g., neutralization, incineration, or reduction) to put it in a form that can be safely buried in a secure landfill or flushed to a sewer. There are relatively few places for approved disposal of hazardous waste. For example, there are none in New England, so most hazardous waste from this area is trucked to South Carolina. The charge to small generators of waste is usually based on the volume of waste. So, 1000 mL of a 2% cyanide solution would cost far more to dispose of than 20 g of solid cyanide, even though the total amount of this poisonous substance is the same. It now costs far more to dispose of most hazardous chemicals than it does to purchase them new.

Waste disposal is very expensive.

American law states that a material is not a waste until the laboratory worker declares it a waste. So—for pedagogical and practical reasons—we want you to regard the chemical treatment of the byproducts of each reaction in this text as a part of the experiment.

The law: A waste is not a waste until the laboratory worker declares it a waste.

In the section titled "Cleaning Up" at the end of each experiment, the goal is to reduce the volume of hazardous waste, to convert hazardous waste to less hazardous waste, or to convert it to nonhazardous waste. The simplest example is concentrated sulfuric acid. As a byproduct from a reaction, it is obviously hazardous. But after careful dilution with water and neutralization with sodium carbonate, the sulfuric acid becomes a dilute solution of sodium sulfate, which in almost every locale can be flushed down the drain with a large quantity of water. Anything flushed down the drain must be accompanied by a large excess of water. Similarly, concentrated bases can be neutralized, oxidants such as Cr^{61} can be reduced, and reductants such as hydrosulfite can be oxidized (by hypochlorite or household bleach). Dilute solutions of heavy metal ions can be precipitated as their insoluble sulfides or hydroxides. The precipitate may still be a hazardous waste, but it will have a much smaller volume.

Cleaning up: reducing the volume of hazardous waste or converting hazardous waste to less hazardous or nonhazardous waste.

One type of hazardous waste is unique: a harmless solid that is damp with an organic solvent. Alumina from a chromatography column and calcium chloride used to dry an ether solution are examples. Being solids, they obviously cannot go in the organic solvents container, and being flammable they cannot go in the nonhazardous waste container. A solution to this problem is to spread the solid out in the hood to let the solvent evaporate. You can then place the solid in the nonhazardous waste container. The savings in waste disposal costs by this operation are enormous. However, be aware of the regulations in your area, as they may not allow evaporation of small amounts of organic solvents in a hood. If this is the case, special containers should be available for disposal of these wet solids.

Disposing of solids wet with organic solvents: alumina and anhydrous calcium chloride pellets.

Our goal in "Cleaning Up" is to make you more aware of all aspects of an experiment. Waste disposal is now an extremely important aspect. Check to be sure the procedure you use is permitted by law in your location. Three sources of information have been used as the basis of the procedures at the end of each experiment: the *Aldrich Catalog Handbook of Fine Chemicals*,[8] which gives brief disposal procedures for every chemical in their catalog; *Prudent Practices in the Laboratory: Handling and Disposal of Chemicals*[9]; and the *Hazardous Laboratory Chemicals Disposal Guide*.[10] The last title listed here should be on the bookshelf of every laboratory. This 464-page book gives detailed information about hundreds of hazardous substances, including their physical properties, hazardous reactions, physiological properties, health hazards, spillage disposal, and waste disposal. Many of the treatment procedures in "Cleaning Up" are adaptations of these procedures. *Destruction of Hazardous Chemicals in the Laboratory*[11] complements this book.

---

[8]See footnote 6 on page 34.
[9]National Research Council. *Prudent Practices in the Laboratory: Handling and Disposal of Chemicals* National Academy Press: Washington, DC, 1995.
[10]See footnote 7 on page 34.
[11]Lunn, G.; Sansone, E. B. *Destruction of Hazardous Chemicals in the Laboratory*; Wiley: New York, 1994.

The area of waste disposal is changing rapidly. Many levels of laws apply—local, state, and federal. What may be permissible to wash down the drain or evaporate in the hood in one jurisdiction may be illegal in another, so before carrying out any waste disposal, check with your college or university waste disposal officer.

BIOHAZARDS

The use of microbial growth bioassays is becoming common in chemistry laboratories. The use of infectious materials presents new hazards that must be recognized and addressed. The first step in reducing hazards when using these materials is to select infectious materials that are known not to cause illness in humans and are of minimal hazard to the environment. A number of procedures should be followed to ensure safety when these materials are used: Individuals need to wash their hands after they handle these materials and before they leave the laboratory; work surfaces need to be decontaminated at the end of each use; and all infectious materials need to be decontaminated before disposal.

QUESTIONS

1. Write a balanced equation for the reaction between the iodide ion, a peroxide, and the hydrogen ion. What causes the orange or brown color?

2. Why does the horn of the carbon dioxide fire extinguisher become cold when the extinguisher is used?

3. Why is water not used to extinguish most fires in an organic laboratory? Consider the following scenario. An organic chemistry student is setting up an experiment on the benchtop, just outside the hood. He is wearing gloves as he dispenses diethyl ether, a volatile, flammable solvent. By accident he spills some ether on his hand but continues on with the experiment. The experiment is complete, and he cleans up. He puts the ether down the drain and washes the glassware. He then takes off his gloves and washes his hands. List all of the safety issues (if any) with this scenario.

CHAPTER 3

Melting Points and Boiling Points

When you see this icon, sign in at this book's premium website at **www.cengage.com/login** to access videos, Pre-Lab Exercises and other online resources.

PRELAB EXERCISE: Draw the organic compounds, identify the intermolecular attractive forces for each, and list them in order of increasing boiling point as predicted by the relative strength of those intermolecular forces: (a) butane, (b) *i*-butanol, (c) potassium acetate, (d) acetone.

PART 1: FIVE CONCEPTS FOR PREDICTING PHYSICAL PROPERTIES

In organic chemistry, structure is everything. A molecule's structure determines both its physical properties and its reactivity. Since the dawn of modern chemistry 200 years ago, over 20 million substances, most of them organic compounds, have been isolated, and their properties and reactions have been studied. It became apparent from these studies that certain structural features in organic molecules would affect the observed properties in a predictable way and that these millions of organic compounds could be organized into classes based on molecular size, composition, and the pattern of bonds between atoms. Chemists also saw trends in certain properties based on systematic changes in these structural features. This organized knowledge allows us to look at a compound's structure and to predict the physical properties of that compound.

Physical properties, such as melting point, boiling point, and solubility, are largely determined by *intermolecular attractive forces*. You learned about these properties in previous chemistry courses. Because a solid understanding of these concepts is critical to understanding organic chemistry, we will review the different types of forces in the context of structural organic chemistry. Using five simple concepts, you should be able to look at the structures of a group of different organic molecules and predict which might be liquids, gases, or solids and which might be soluble in water. You can often predict the boiling point, melting point, or solubility of one structure relative to other structures. In fact, as your knowledge grows, you may be able to predict a compound's approximate melting or boiling temperature based on its structure. Your understanding of intermolecular attractive forces will be very useful in this chapter's experiments on melting and boiling points, and those in Chapters 5 and 6 that involve distillation and boiling points.

41

1. LONDON ATTRACTIVE FORCES (OFTEN CALLED VAN DER WAALS FORCES)

Organic molecules that contain only carbon and hydrogen (hydrocarbons) are weakly attracted to each other by London forces. Though weak, these attractive forces increase as molecular size increases. Thus, the larger the molecule, the greater the attractive force for neighboring molecules and the greater the energy required to get two molecules to move apart. This trend can be seen if we compare the melting points and boiling points of three hydrocarbons of different size: methane, hexane, and tetracosane.

CH_4

Methane
mp −182°C
bp −162°C
Gas at room temp.

Hexane, C_6H_{14}
mp −95°C
bp +69°C
Liquid at room temp.

Tetracosane, $C_{24}H_{50}$
mp +51°C
bp +391°C
Solid at room temp.

We know that methane is called natural gas because methane's physical state at room temperature (20°C = 68°F) is a gas. Its London forces are so weak that methane must be cooled to −162°C at 1 atm of pressure before the molecules will stick together enough to form a liquid. Hexane is a very common liquid solvent found on most organic laboratory shelves. The intermolecular forces between its molecules are strong enough to keep them from flying apart, but the molecules are still able to flex and slide by each other to form a fluid. Hexane must be heated above 69°C, which is 231°C hotter than methane, to convert all its molecules to a gas. Tetracosane, a C_{24} solid hydrocarbon, is four times larger than hexane, and its London forces are strong enough to hold the molecules rigidly in place at room temperature. Tetracosane is one of the many long-chain hydrocarbons found in candle wax, which must be heated in order to disrupt the intermolecular forces and melt the wax into a liquid. A lot of energy is required to convert liquid tetracosane to a gas, as evidenced by its extremely high boiling point (391°C).

2. DIPOLE-DIPOLE ATTRACTIVE FORCES

The attractive forces between molecules increases when functional groups containing electronegative atoms such as chlorine, oxygen, and nitrogen are present because these atoms are more electronegative than carbon. These atoms pull electrons toward themselves, making their end of the bond slightly negatively charged (δ^-) and leaving the carbon slightly positively charged (δ^+), as shown for isopropyl chloride and acetone.

Isobutane
mp −137°C
bp 0°C
Gas at room temp.

Isopropyl chloride
mp −117°C
bp +35°C
Liquid at room temp.

Acetone
mp −94°C
bp +56°C
Liquid at room temp.

A bond with a slight charge separation is termed a *polar* bond, and polar atomic bonds often give a molecule a *dipole*: slightly positive and negative ends symbolized by an arrow in the direction of the negative charge (+→). Attraction of the positive end of one molecule's dipole to the negative end of another's dipole occurs between polar molecules, which increases the intermolecular attractive force. Dipole-dipole attractive forces are stronger than London forces, as demonstrated in the previous examples that show an increase in melting point and boiling point when a methyl group of isobutane is replaced by chlorine or oxygen.

3. HYDROGEN BONDING

Hydrogen bonding is an even stronger intermolecular attractive force, as evidenced by the large increase in the melting point and boiling points of the alcohol methanol (MW = 32) relative to those of the hydrocarbon ethane (MW = 30), both of comparable molecular weight. Hydrogen bonding occurs with organic molecules containing O—H groups (for example, alcohols and carboxylic acids) or N—H groups (for example, amines or amides). The hydrogen in these groups is attracted to the unshared pair of electrons on the O or N of another molecule, forming a hydrogen bond, often symbolized by a dashed line, which is shown for methanol.

$$CH_3—CH_3$$

Ethane
mp −172°C
bp −88°C
Gas at room temp.

Methanol
mp −97°C
bp +65°C
Liquid at room temp.

As this example indicates, the hydrogen bonds extend throughout the liquid. One can think of these hydrogen bonds as molecular Velcro that can be pulled apart if there is sufficient energy. Hydrogen bonding plays a major role in the special physical behavior of water and is a major determinant of the chemistry of proteins and nucleic acids in living systems.

4. IONIC ATTRACTIVE FORCES

Recall that ionic substances, such as table salt (NaCl), are usually solids with high melting points (>300°C) due to the strong attractive forces between positive and negative ions. Most organic molecules contain only covalent bonds and have no ionic attractive forces between them. However, there are three important exceptions involving acidic or basic functional groups that can form ionic structures as the pH is raised or lowered.

1. The hydrogen on the —OH of the carboxyl group in carboxylic acids, such as acetic acid, is acidic (H⁺ donating) and reacts with bases such as potassium hydroxide (KOH) and sodium bicarbonate (NaHCO₃) to form salts. The process is reversed by adding an acid to lower the pH.

Potassium acetate
mp 306°C

$$\underset{\text{H}^+}{\overset{\text{KOH}}{\rightleftharpoons}}$$

Acetic acid
mp 17°C

$$\underset{\text{H}^+}{\overset{\text{NaHCO}_3}{\rightleftharpoons}}$$

Sodium acetate
mp >300°C

The dry salts are ionic and have very high melting points, which is expected for ionic substances. Note that this acidity is *not* observed for alcohols where the —OH group is attached to a singly bonded (sp³ or saturated) carbon.

2. The hydrogen on an —OH group that is attached to an aromatic ring is weakly acidic and reacts with strong bases such as sodium hydroxide (NaOH) to form high melting ionic salts, as evidenced by the reaction of phenol to sodium phenolate. Again, the reaction is reversed by the addition of an acid.

Phenol
mp 41°C

$$\underset{\text{H}^+}{\overset{\text{NaOH}}{\rightleftharpoons}}$$

Sodium phenolate
mp 382°C

Note again that this acidity is *not observed* for alcohols where the —OH group is attached to a singly bonded (sp³ or saturated) carbon.

3. Amines (but not amides) are basic (H⁺ accepting) and will react with acid to form ionic amine salts with elevated melting points, as shown, for example, for isopropyl amine.

$$CH_3\text{—}\underset{\underset{\displaystyle CH_3}{|}}{CH}\text{—}NH_2 \quad \underset{\text{base}}{\overset{HCl}{\rightleftharpoons}} \quad CH_3\text{—}\underset{\underset{\displaystyle CH_3}{|}}{CH}\text{—}NH_3^+\ Cl^-$$

Isopropyl amine   **Isopropyl amine hydrochloride**
mp −95°C   mp 162°C

Amine salts can be converted back to amines by adding a base to raise the pH.

---

5. COMPETING INTERMOLECULAR FORCES AND SOLUBILITY

For pure compounds containing identical molecules, the total attractive force between molecules is the sum of all the attractive forces listed previously, both weak and strong. These forces tend to work together to raise melting and boiling points as the size of the molecule's hydrocarbon skeleton increases and as polar, hydrogen bonded, or ionic functional groups are incorporated into the molecule. However, solubility involves the interaction of two different molecules, which may have different types of attractive forces. When we try to dissolve one substance in another, we have to disrupt the attractive forces in both substances to get the molecules of the two substances to intermingle. For example, to get water (polar with hydrogen bonding) and the hydrocarbons (nonpolar and no hydrogen bonding) in motor oil to mix and dissolve in one another, we would have to disrupt the London attractive forces between the oil molecules and the hydrogen bonds between the water molecules. Because London forces are weak, separating the oil molecules does not require much energy. However, breaking apart the much stronger hydrogen bonds by inserting oil molecules between the water molecules requires considerable energy and is unfavorable. Therefore, oil or even the simplest hydrocarbon, methane, is insoluble in water. This is the molecular basis of the old adage "Oil and water don't mix."

In addition to carbon and hydrogen, the majority of organic molecules contain other elements, such as nitrogen and oxygen, in functional groups that can be polar, exhibit hydrogen bonding, show ionic tendencies, or have any combination thereof. Can we predict the water solubility of these organic substances? Let's look at some examples and see.

Figure 3.1 shows a collection of small organic molecules of about the same size and molecular weight, listed in order of increasing boiling point or melting point, which is consistent with the types of intermolecular forces discussed. With the exception of the hydrocarbon butane, all of these substances are very soluble in water—at least 100 g will dissolve in 1 L of water. It appears that the intermolecular attractive forces between these polar, hydrogen bonded, or ionic molecules and water compensates for the disruption of hydrogen bonding between water molecules so the organic molecules can move into and intermingle with the water molecules—in other words, dissolve.

Figure 3.2 shows a collection of larger organic molecules than those in Figure 3.1, again listed in order of increasing melting and boiling point, which is consistent with our knowledge of the strength of intermolecular attractive forces. The important difference for this group is that the hydrocarbon portion of each molecule is

FIG. 3.1

Some small organic molecules containing 4 atoms (carbon, oxygen, and nitrogen) in order of increasing melting or boiling points.

C₄ Hydrocarbon, butane
mp –138°C; bp 0°C
Insoluble in H₂O

C₃ Amine
mp –43°C; bp 48°C
Soluble in H₂O; Soluble in organic solvents

C₃ Ketone, acetone
mp –94°C; bp 56°C
Soluble in H₂O; Soluble in organic solvents

C₃ Alcohol
mp –127°C; bp 97°C
Soluble in H₂O; Soluble in organic solvents

C₂ Carboxylic acid. acetic acid
mp 17°C; bp 117°C
Soluble in H₂O; Soluble in organic solvents

C₃ Amine hydrochloride
mp 161°C
Soluble in H₂O; Insoluble in organic solvents

Sodium salt of C₂ carboxylic acid
mp 324°C
Soluble in H₂O; Insoluble in organic solvents

FIG. 3.2

Some organic molecules containing 8 atoms (carbon, oxygen, and nitrogen) in order of increasing melting or boiling points.

C₈ Hydrocarbon, octane
mp –57°C; bp 126°C
Insoluble in H₂O

C₇ Amine
mp –18°C; bp 154°C
Insoluble in H₂O; Soluble in organic solvents

C₇ Ketone
mp –35°C; bp 150°C
Insoluble in H₂O; Soluble in organic solvents

C₇ Alcohol
mp –34°C; bp 175°C
Insoluble in H₂O; Soluble in organic solvents

C₆ Carboxylic acid
mp –2°C; bp 200°C
Insoluble in H₂O; Soluble in organic solvents

C₇ Amine hydrochloride
mp 242°C
Soluble in H₂O; Insoluble in organic solvents

Sodium salt of C₆ carboxylic acid
mp 245°C
Soluble in H₂O; Insoluble in organic solvents

four carbons larger than for those in Figure 3.1. We might predict that the larger hydrocarbon portion makes them behave more like the water-insoluble hydrocarbon octane. Indeed, the larger hydrocarbon portion of these molecules greatly reduces their solubility in water to less than 5 g/L of water except for the two ionic compounds. These two, the amine hydrochloride and the sodium carboxylate compounds, have higher solubility—tens of grams per liter of water—proof that ionic charges can interact strongly with water molecules.

FIG. 3.3
Some organic molecules containing 18 atoms (carbon, oxygen, and nitrogen) in order of increasing melting or boiling points.

C₁₈ Hydrocarbon
mp 6°C
Insoluble in H₂O

C₁₇ Ketone
mp 48°C
Insoluble in H₂O; Soluble in organic solvents

C₁₇ Amine
mp 49°C
Insoluble in H₂O; Soluble in organic solvents

C₁₇ Alcohol
mp 53°C
Insoluble in H₂O; Soluble in organic solvents

C₁₆ Carboxylic acid
mp 63°C
Insoluble in H₂O; Soluble in organic solvents

C₁₇ Amine hydrochloride
mp 165°C
Soluble in H₂O; Slightly soluble in organic solvents

Sodium salt of C₁₆ carboxylic acid
mp 270°C
Soluble in H₂O; Slightly soluble in organic solvents

This trend in water solubility based on the size of the hydrocarbon portion continues for the set of even larger organic molecules shown in Figure 3.3 containing C_{16} to C_{18} hydrocarbon chains. Most are virtually insoluble in water, and even the ionic forms have solubilities of less than 1 g/L of water.

In addition to water, many other liquid solvents are used in the organic laboratory to dissolve substances, including acetone, dichloromethane (CH_2Cl_2), ethanol (CH_3CH_2OH), diethyl ether ($CH_3CH_2OCH_2CH_3$), hexane, methanol, and toluene ($C_6H_5CH_3$). Predicting the solubility of different organic compounds, such as those shown in Figures 3.1, 3.2, and 3.3, in these solvents can be done using the intermolecular attractive force concepts discussed here. For example, because the molecules in Figure 3.3 have long hydrocarbon skeletons, you would predict that these would probably be soluble in the hydrocarbon hexane. This predictive rule can be summed up as "Like dissolves like." You might also predict that the two ionic materials would be the least soluble in hexane because of the strong intermolecular forces in these solids, as evidenced by their high melting points, which are so unlike the weak London forces in hexane. The solubility of organic compounds in organic solvents and water at low, neutral, and high pH will be considered in more detail when you learn about recrystallization in Chapter 4 and extraction in Chapter 7.

PART 2: MELTING POINTS

A. THERMOMETERS

There are a few types of thermometers that can be used to read melting point (and boiling point) temperatures: mercury-in-glass thermometers, non-mercury thermometers, and digital thermometers. Mercury-in-glass thermometers provide highly accurate readings and are ideal for use at high temperatures (260°C–400°C). Care should be taken not to break the thermometer, which will release the toxic mercury. Teflon-coated mercury thermometers are usable up to 260°C and are less likely to spill mercury if broken. If breakage does happen, inform your instructor immediately because special equipment is required to clean up mercury spills. A digital thermometer (Fig. 3.4) has a low heat capacity and a fast response time. It is more robust than a glass thermometer and does not, of course, contain mercury. Non-mercury thermometers may be filled with isoamyl benzoate (a biodegradable liquid) or with a custom organic red-spirit liquid instead of mercury. These thermometers give reasonably accurate readings at temperatures up to 150°C, but above this temperature they need to be carefully calibrated. These thermometers should be stored vertically to prevent thread separation.

⚠ Mercury is toxic. Immediately report any broken thermometers to your instructor so that proper clean-up with a mercury disposal kit can occur.

B. MELTING POINTS

The melting point of a pure solid organic compound is one of its characteristic physical properties, along with molecular weight, boiling point, refractive index, and density. A pure solid will melt reproducibly over a narrow range of temperatures, typically less than 1°C. The process of determining this melting point is done on a truly micro scale using less than 1 mg of material. The apparatus is simple, consisting of a thermometer, a capillary tube to hold the sample, and a heating bath.

Melting points—a micro technique

Characterization

An indication of purity

Melting points are determined for three reasons: (1) If the compound is a known one, the melting point will help to characterize the sample; (2) If the compound is new, then the melting point is recorded to allow future characterization by others; (3) The range of the melting point is indicative of the purity of the compound – an impure compound will melt over a wide range of temperatures. Recrystallization of the compound will purify it and decrease the melting point range. In addition, the entire range will be displaced upward. For example, an impure sample might melt from 120°C to 124°C, and after recrystallization will melt at 125°C–125.5°C. A solid is considered pure if the melting point does not rise after recrystallization.

A crystal is an orderly arrangement of molecules in a solid. As heat is added to the solid, the molecules will vibrate and perhaps rotate, but still remain a solid. At a characteristic temperature, the crystal will suddenly acquire the necessary

FIG. 3.4
A digital thermometer.

Digital
thermometer

Surface
probe

FIG. 3.5
A melting point–composition diagram for mixtures of the solids X and Y.

| Mole % X | 100 | 75 | 60 | | 0 |
| Mole % Y | 0 | 25 | 40 | | 100 |

Melting point generalizations

A phase diagram

Melting point depression

energy to overcome the forces that attract one molecule to another and will undergo translational motion—in other words, it will become a liquid.

The forces by which one molecule is attracted to another include ionic attractions, London forces, hydrogen bonds, and dipole-dipole attractions. Most, but by no means all, organic molecules are covalent in nature and melt at temperatures below 300°C. Typical inorganic compounds are ionic and have much higher melting points (e.g., sodium chloride melts at 800°C). Ionic organic molecules often decompose before melting, as do compounds having many strong hydrogen bonds, such as sucrose.

Other factors being equal, larger molecules melt at higher temperatures than smaller molecules. Among structural isomers, the more symmetrical isomer will have the higher melting point. Among optical isomers, the R and S enantiomers will have the same melting points, but the racemate (a mixture of equal parts of R and S) will usually possess a different melting point. Diastereomers, another type of stereoisomer, will have different melting points. Molecules that can form hydrogen bonds will usually possess higher melting points than their counterparts of similar molecular weight.

The melting point behavior of impure compounds is best understood by considering a simple binary mixture of compounds X and Y (Fig. 3.5). This melting point–composition diagram shows melting point behavior as a function of composition. The melting point of a pure compound is the temperature at which the vapor pressures of the solid and liquid are equal. But in dealing with a mixture, the situation is different. Consider the case of a mixture of 75% X and 25% Y. At a temperature below the eutectic temperature (ET), the mixture is solid Y and solid X. At ET, the solid begins to melt. The melt is a solution of Y dissolved in liquid X. The vapor pressure of the solution of X and Y together is less than that of pure X at the melting point; therefore, the temperature at which X will melt is lower when mixed with Y. This is an application of Raoult's law (*see* Chapter 5). As the temperature is increased, more and more of solid X melts until it is all gone at point **M** (temperature m). The melting point range is thus from ET to *m*. In practice, it is very difficult to detect the ET when a melting point is determined in a capillary because it represents the point at which an infinitesimal amount of the solid mixture has begun to melt.

In this hypothetical example, the liquid solution becomes saturated with Y at the eutectic point (EP). This is the point at which X and Y and their liquid solutions are in equilibrium. A mixture of X and Y containing 60% X will appear to have a sharp melting point at the ET.

The melting point range of a mixture of compounds is generally broad, and the breadth of the range is an indication of purity. The chances of accidentally coming on the eutectic composition are small. Recrystallization will enrich the predominant compound while excluding the impurity and will, therefore, decrease the melting point range.

It should be apparent that the impurity must be soluble in the compound, so an insoluble impurity such as sand or charcoal will not depress the melting point. The impurity does not need to be a solid. It can be a liquid such as water (if it is soluble) or an organic solvent, such as the one used to recrystallize the compound; this advocates the necessity for drying the compound before determining its melting point.

Advantage is taken of the depression of melting points of mixtures to prove whether or not two compounds having the same melting points are identical. If X and Y are identical, then a mixture of the two will have the same melting point; if X and Y are not identical, then a small amount of X in Y or of Y in X will reduce the melting point.

The eutectic point

Mixed melting points

FIG. 3.6
Sealing a melting point capillary tube.

Samples that sublime

Apparatus

Melting Point Capillaries

Before using a melting point apparatus, the sample needs to be prepared for analysis. Most melting point determinations require that the sample be placed in a capillary tube. The experiments in this book require capillary tubes for sample preparation. Capillaries may be obtained commercially or may be produced by drawing out 12-mm soft-glass tubing. The tubing is rotated in the hottest part of a Bunsen burner flame until it is very soft and begins to sag. It should not be drawn out during heating; it is removed from the flame and after a slight hesitation drawn steadily and not too rapidly to arm's length. With some practice it is possible to produce 10–15 good tubes in a single drawing. The long capillary tube can be cut into 100-mm lengths with a glass scorer. Each tube is sealed by rotating one open end in the edge of a small flame until the glass melts and seals the bottom, as seen in Figure 3.6.

Filling Melting Point Capillaries. The dry sample is ground to a fine powder on a watch glass or a piece of weighing paper on a hard surface using the flat portion of a spatula. It is formed into a small pile, and the open end of the melting point capillary is forced down into the pile. The sample is shaken into the closed end of the capillary by rapping sharply on a hard surface or by dropping it down a 2-ft length of glass tubing onto a hard surface. The height of the sample should be no more than 2–3 mm.

Sealed Capillaries. Some samples sublime (go from a solid state directly to the vapor phase without appearing to melt), or undergo rapid air oxidation and decompose at the melting point. These samples should be sealed under vacuum. This can be accomplished by forcing a capillary through a hole previously made in a rubber septum and evacuating the capillary using a water aspirator or a mechanical vacuum pump (Fig. 3.7). Using the flame from a small micro burner, the tube is gently heated about 15 mm above the tightly packed sample. This will cause any

FIG. 3.7
Evacuation of a melting point capillary prior to sealing.

A small rubber band can be made by cutting off a very short piece of 1/4" gum rubber tubing.

Thomas–Hoover Uni-Melt

FIG. 3.8
A simple melting point apparatus.

FIG. 3.9
The Thomas–Hoover Uni-Melt melting point apparatus.

material in this region to sublime away. It is then heated more strongly in the same place to collapse and seal the tube, taking care that the tube is straight when it cools. It is also possible to seal the end of a long Pasteur pipette, add the sample, pack it down, and seal off a sample under vacuum in the same way.

Melting Point Devices. The apparatus required for determining an accurate melting point need not be elaborate. The same results are obtained on the simplest as on the most complex devices. The simplest setup involves attaching the sample-filled, melting point capillary to a thermometer using a rubber band and immersing them into a silicone oil bath (Fig. 3.8). This rubber band must be above the level of the oil bath; otherwise, it will break in the hot oil. The sample should be close to and on a level with the center of the thermometer bulb. This method can analyze compounds whose melting points go up to ~350°C. If determinations are to be done on two or three samples that differ in melting point by as much as 10°C, two or three capillaries can be secured to the thermometer together; the melting points can be observed in succession without removing the thermometer from the bath. As a precaution against the interchange of tubes while they are being attached, use some system of identification, such as one, two, and three dots made with a marking pencil.

More sophisticated melting point devices, some of which can attain temperatures of 500°C, will now be described.

The Thomas–Hoover Uni-Melt apparatus (Fig. 3.9) will accommodate up to seven capillaries in a small, magnified, lighted beaker of high-boiling silicone oil that is stirred and heated electrically. The heating rate is controlled with a variable transformer that is part of the apparatus. The rising mercury column of the thermometer can be observed with an optional traveling periscope device so the eye need not move away from the capillary. For industrial, analytical, and control work, the Mettler apparatus determines the melting point automatically and displays the result in digital form.

FIG. 3.10

The Mel-Temp melting point apparatus.

FIG. 3.11

The Fisher-Johns melting point apparatus.

The Mel-Temp apparatus (Fig. 3.10) consists of an electrically heated aluminum block that accommodates three capillaries. The sample is illuminated through the lower port and observed with a six-power lens through the upper port. The heating rate can be controlled and, with a special thermometer, the apparatus can be used up to 500°C—far above the useful limit of silicone oil (which is about 350°C). For this melting point apparatus, it is advisable to use a digital thermometer rather than a mercury-in-glass thermometer.

The Fisher-Johns melting point apparatus (Fig. 3.11) is used to determine the melting point of a single sample. Instead of a capillary tube, the sample is placed between two thin glass disks that are placed on an aluminum heating stage. Heating is controlled by a variable transformer, and melting is observed through a magnifier; the melting temperature is read from a mercury-in-glass thermometer. This apparatus can be used for compounds that melt between 20°C and 300°C.

Determining the Melting Point

⚠️

The rate of heating is the most important factor in obtaining accurate melting points. Heat no faster than 1°C per minute.

The accuracy of the melting point depends on the accuracy of the thermometer, so the first exercise in the following experiments will be to calibrate the thermometer. Melting points of pure, known compounds will be determined and deviations recorded so a correction can be applied to future melting points. Be forewarned, however, that thermometers are usually fairly accurate.

The most critical factor in determining an accurate melting point is the rate of heating. At the melting point, the temperature increase should not be greater than 1°C per minute. This may seem extraordinarily slow, but it is necessary in order for heat from the oil bath or the heating block to be transferred equally to the sample and to the glass and mercury of the thermometer.

From your own experience, you know the rate at which ice melts. Consider performing a melting point experiment on an ice cube. Because water melts at 0°C, you would need to have a melting point bath a few degrees below zero. To observe the true melting point of the ice cube, you would need to raise the temperature extraordinarily slowly. The ice cube would appear to begin to melt at 0°C and, if you waited for temperature equilibrium to be established, it would all be melted at

0.5°C. If you were impatient and raised the temperature too rapidly, the ice might appear to melt over a range of 0°C to 20°C. Similarly, melting points determined in capillaries will not be accurate if the rate of heating is too fast.

EXPERIMENTAL PROCEDURES

1. CALIBRATION OF THE THERMOMETER

Determine the melting point of standard substances (Table 3.1) over the temperature range of interest. The difference between the values found and those expected constitutes the correction that must be applied to future temperature readings. If the thermometer has been calibrated previously, then determine one or more melting points of known substances to familiarize yourself with the technique. If the determinations do not agree within 1°C, then repeat the process. Both mercury-in-glass and digital thermometers will need to be calibrated; non-mercury thermometers are not typically used for melting point determination.

TABLE 3.1 *Melting Point Standards*

Compound		Structure	Melting Point (°C)
Naphthalene	(a)		80–82
Urea	(b)	H_2NCNH_2	132.5–133
Sulfanilamide	(c)		164–165
4-Toluic acid	(d)		180–182
Anthracene	(e)		214–217
Caffeine (evacuated capillary)	(f)		234–236.5

2. MELTING POINTS OF PURE UREA AND CINNAMIC ACID

—CH=CH—COOH

Cinnamic acid

Heat rapidly to within 20°C of the melting point.

Heat slowly (<1°C/min) near the melting temperature.

Using a metal spatula, crush the sample to a fine powder on a hard surface such as a watch glass. Push the open end of a melting point capillary into the powder and force the powder down in the capillary by tapping the capillary or by dropping it through a long glass tube held vertically and resting on a hard surface. The column of solid should be no more than 2–3 mm in height and should be tightly packed.

If the approximate melting temperature is known, the bath can be heated rapidly until the temperature is about 20°C below this point; the heating during the last 15°C–20°C should slow down considerably *so the rate of heating at the melting point is no more than 1°C per minute* while the sample is melting. As the melting point is approached, the sample may shrink because of crystalline structure changes. However, the melting process begins when the first drops of liquid are seen in the capillary and ends when the last trace of solid disappears. For a pure compound this whole process may occur over a range of only 0.5°C; hence, it is necessary to slowly increase the temperature during the determination.

Determine the melting point (mp) of either urea (mp 132.5°C–133°C) or cinnamic acid (mp 132.5°C–133°C). Repeat the determination; if the two determinations do not check within 1°C, repeat a third time.

3. MELTING POINTS OF UREA-CINNAMIC ACID MIXTURES

> **IN THIS EXPERIMENT** you will see dramatic evidence of the phenomenon of melting point depression, which will allow you to prepare a phase diagram like that shown in Figure 3.5 (on page 49).

Make mixtures of urea and cinnamic acid in the approximate proportions 1:4, 1:1, and 4:1 by putting side by side the correct number of equal-sized small piles of the two substances and then mixing them. Grind the mixture thoroughly for at least a minute on a watch glass using a metal spatula. Note the ranges of melting of the three mixtures and use the temperatures of complete liquefaction to construct a rough diagram of melting point versus composition.

4. UNKNOWNS

Determine the melting point of one or more of the unknowns selected by your instructor and identify the substance based on its melting point (Table 3.2). Prepare two capillaries of each unknown. Run a very fast determination on the first sample to ascertain the approximate melting point. Cool the melting point bath to just below the melting point and make a slow, careful determination using the other capillary.

5. AN INVESTIGATION: DETERMINATION OF MOLECULAR WEIGHT USING MELTING POINT DEPRESSION

Before the mass spectrometer came into common usage, the molal freezing point depression of camphor was used to determine molecular weights. Whereas a 1% solid solution of urea in cinnamic acid will cause a relatively small melting

TABLE 3.2 *Melting Point Unknowns*

Compound	Melting Point (°C)
Benzophenone	49–51
Maleic anhydride	52–54
4-Nitrotoluene	54–56
Naphthalene	80–82
Acetanilide	113.5–114
Benzoic acid	121.5–122
Urea	132.5–133
Salicylic acid	158.5–159
Sulfanilamide	165–166
Succinic acid	184.5–185
3,5-Dinitrobenzoic acid	205–207
p-Terphenyl	210–211

point depression, a 1%-by-weight solid solution in camphor of any organic compound with a molecular weight of 100 will cause a 4.0°C depression in the melting point of the camphor. Quantitative use of this relationship can be used to determine the molecular weight of an unknown. You can learn more about the details of this technique in very old editions of *Organic Experiments*[1] or by searching the Web for "colligative properties, molal freezing point depression." Visit this book's website for more information.

PART 3: BOILING POINTS

The boiling point of a pure organic liquid is one of its characteristic physical properties, just like its density, molecular weight, and refractive index, and the melting point of its solid state. The boiling point is used to characterize a new organic liquid, and knowledge of the boiling point helps to compare one organic liquid to another, as in the process of identifying an unknown organic substance.

A comparison of boiling points with melting points is instructive. The process of determining the boiling point is more complex than that for the melting point: It requires more material, and because it is less affected by impurities, it is not as good an indication of purity. Boiling points can be determined on a few microliters of a liquid, but on a small scale it is difficult to determine the boiling point range. This requires enough material to distill—about 1 to 2 mL. Like the melting point, the boiling point of a liquid is affected by the forces that attract one molecule to another—ionic attraction, London forces, dipole-dipole interactions, and hydrogen bonding, as discussed in Part 1 of this chapter.

STRUCTURE AND BOILING POINT

In a homologous series of molecules, the boiling point increases in a perfectly regular manner. The normal saturated hydrocarbons have boiling points ranging from −161°C for methane to 330°C for n-$C_{19}H_{40}$, an increase of about 27°C for each

[1]Fieser L. F. *Organic Experiments*, 2nd ed.; D.C. Heath: Lexington, MA, 1968; 38–42.

CH$_2$ group. It is convenient to remember that *n*-heptane with a molecular weight of 100 has a boiling point near 100°C (98.4°C). A spherical molecule such as 2,2-dimethylpropane has a lower boiling point than *n*-pentane because it does not have as many points of attraction to adjacent molecules. For molecules of the same molecular weight, those with dipoles, such as carbonyl groups, will have higher boiling points than those without, and molecules that can form hydrogen bonds will boil even higher. The boiling point of such molecules depends on the number of hydrogen bonds that can be formed. An alcohol with one hydroxyl group will boil at a lower temperature than an alcohol with two hydroxyl groups if they both have the same molecular weight. A number of other generalizations can be made about boiling point behavior as a function of structure; you will learn about these throughout your study of organic chemistry.

BOILING POINT AS A FUNCTION OF PRESSURE

Boiling points decrease about 0.5°C for each 10-mm decrease in atmospheric pressure.

Because the boiling point of a pure liquid is defined as the temperature at which the vapor pressure of the liquid exactly equals the pressure exerted on it, the boiling point will be a function of atmospheric pressure. At an altitude of 14,000 ft, the boiling point of water is 81°C. At pressures near that of the atmosphere at sea level (760 mm), the boiling point of most liquids decreases about 0.5°C for each 10-mm decrease in atmospheric pressure. This generalization does not hold for greatly reduced pressures because the boiling point decreases as a nonlinear function of pressure (see Fig. 5.2 on page 89). Under these conditions, a nomograph relating the observed boiling point, the boiling point at 760 mm, and the pressure in millimeters should be consulted (see Fig. 6.19 on page 124). This nomograph is not highly accurate because the change in boiling point as a function of pressure also depends on the type of compound (polar, nonpolar, hydrogen bonding, etc.). Consult the *CRC Handbook of Chemistry and Physics*[2] for the correction of boiling points to standard pressure.

Mercury is toxic. Immediately report any broken thermometers to your instructor.

Most mercury-in-glass laboratory thermometers have a mark around the stem that is 3 in. (76 mm) from the bottom of the bulb. This is the immersion line; the thermometer will record accurate temperatures if immersed to this line. If you break a mercury thermometer, immediately inform your instructor, who will use special apparatus to clean up the mercury. Mercury vapor is very toxic and can be fatal if the fumes are produced by the heating of liquid mercury.

CALIBRATING THE THERMOMETER

If you have not previously carried out a calibration, test the 0°C point of your thermometer with a well-stirred mixture of crushed ice and distilled water. To check the 100°C point, put 2 mL of water in a test tube with a boiling chip to prevent bumping, and boil the water gently over a hot sand bath with the thermometer in the vapor from the boiling water. Make sure that the thermometer does not touch the side of the test tube. Then immerse the bulb of the thermometer into the liquid and see if you can observe superheating. Check the atmospheric pressure to determine the true boiling point of the water.

[2]Lide, D. R., ed. *CRC Handbook of Chemistry and Physics*, 86th ed.; CRC Press: Boca Raton, FL, 2005.

DISTILLATION CONSIDERATIONS

Prevention of Superheating—Boiling Sticks and Boiling Stones

Superheating occurs when a very clean liquid in a very clean vessel is heated to a temperature above its boiling point without ever actually boiling. That is, if a thermometer is placed in the superheated liquid, the thermometer will register a temperature higher than the boiling point of the liquid. If boiling does occur under these conditions, it occurs with explosive violence. To avoid this problem, boiling stones or boiling sticks are always added to liquids before heating them to boiling—whether to determine a boiling point or to carry out a reaction or distillation. These boiling stones or sticks provide the nuclei on which the bubbles of vapor indicative of a boiling liquid can form; be careful not to confuse the bubbling for boiling. Some boiling stones, also called boiling chips, are composed of porous unglazed porcelain. When dry, this material is filled with air in numerous fine capillaries. With heating, this air expands to form the fine bubbles upon which even boiling can take place. Once the liquid cools, it will fill these capillaries and the boiling chip will become ineffectual, so another chip must be added each time the liquid is reheated to boiling. Wooden boiling sticks about 1.5 mm in diameter—often called applicator sticks—also promote even boiling and, unlike stones, are removed easily from the solution. Neither boiling sticks nor stones work well for vacuum distillation (*see* Chapter 6).

Closed Systems

Distillations that are run at atmospheric pressure need to be open to the atmosphere to avoid pressure buildup, which could lead to an explosion. Therefore, always make sure that a distillation setup is not a closed system—unless, of course, you are running a vacuum distillation.

BOILING POINT DETERMINATION: APPARATUS AND TECHNIQUE

Boiling Point Determination by Distillation

When enough material is available (at least 3 mL), the best method for determining the boiling point of a liquid is to distill it (*see* Chapter 5). Distillation allows the boiling range to be determined and thus gives an indication of purity. Bear in mind, however, that a constant boiling point is not a guarantee of homogeneity and thus purity. Constant-boiling azeotropes such as 95% ethanol are common.

All procedures involving volatile and/or flammable solvents should be conducted in a fume hood.

Boiling Point Determination Using a Digital Thermometer and a Reaction Tube

Boiling points can be measured rapidly and accurately using an electronic digital thermometer, as depicted in Figure 3.12. Although digital thermometers are currently too expensive for each student to have, several of these in the laboratory can greatly speed up the determination of boiling points. Also, digital thermometers are much safer to use because there is no danger from toxic mercury vapor if the thermometer is accidentally dropped.

Photo: *Boiling Point Determination with a Digital Thermometer*

FIG. 3.12

Using a digital thermometer for determining boiling points.

FIG. 3.13

A small-scale boiling-point apparatus. Be sure the thermometer does not touch the tube.

The surface probe of the digital thermometer is the active element. Unlike the bulb of mercury at the end of a thermometer, this element has a very low heat capacity and a very fast response time, so boiling points can be determined very quickly with this apparatus. About 0.2 mL to 0.3 mL of the liquid and a boiling chip are heated on a sand bath until the liquid refluxes about 3 cm up the tube. The thermometer probe should not touch the side of the reaction tube, but should be placed approximately 5 mm above the liquid. The boiling point is the highest temperature recorded by the thermometer and is maintained for about 1 min. The application of heat will drive tiny bubbles of air from the boiling chip; do not mistake these tiny bubbles for true boiling; this mistake can readily happen if the unknown has a very high boiling point.

Boiling Point Determination in a Reaction Tube

If a digital thermometer is not available, use the apparatus shown in Figure 3.13. Using a distilling adapter at the top of a reaction tube allows access to the atmosphere. Place 0.3 mL of the liquid along with a boiling stone in a 10 × 100-mm reaction tube, clamp a thermometer so that the bulb is just above the level of the liquid, and then heat the liquid with a sand bath. It is *very important* that no part of the thermometer touch the reaction tube. Heating is regulated so that the boiling liquid refluxes about 3 cm up the thermometer, but does not boil out of the apparatus. If you cannot see the refluxing liquid, carefully run your finger down the side of the reaction tube until you feel heat. This indicates where the liquid is refluxing. Droplets of liquid must drip from the thermometer bulb to thoroughly heat the mercury. The boiling point is the highest temperature recorded by the thermometer and is maintained over about a 1-minute time interval.

The application of heat will drive out tiny air bubbles from the boiling chip. Do not mistake these tiny bubbles for true boiling. This can occur if the unknown has a very high boiling point. It may take several minutes to heat up the mercury in the thermometer bulb. True boiling is indicated by drops dripping from the thermometer, with a constant temperature recorded on the thermometer. If the temperature is not constant, then you are probably not observing true boiling.

Boiling Point Determination Using a 3-mm to 5-mm Tube

For smaller quantities, a 3-mm to 5-mm diameter tube is attached to the side of a thermometer by a rubber band (Fig. 3.14) and heated in a liquid bath. The tube, which can be made from tubing 3 mm to 5 mm in diameter, contains a small inverted capillary. This is made by cutting a 6-mm piece from the sealed end of a melting point capillary, inverting it, and sealing the closed end of the capillary. A centimeter ruler is printed on the inside back cover of this book.

When the sample is heated in this device, the air in the inverted capillary will expand, and an occasional bubble will escape. At the true boiling point, a continuous and rapid stream of bubbles will emerge from the inverted capillary. When this occurs, the heating is stopped, and the bath is allowed to cool. A time will come when bubbling ceases and the liquid just begins to rise in the inverted capillary. The temperature at which this happens is recorded. The liquid is allowed to partially fill the small capillary, and then heat is applied carefully until the first bubble emerges from the capillary. The temperature is recorded at that point. The two temperatures approximate the boiling point range for the liquid.

As the liquid was being heated, the air expanded in the inverted capillary and was replaced by vapor of the liquid. The liquid was actually slightly superheated when rapid bubbles emerged from the capillary, but on cooling, a point was

Smaller-scale boiling point apparatus

FIG. 3.14
A smaller-scale boiling point apparatus.

reached at which the pressure on the inside of the capillary matched the outside (atmospheric) pressure. This is, by definition, the boiling point.

Cleaning Up. Place the boiling point sample in either the halogenated or nonhalogenated waste container. Do not pour it down the sink.

QUESTIONS

1. What effect would poor circulation of the melting point bath liquid have on the observed melting point?

2. What is the effect of an insoluble impurity, such as sodium sulfate, on the observed melting point of a compound?

3. Three test tubes, labeled A, B, and C, contain substances with approximately the same melting points. How could you prove that the test tubes contain three different chemical compounds?

4. One of the most common causes of inaccurate melting points is too rapid heating of the melting point bath. Under these circumstances, how will the observed melting point compare to the true melting point?

5. Strictly speaking, why is it incorrect to speak of a melting *point?*

6. What effect would the incomplete drying of a sample (for example, the incomplete removal of a recrystallization solvent) have on the melting point?

7. Why should the melting point sample be finely powdered?

8. You suspect that an unknown is acetanilide (mp 113.5°C–114°C). Give a qualitative estimation of the melting point when the acetanilide is mixed with 10% by weight of naphthalene.

9. You have an unknown with an observed melting point of 90°C–93°C. Is your unknown compound A with a reported melting point of 95.5°C–96°C, or compound B with a reported melting point of 90.5°C–91°C? Explain.

10. Why is it important to heat the melting point bath or block slowly and steadily when the temperature gets close to the melting point?

11. Why is it important to pack the sample tightly in the melting point capillary?

12. An unknown compound is suspected to be acetanilide (mp 113.5°C–114°C). What would happen to the melting point if this unknown were mixed with (a) an equal quantity of pure acetanilide? (b) an equal quantity of benzoic acid?

13. Which would be expected to have the higher boiling point, *t*-butyl alcohol (2-methyl-2-propanol) or *n*-butyl alcohol (1-butanol)? Explain.

14. What is the purpose of the side arm of the thermometer adapter in Figure 3.13?

See *Web Links*

REFERENCES

Weissberger, Arnold, and Bryant W. Rossiter (eds.). *Physical Methods of Chemistry,* Vol. 1, Part V. New York: Wiley-Interscience, 1971.

J. Kofron and J.K. Hardy of the University of Akron have an excellent website with photographs illustrating mixed melting points: http://ull.chemistry.uakron.edu/organic_lab/melting_point.

CHAPTER 4

Recrystallization

PRELAB EXERCISE: Write an expanded outline for the seven-step process of recrystallization.

Recrystallization: the most important purification method for solids, especially for small-scale experiments.

Recrystallization is the most important method for purifying solid organic compounds. It is also a very powerful, convenient, and efficient method of purification, and it is an important industrial technique that is still relevant in the chemical world today. For instance, the commercial purification of sugar is done by recrystallization on an enormous scale.

A pure, crystalline organic substance is composed of a three-dimensional array of molecules held together primarily by London forces. These attractive forces are fairly weak; most organic solids melt in the range between 22°C and 250°C. An impure organic solid will not have a well-defined crystal lattice because impurities do not allow the crystalline structure to form. The goal of recrystallization is to remove impurities from a solid to allow a perfect crystal lattice to grow.

There are four important concepts to consider when discussing the process of recrystallization:

1. Solubility
2. Saturation level
3. Exclusion
4. Nucleation

Recrystallization involves dissolving the material to be purified (the *solute*) in an appropriate hot *solvent* to yield a solution (*solubility*). As the solvent cools, the solution becomes saturated with respect to the solute (*saturation level*), which then recrystallizes. As the perfectly regular array of a crystal is formed, impurities are excluded (*exclusion*), and the crystal is thus a single pure substance. Soluble impurities remain in solution because they are not concentrated enough to saturate the solution. Recrystallization of a solute is initiated at a point of *nucleation*, which can be a seed crystal, a speck of dust, or a scratch on the wall of the test tube.

In this chapter, you will carry out the recrystallization process, one of the most important laboratory operations of organic chemistry, by following its seven steps. Then you will perform several actual recrystallization experiments.

61

THE SEVEN STEPS OF RECRYSTALLIZATION

The process of recrystallization can be broken into seven discrete steps: (1) choosing the solvent and solvent pairs; (2) dissolving the solute; (3) decolorizing the solution with pelletized Norit; (4) filtering suspended solids; (5) recrystallizing the solute; (6) collecting and washing the crystals; and (7) drying the crystals. A detailed description of each of these steps is given in the following sections.

STEP 1. CHOOSING THE SOLVENT AND SOLVENT PAIRS

Similia similibus solvuntur.

Video: *The Reaction Tube in Use*

The ideal solvent

In choosing the solvent, the chemist is guided by the dictum "like dissolves like." Even the nonchemist knows that oil and water do not mix, and that sugar and salt dissolve in water but not in oil. Hydrocarbon solvents such as hexane will dissolve hydrocarbons and other nonpolar compounds, and hydroxylic solvents such as water and ethanol will dissolve polar compounds. It is often difficult to decide, simply by looking at the structure of a molecule, just how polar or nonpolar it is and which solvent would be best. Therefore, the solvent is often chosen by experimentation. If an appropriate single solvent cannot be found for a given substance, a solvent pair system may be used. The requirement for this solvent pair is miscibility; both solvents should dissolve in each other for use as a recrystallization solvent system.

The best recrystallization solvent (and none is ideal) will dissolve the solute when the solution is hot but not when the solution is cold; it will either not dissolve the impurities at all or it will dissolve them very well (so they do not recrystallize out along with the solute); it will not react with the solute; and it will be nonflammable, nontoxic, inexpensive, and very volatile (so it can be removed from the crystals).

Miscible: capable of being mixed

Some common solvents and their properties are presented in Table 4.1 in order of decreasing polarity of the solvent. Solvents adjacent to each other in the list will dissolve in each other; that is, they are miscible with each other, and each solvent will, in general, dissolve substances that are similar to it in chemical structure. These solvents are used both for recrystallization and as solvents in which reactions are carried out.

Procedure

Choosing a Solvent

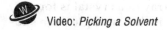
Video: *Picking a Solvent*

To choose a solvent for recrystallization, place a few crystals of the impure solute in a small test tube or centrifuge tube and add a very small drop of the solvent. Allow the drop to flow down the side of the tube and onto the crystals. If the crystals dissolve instantly at about 22°C, that solvent cannot be used for recrystallization because too much of the solute will remain in solution at low temperatures. If the crystals do not dissolve at about 22°C, warm the tube on a hot sand bath and observe the crystals. If they do not go into solution, add 1 more drop of the solvent. If the crystals go into solution at the boiling point of the solvent and then recrystallize when the tube is cooled, you have found a good recrystallization solvent. If not, remove the solvent by evaporation and try a different solvent. In this trial-and-error process, it is easiest to try low-boiling solvents first because they can be easily removed. Occasionally, no single satisfactory solvent can be found, so mixed solvents, or *solvent pairs*, are used.

TABLE 4.1 *Recrystallization Solvents*

Solvent	Boiling Point (°C)	Density (g/mL)	Remarks
Water (H_2O)	100	1.000	It is the solvent of choice because it is cheap, non-flammable, nontoxic, and will dissolve a large variety of polar organic molecules. Its high boiling point and high heat of vaporization make it difficult to remove from crystals.
Acetic acid (CH_3COOH)	118	1.049	It will react with alcohols and amines, and it is difficult to remove from crystals. It is not a common solvent for recrystallizations, although it is used as a solvent when carrying out oxidation reactions.
Dimethyl sulfoxide (DMSO; CH_3SOCH_3)	189	1.100	It is not a commonly used solvent for recrystallization, but it is used for reactions.
Methanol (CH_3OH)	64	0.791	It is a very good solvent that is often used for recrystallization. It will dissolve molecules of higher polarity than other alcohols.
95% Ethanol (CH_3CH_2OH)	78	0.789	It is one of the most commonly used recrystallization solvents. Its high boiling point makes it a better solvent for less polar molecules than methanol. It evaporates readily from crystals. Esters may undergo an interchange of alcohol groups on recrystallization.
Acetone (CH_3COCH_3)	56	0.791	It is an excellent solvent, but its low boiling point means there is not much difference in the solubility of a compound at its boiling point compared to about 22°C.
2-Butanone; also known as methyl ethyl ketone (MEK; $CH_3COCH_2CH_3$)	80	0.805	It is an excellent solvent that has many of the most desirable properties of a good recrystallization solvent.
Ethyl acetate ($CH_3COOC_2H_5$)	78	0.902	It is an excellent solvent that has about the right combination of moderately high boiling point and the volatility needed to remove it from crystals.
Dichloromethane; also known as methylene chloride (CH_2Cl_2)	40	1.325	Although a common extraction solvent, dichloromethane has too low a boiling point to make it a good recrystallization solvent. It is useful in a solvent pair with ligroin.
Diethyl ether; also known as ether ($CH_3CH_2OCH_2CH_3$)	35	0.706	Its boiling point is too low for recrystallization, although it is an extremely good solvent and fairly inert. It is used in a solvent pair with hexanes.
Methyl *t*-butyl ether ($CH_3OC(CH_3)_3$)	52	0.741	It is a relatively new and inexpensive solvent. It does not easily form peroxides; it is less volatile than diethyl ether, but it has the same solvent characteristics. (*See also* Chapter 7.)
1,4-Dioxane ($C_4H_8O_2$)	101	1.034	It is a very good solvent that is not too difficult to remove from crystals; it is a mild carcinogen, and it forms peroxides.
Toluene ($C_6H_5CH_3$)	111	0.865	It is an excellent solvent that has replaced the formerly widely used benzene (a weak carcinogen) for the recrystallization of aryl compounds. Because of its boiling point, it is not easily removed from crystals.

(continued)

TABLE 4.1 (*continued*)

Solvent	Boiling Point (°C)	Density (g/mL)	Remarks
Pentane (C_5H_{12})	36	0.626	It is a widely used solvent for nonpolar substances. It is not often used alone for recrystallization, but it is good in combination with several other solvents as part of a solvent pair.
Hexane (C_6H_{14})	69	0.659	It is frequently used to recrystallize nonpolar substances. It is inert and has the correct balance between boiling point and volatility. It is often used as part of a solvent pair.
Cyclohexane (C_6H_{12})	81	0.779	It is similar in all respects to hexane.

Note: The solvents in this table are listed in decreasing order of polarity. Adjacent solvents in the list are, in general, miscible with each other.

TABLE 4.2 *Solvent Pairs*

Acetic acid–water	Ethyl acetate–cyclohexane
Ethanol-water	Acetone-hexanes
Acetone-water	Ethyl acetate–hexanes
Dioxane-water	*t*-Butyl methyl ether–hexanes
Acetone-ethanol	Dichloromethane-hexanes
Ethanol–*t*-butyl methyl ether	Toluene-hexanes

Solvent Pairs

To use a mixed solvent pair, dissolve the crystals in the better solvent (more solubilizing) and add the poorer solvent (less solubilizing) to the hot solution until it becomes cloudy, and the solution is saturated with the solute. The two solvents must, of course, be miscible with each other. Some useful solvent pairs are given in Table 4.2.

STEP 2. DISSOLVING THE SOLUTE

 Microscale Procedure

Once a recrystallization solvent has been found, the impure crystals are placed in a reaction tube, the solvent is added dropwise, the crystals are stirred with a microspatula or a small glass rod, and the tube is warmed on a steam bath or a sand bath until the crystals dissolve. Care must be exercised to use the minimum amount of solvent at or near the boiling point. Observe the mixture carefully as solvent is being added. Allow sufficient time for the boiling solvent to dissolve the solute and note the rate at which most of the material dissolves. To hasten the solution process, crush large crystals with a stirring rod, taking care not to break the reaction tube. When you believe most of the material has been dissolved, stop adding solvent. There is a possibility that your sample is contaminated with a small quantity of an insoluble impurity that never will dissolve.

Do not use too much solvent.

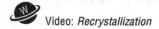 Video: *Recrystallization*

If the solution contains no undissolved impurities and is not colored from impurities, you can simply let it cool, allowing the solute to recrystallize (step 5), and then collect the crystals (step 6). On the other hand, if the solution is colored, it must be treated with activated (decolorizing) charcoal and then filtered before recrystallization (step 3). If it contains solid impurities, it must be filtered before recrystallization takes place (step 4).

On a microscale, there is a tendency to use too much solvent so that on cooling the hot solution, little or no material recrystallizes. This is not a hopeless situation. The remedy is to evaporate some of the solvent (by careful boiling) and repeat the cooling process. Inspect the hot solution to see if crystals form, and if not, continue to evaporate solvent.

A solution (solute dissolved in solvent) can become *superheated*; that is, heated above its boiling point without actually boiling. When boiling does suddenly occur, it can happen with almost explosive violence, a process called *bumping*. To prevent this from happening, a *wood applicator stick* can be added to the solution (Fig. 4.1). Air trapped in the wood comes out of the stick and forms the nuclei on which even boiling can occur. Porous porcelain *boiling chips* work in the same way; only a single chip is required to prevent bumping. Never add a boiling chip or a boiling stick to a hot solution because the hot solution may be superheated and boil over or bump.

Prevention of bumping

Do not use wood applicator sticks (boiling sticks) in place of boiling chips in a reaction. Use them only for recrystallization.

Macroscale Procedure

Place the substance to be recrystallized in an Erlenmeyer flask (never use a beaker), add enough solvent to cover the crystals, and then heat the flask on a steam bath (if the solvent boils below 90°C) or a hot plate until the solvent boils. (Note: Adding a boiling stick or a boiling chip to the solution will promote even boiling. It is easy to superheat the solution; that is, heat it above the boiling point with no boiling taking place. Once the solution does boil, it does so with explosive violence; it bumps.) Never add a boiling chip or boiling stick to a hot solution because this might cause the solution to boil over.

Video: *Macroscale Crystallization*

Stir the mixture or, better, swirl it (Fig. 4.2) to promote dissolution. Add solvent gradually, keeping it at the boiling point, until all of the solute dissolves. A glass rod with a flattened end can sometimes be useful in crushing large particles of solute to speed up the dissolving process. Be sure no flames are nearby when working with flammable solvents.

All procedures involving volatile and/or flammable solvents should be conducted in a fume hood.

Be careful not to add too much solvent. Note how rapidly most of the material dissolves; stop adding solvent when you suspect that almost all of the desired material has dissolved. It is best to err on the side of too little solvent rather than too much. Undissolved material noted at this point could be an insoluble impurity

FIG. 4.1

A reaction tube being used for recrystallization. The wood applicator stick ("boiling stick") promotes even boiling and is easier to remove than a boiling chip. The Thermowell sand is cool on top and hotter deeper down, so it provides a range of temperatures. The reaction tube is long and narrow; it can be held in the hand while the solvent refluxes. Do not use a boiling stick in place of a boiling chip in a reaction.

Wood applicator stick

Cool at this point

Air condenser

Boiling solvent

Temperature controlled by depth in sand

FIG. 4.2

Swirling of a solution to mix contents and help dissolve material to be recrystallized.

that never will dissolve. Allow the solvent to boil, and if no further material dissolves, proceed to step 4 to remove suspended solids from the solution by filtration, or if the solution is colored, go to step 3 to carry out the decolorization process. If the solution is clear, proceed to step 5.

STEP 3. DECOLORIZING THE SOLUTION WITH PELLETIZED NORIT

 Video: *Decolorization of a Solution with Norit*

Activated charcoal = decolorizing carbon = Norit

The vast majority of pure organic chemicals are colorless or a light shade of yellow; consequently, this step is not usually required. Occasionally, a chemical reaction will produce high molecular weight byproducts that are highly colored. The impurities can be adsorbed onto the surface of activated charcoal by simply boiling the solution with charcoal. Activated charcoal is made by the pyrolysis of carbonaceous material such as coconut shells, wood and lignite and activated with steam. It has an extremely large surface area per gram (several hundred square meters) and can bind a large number of molecules to this surface. On a commercial scale, the impurities in brown sugar are adsorbed onto charcoal in the process of refining sugar.

Add a small amount (0.1% of the solute weight is sufficient) of pelletized Norit to the colored solution and then boil the solution for a few minutes. Be careful not to add the charcoal pieces to a superheated solution; the charcoal will function like hundreds of boiling chips and will cause the solution to boil over. Remove the Norit by filtration as described in step 4.

STEP 4. FILTERING SUSPENDED SOLIDS

The filtration of a hot, saturated solution to remove solid impurities or charcoal can be performed in a number of ways. These processes include gravity filtration, pressure filtration, decantation, or removing the solvent with a Pasteur pipette. Vacuum filtration is not used because the hot solvent will cool during the process, and the product will recrystallize in the filter. Filtration can be one of the most vexing operations in the laboratory if the desired compound recrystallizes during filtration. Test the solution or a small portion of it before filtration to ensure that no crystals form at about 22°C. Like decolorization with charcoal, the removal of solid impurities by filtration is usually not necessary.

Microscale Procedure

(A) Removal of Solution with a Pasteur Pipette

If the solid impurities are large in size, they can be removed by filtration of the liquid through the small space between the flat end of a Pasteur pipette and the bottom of a reaction tube (Fig. 4.3). Expel air from the pipette by squeezing the pipette bulb as the pipette is being pushed to the bottom of the tube. Use a small additional quantity of solvent to rinse the tube and pipette. Anhydrous calcium chloride, a drying agent, is easily removed in this way. The removal of very fine material, such as traces of charcoal, is facilitated by filtration of the solution through a small piece of filter paper ($3\ mm^2$) placed in a reaction tube. This process is even easier if the filter paper is the thick variety, such as that from which Soxhlet extraction thimbles are made.[1]

 Video: *Filtration of Crystals Using the Pasteur Pipette*

[1]Belletire, J. L.; Mahmoodi, N. O. *J. Chem. Educ.* **1989**, 66, 964.

FIG. 4.3
Filtration using a Pasteur pipette and a reaction tube.

FIG. 4.4
Filtration of a solution in a Pasteur pipette.

Pipette bulb

Pasteur pipette

Reaction tube

Note square, flat tip

Solution to be filtered

Cotton

Celite (optional)

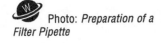
Photo: *Preparation of a Filter Pipette*

(B) Filtration in a Pasteur Pipette

To filter 0.1 mL to 2 mL of a solution, dilute the solution with enough solvent so that the solute will not recrystallize at about 22°C. Prepare a filter pipette by pushing a tiny bit of cotton into a Pasteur pipette, put the solution to be filtered into this filter pipette using another Pasteur pipette, and then force the liquid through the filter using air pressure from a pipette bulb (Fig. 4.4). Fresh solvent should be added to rinse the pipette and cotton. The filtered solution is then concentrated by evaporation. One problem encountered with this method is using too much cotton packed too tightly in the pipette so that the solution cannot be forced through it. To remove very fine impurities such as traces of decolorizing charcoal, a 3-mm to 4-mm layer of Celite filter aid can be added to the top of the cotton.

(C) Removal of Fine Impurities by Centrifugation

To remove fine solid impurities from up to 4 mL of solution, dilute the solution with enough solvent so that the solute will not recrystallize at about 22°C. Counterbalance the reaction tube and centrifuge for about 2 minutes at high speed in a laboratory centrifuge. The clear supernatant can be decanted (poured off) from the solid on the bottom of the tube. Alternatively, with care, the solution can be removed with a Pasteur pipette, leaving the solid behind.

(D) Pressure Filtration with a Micro Büchner Funnel

The technique applicable to volumes from 0.1 mL to 5 mL is to use a micro Büchner funnel. It is made of polyethylene and is fitted with a porous polyethylene frit that is 6 mm in diameter. This funnel fits in the bottom of an inexpensive disposable polyethylene pipette in which a hole is cut (Fig. 4.5). The solution to be filtered is placed in the polyethylene pipette using a Pasteur pipette. The thumb covers the hole in the plastic pipette and pressure is applied to filter the solution. It is good practice to place a 6-mm-diameter piece of filter paper over the frit, which would otherwise become clogged with insoluble material.

The glass chromatography column from the kit can be used in the same way. A piece of filter paper is placed over the frit. The solution to be filtered is placed in the chromatography column, and pressure is applied to the solution using a pipette bulb. In both procedures, dilute the solution to be filtered so that it does not recrystallize in the apparatus, and use a small amount of clean solvent to rinse the apparatus. The filtered solution is then concentrated by evaporation.

Video: *Microscale Crystallization*

Use filter paper on top of the frit.

Using the chromatography column for pressure filtration.

Macroscale Procedure

(A) Decantation

On a large scale, it is often possible to pour off (decant) the hot solution, leaving the insoluble material behind. This is especially easy if the solid is granular like sodium sulfate. The solid remaining in the flask and the inside of the flask should be rinsed with a few milliliters of the solvent in order to recover as much of the product as possible.

Decant: to pour off. A fast, easy separation procedure.

(B) Gravity Filtration

The most common method for the removal of insoluble solid material is gravity filtration through fluted filter paper (Fig. 4.6). This is the method of choice for removing

FIG. 4.5

A pressure filtration apparatus. The solution to be filtered is added through the aperture, which is closed by a finger as pressure is applied.

FIG. 4.6

Gravity filtration of hot solution through fluted filter paper.

— Filling aperture

— Polyethylene transfer pipette

— Polyethylene frit

— Büchner funnel

FIG. 4.7
Fluting a piece of filter paper.

⚠ Be aware that the vapors of low-boiling solvents can ignite on an electric hot plate.

FIG. 4.8
Assemblies for gravity filtration. Stemless funnels have diameters of 2.5, 4.2, 5.0, and 6.0 cm.

finely divided charcoal, dust, lint, and so on. The following equipment is needed for this process: three labeled Erlenmeyer flasks on a steam bath or a hot plate (flask A contains the solution to be filtered, flask B contains a few milliliters of solvent and a stemless funnel, and flask C contains several milliliters of the crystallizing solvent to be used for rinsing purposes), a fluted piece of filter paper, a towel for holding the hot flask and drying out the stemless funnel, and boiling chips for all solutions.

A piece of filter paper is fluted as shown in Figure 4.7 and is then placed in a stemless funnel. Appropriate sizes of Erlenmeyer flasks, stemless funnels, and filter paper are shown in Figure 4.8. The funnel is stemless so that the saturated solution being filtered will not have a chance to cool and clog the stem with crystals. The filter paper should fit entirely inside the rim of the funnel; it is fluted to allow rapid filtration. Test to see that the funnel is stable in the neck of flask B. If not, support it with a ring attached to a ring stand. A few milliliters of solvent and a boiling chip should be placed in flask B into which the solution is to be filtered. This solvent is brought to a boil on a steam bath or hot plate, along with the solution to be filtered.

The solution to be filtered (in flask A) should be saturated with the solute at the boiling point. Note the volume and then add 10% more solvent (from flask C). The resulting slightly dilute solution is not as likely to recrystallize in the funnel during filtration. Bring the solution to be filtered to a boil, grasp flask A with a towel, and pour the solution into the filter paper in the stemless funnel equipped in flask B (Fig. 4.6). The funnel should be warm to prevent recrystallization from occurring in the funnel. This can be accomplished in two ways: (1) Invert the funnel over a steam bath for a few seconds, pick up the funnel with a towel, wipe it perfectly dry, place it on top of flask B, and then add the fluted filter paper; or (2) place the stemless funnel in the neck of flask B and allow the solvent to reflux into the funnel, thereby warming it.

Pour the solution to be filtered (in flask A) at a steady rate onto the fluted filter paper (equipped in flask B). Check to see whether recrystallization is occurring in the filter. If it does, add boiling solvent (from flask C heated on a steam bath or a hot plate) until the crystals dissolve, dilute the solution being filtered, and carry on. Rinse flask A with a few milliliters of boiling solvent (from flask C) and rinse the fluted filter paper with this same solvent.

Because the filtrate has been diluted to prevent it from recrystallizing during the filtration process, the excess solvent must now be removed by boiling the solution. This process can be sped up somewhat by blowing a slow current of air into the flask in the hood or using an aspirator tube to pull vapors into the aspirator (Fig. 4.9 and Fig. 4.10). However, the fastest method is to heat the solvent in the

FIG. 4.9

An aspirator tube in use. A boiling stick may be necessary to promote boiling.

Aspirator tube

To water aspirator

Clamp here

Tared flask

Boiling stick

Steam in

Outlet to sink

Steam bath

FIG. 4.10

A tube being used to remove solvent vapors.

To water aspirator or to nitrogen or air supply

Pasteur pipette

Boiling stick

Hot sand bath

FIG. 4.11

Evaporation of a solvent under a vacuum.

Hirsch funnel

25-mL Filter flask

To water aspirator

⚠

Be sure that you are wearing gloves when doing this step!

filter flask on a sand bath while the flask is connected to a water aspirator. The vacuum is controlled with the thumb (Fig. 4.11).[2] Be sure that you are wearing gloves when doing this step! If your thumb is not large enough, put a one-holed rubber stopper into the Hirsch funnel or the filter flask and again control the vacuum with your thumb. If the vacuum is not controlled, the solution may boil over and go out the vacuum hose.

STEP 5. RECRYSTALLIZING THE SOLUTE

On both a macroscale and a microscale, the recrystallization process should normally start from a solution that is saturated with the solute at the boiling point. If it has been necessary to remove impurities or charcoal by filtration, the solution has been diluted. To concentrate the solution, simply boil off the solvent under an aspirator tube as shown in Figure 4.9 (macroscale) or blow off solvent using a gentle stream of air or, better, nitrogen in the hood as shown in Figure 4.10 (microscale). Be sure to have a boiling chip (macroscale) or a boiling stick (microscale) in the

[2]See also Mayo, D. W.; Pike, R. M.; Butcher, S. M. *Microscale Organic Laboratory;* Wiley: New York, 1986; 97.

solution during this process, but make sure you remove it before initiating recrystallization.

A saturated solution.

Slow cooling is important.

Once it has been ascertained that the hot solution is saturated with the compound just below the boiling point of the solvent, allow it to cool slowly to about 22°C. Slow cooling is a critical step in recrystallization. If the solution is not allowed to cool slowly, precipitation will occur, resulting in impurities "crashing out" of solution along with the desired solute; thus, no exclusion will occur. On a microscale, it is best to allow the reaction tube to cool in a beaker filled with cotton or paper towels which act as insulation, so cooling takes place slowly. Even insulated in this manner, the small reaction tube will cool to about 22°C within a few minutes. Slow cooling will guarantee the formation of large crystals, which are easily separated by filtration and easily washed free of adhering impure solvent. On a small scale, it is difficult to obtain crystals that are too large and occlude impurities. Once the tube has cooled to about 22°C without disturbance, it can be cooled in ice to maximize the amount of product that comes out of solution. On a macroscale, the Erlenmeyer flask is set atop a cork ring or other insulator and allowed to cool gradually to about 22°C. If the flask is moved during recrystallization, many nuclei will form, and the crystals will be small and have a large surface area. They will not be easy to filter and wash clean of the mother liquor. Once recrystallization ceases at about 22°C, the flask should be placed in ice to cool further. Make sure to clamp the flask in the ice bath so that it does not tip over.

 Videos: *Recrystallization, Microscale Crystallization*

Add a seed crystal or scratch the tube.

With slow cooling, recrystallization should begin immediately. If not, add a seed crystal or scratch the inside of the tube with a glass rod at the liquid-air interface. Recrystallization must start on some nucleation center. A minute crystal of the desired compound saved from the crude material will suffice. If a seed crystal is not available, recrystallization can be started on the rough surface of a fresh scratch on the inside of the container.

STEP 6. COLLECTING AND WASHING THE CRYSTALS

Once recrystallization is complete, the crystals must be separated from the ice-cold mother liquor, washed with ice-cold solvent, and dried.

Microscale Procedure

(A) Filtration Using a Pasteur Pipette

The most important filtration technique used in microscale organic experiments employs a Pasteur pipette (Fig. 4.12). About 70% of the crystalline products from the experiments in this text can be isolated in this way. The others will be isolated by filtration on a Hirsch funnel.

Videos: *Filtration of Crystals Using the Pasteur Pipette*

The ice-cold crystalline mixture is stirred with a Pasteur pipette and, while air is being expelled from the pipette, forced to the bottom of the reaction tube. The bulb is released, and the solvent is drawn into the pipette through the very small space between the flat tip of the pipette and the curved bottom of the reaction tube. When all the solvent has been withdrawn, it is expelled into another reaction tube. It is sometimes useful to rap the tube containing the wet crystals against a hard surface to pack them so that more solvent can be removed. The tube is returned to the ice bath, and a few drops of cold solvent are added to the crystals. The mixture is stirred to wash the crystals, and the solvent is again removed. This process can be repeated as many times as necessary. Volatile solvents can be removed from the

FIG. 4.12
Filtration using a Pasteur pipette and a reaction tube.

Pipette bulb

Pasteur pipette

Reaction tube

Note square, flat tip

FIG. 4.13
Drying crystals under reduced pressure in a reaction tube.

To aspirator

Glass tube

Thermometer adapter

Reaction tube

Beaker of warm water

Crystals to be dried

damp crystals under vacuum (Fig. 4.13). Alternatively, the last traces of solvent can be removed by centrifugation using a Wilfilter (Fig. 4.14).

(B) Filtration Using a Hirsch Funnel

When the volume of material to be filtered is greater than 1.5 mL, collect the material on a Hirsch funnel. The Hirsch funnel in the Williamson/Kontes kit[3] is unique. It is composed of polypropylene and has an integral molded stopper that fits a 25-mL filter flask. It comes fitted with a 20-μm polyethylene fritted disk, which is not meant to be disposable, although it costs only about twice as much as an 11-cm piece of filter paper (Fig. 4.15). Although products can be collected directly on this disk, it is good practice to place an 11- or 12-mm diameter piece of No. 1 filter paper on the disk. In this way, the frit will not become clogged with insoluble impurities. The disk of filter paper can be cut to size with a cork borer or leather punch. A piece of filter paper *must* be used on the old-style porcelain Hirsch funnels.

Clamp the clean, dry 25-mL filter flask in an ice bath to prevent it from falling over and place the Hirsch funnel with filter paper in the flask. The reason for cooling the filter flask is to keep the mother liquor cold so it will not dissolve the crystals on the Hirsch funnel when fresh cold solvent is used to wash crystals from the container onto the funnel. In a separate flask, cool ~10 mL of solvent in an ice bath; this solvent is used for washing the recrystallization flask and for washing the crystals. Wet the filter paper with the solvent used in the recrystallization, turn on the water aspirator (see "The Water Aspirator and the Trap"), and ascertain that

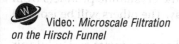

Video: *Microscale Filtration on the Hirsch Funnel*

[3]The microscale kit is available through Kontes (www.kontes.com).

FIG. 4.14

The Wilfilter filtration apparatus. Filtration occurs between the flat face of the polypropylene Wilfilter and the top of the reaction tube.

(a)   (b)

Break the vacuum, add a very small quantity of ice-cold wash solvent, and reapply the vacuum.

FIG. 4.15

The Hirsch funnel being used for vacuum filtration. This unique design has a removable and replaceable 20-μm polyethylene frit. No adapter is needed because there is a vacuum-tight fit to the filter flask. Always use a piece of filter paper with this funnel.

the filter paper is pulled down onto the frit. Pour and scrape the crystals and mother liquor onto the Hirsch funnel and, as soon as the liquid is gone from the crystals, break the vacuum at the filter flask by removing the rubber hose.

Rinse the recrystallization flask with ice-cold fresh solvent. Pour this rinse through the Hirsch funnel and reapply vacuum to the filter flask. As soon as all the liquid has disappeared from the crystals, wash the crystals with a few drops of ice-cold solvent. Repeat this washing process as many times as necessary to remove colored material or other impurities from the crystals. In some cases, only one very small wash will be needed. After the crystals have been washed with ice-cold solvent, the vacuum can be left on to dry the crystals. A cork can be used to press the solvent from the crystals, if necessary.

(C) Filtration with a Wilfilter (Replacing a Craig Tube)

The isolation of less than 100 mg of recrystallized material from a reaction tube (or any other container) is not easy. If the amount of solvent is large enough (1 mL or more), the material can be recovered by filtration with a Hirsch funnel. But when the volume of liquid is less than 1 mL, much product is left in the tube during the transfer to a Hirsch funnel. The solvent can be removed with a Pasteur pipette pressed against the bottom of the tube, a very effective filtration technique, but scraping the damp crystals from the reaction tube results in major losses. If the solvent has a relatively low boiling point, it can be evaporated by connecting the tube to a water aspirator (*see* Fig. 4.13 on page 72). Once the crystals are dry, they are easily scraped from the tube with little or no loss. Some solvents—and water is the principal culprit—are not easily removed by evaporation. And even though removal of the solvent under vacuum is not terribly difficult, it takes time.

We have invented a filtration device that circumvents these problems: the Wilfilter. After recrystallization has ceased, most of the solvent is removed from the crystals using a Pasteur pipette in the usual way (*see* Fig. 4.12 on page 72). Then the polypropylene Wilfilter is placed on the top of the reaction tube, followed by a 15-mL polypropylene centrifuge tube (*see* Fig. 4.14 on page 73). The assembly is inverted and placed in a centrifuge such as the International Clinical Centrifuge that holds twelve 15-mL tubes. The assembly, properly counterbalanced, is centrifuged for about 1 minute at top speed. The centrifuge tube is removed from the centrifuge, and the reaction tube is then removed from the centrifuge tube. The three fingers on the Wilfilter keep it attached to the reaction tube. The filtrate is left in the centrifuge tube.

Filtration with the Wilfilter occurs between the top surface of the reaction tube and the flat surface of the Wilfilter. Liquid will pass through that space during centrifugation, but crystals will not. The crystals will be found on top of the Wilfilter and inside the reaction tube. The very large centrifugal forces remove all the liquid, so the crystals will be virtually dry and thus easily removed from the reaction tube by shaking or scraping with the metal spatula.

The Wilfilter replaces an older device known as a Craig tube (Fig. 4.16), which consists of an outer tube of 1-, 2-, or 3-mL capacity with an inner plunger made of Teflon (expensive) or glass (fragile). The material to be recrystallized is transferred to the outer tube and recrystallized in the usual way. The inner plunger is added, and a wire hanger is fashioned so that the assembly can be removed from the centrifuge tube without the plunger falling off. Filtration in this device occurs through the rough surface that has been ground into the shoulder of the outer tube.

The Wilfilter possesses several advantages: a special recrystallization device is not needed, no transfers of material are needed, it is not as limited in capacity (which is 4.5 mL), and its cost is one-fifth that of a Craig tube assembly.

FIG. 4.16
The Craig tube filtration apparatus. Filtration occurs between the rough ground glass surfaces when the apparatus is centrifuged.

Rough ground glass surfaces

Crystals and solvent

Crystals

Centrifuge tube

Solvent

(D) Filtration into a Reaction Tube on a Hirsch Funnel

If it is desired to have the filtrate in a reaction tube instead of spread on the bottom of a 25-mL filter flask, then the process described in the previous section can be carried out in the apparatus shown in Figure 4.17. The vacuum hose is connected to the side arm of the flask using a thermometer adapter and a short length of glass tubing. Evaporate the filtrate in the reaction tube to collect a second crop of crystals.

(E) Filtration into a Reaction Tube with a Micro Büchner Funnel

If the quantity of material being collected is very small, use the bottom of the chromatography column as a micro Büchner funnel, which can be fitted into the top of the thermometer adapter, as shown in Figure 4.18. Again, it is good practice to cover the frit with a piece of 6-mm filter paper (cut with a cork borer).

(F) The Micro Büchner Funnel in an Enclosed Filtration Apparatus

In the apparatus shown in Figure 4.19, recrystallization is carried out in the upper reaction tube in the normal way. The apparatus is then turned upside down, the crystals are shaken down onto a micro Büchner funnel, and a vacuum is applied through the side arm. In this apparatus, crystals can be collected in an oxygen-free atmosphere (Schlenk conditions).

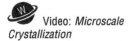
Photo: *Vacuum Filtration into a Reaction Tube through a Hirsch Funnel*

Video: *Microscale Crystallization*

FIG. 4.17
A microscale Hirsch filtration assembly. The Hirsch funnel gives a vacuum-tight seal to the 105° adapter.

FIG. 4.18
Filtration using a microscale Büchner funnel.

FIG. 4.19
The Schlenk-type filtration apparatus. The apparatus is inverted to carry out the filtration.

FIG. 4.20

Matching filter assemblies. The 6.0-cm polypropylene Büchner funnel (right) resists breakage and can be disassembled for cleaning.

Büchner funnels

Hirsch funnel
Neoprene adapter

 Macroscale Apparatus

Filtration on a Hirsch Funnel and a Büchner Funnel

If the quantity of material is small (<2 g), a Hirsch funnel can be used in exactly the way that was described in a previous section. For larger quantities, a Büchner funnel is used. Properly matched Büchner funnels, filter paper, and flasks are shown in Figure 4.20. The Hirsch funnel shown in the figure has a 5-cm bottom plate to accept 3.3-cm round filter paper.

Place a piece of filter paper in the bottom of the Büchner funnel. Wet it with solvent and be sure it lies flat so that crystals cannot escape around the edge and go under the filter paper. Then, with the vacuum off, pour the cold slurry of crystals into the center of the filter paper. Apply the vacuum; as soon as the liquid disappears from the crystals, break the vacuum to the flask by disconnecting the hose. Rinse the Erlenmeyer flask with cold solvent. Add this to the crystals and reapply the vacuum just until the liquid disappears from the crystals. Repeat this process as many times as necessary to recover all the crystals from the Erlenmeyer flask, and then leave the vacuum on to dry the crystals.

The Water Aspirator and Trap

The most common way to produce a vacuum for filtration in the organic laboratory is by employing a *water aspirator*. Air is entrained efficiently in the water rushing through the aspirator to produce a vacuum roughly equal to the vapor pressure of the water going through it (17 torr at 20°C, 5 torr at 4°C). A check valve is built into the aspirator, but when the water is turned off, it will often back up into the evacuated system. For this reason, a trap is always installed in the line (Fig. 4.21). *The water passing through the aspirator should always be turned on full force.*

Opening the screw clamp on the trap can open the system to the atmosphere, as well as removing the hose from the small filter flask. Open the system and then turn off the water to avoid having water sucked back into the filter trap. Thin rubber tubing on the top of the trap will collapse and bend over when a good vacuum is established. You will, in time, learn to hear the differences in the sound of an aspirator when it is pulling a vacuum and when it is working on an open system.

Collecting a Second Crop of Crystals

Regardless of the method used to collect crystals on either a macroscale or a microscale, the filtrate and washings can be combined and evaporated to the point of saturation to obtain a second crop of crystals—hence this advocates having a

Video: *Microscale Filtration with the Hirsch Funnel*

Clamp the filter flask

FIG. 4.21
An aspirator, a filter trap, and a funnel. Clamp the small filter flask to prevent it from tipping over.

clean receptacle for the filtrate. This second crop will increase the overall yield, but the crystals will not usually be as pure as the first crop.

STEP 7. DRYING THE PRODUCT

 Microscale Procedure

Video: *Recrystallization*

FIG. 4.22
Drying a solid by reduced air pressure.

If possible, dry the product in the reaction tube after removing the solvent with a Pasteur pipette. Simply connecting the tube to the water aspirator can do this. If the tube is clamped in a beaker of hot water, the solvent will evaporate more rapidly under vacuum, but make sure not to melt the product (*see* Fig. 4.13 on page 72). Water, which has a high heat of vaporization, is difficult to remove in this way. Scrape the product onto a watch glass and allow it to dry to constant weight, which will indicate that all the solvent has been removed. If the product is collected on a Hirsch funnel or a Wilfilter, the last traces of solvent can be removed by squeezing the crystals between sheets of filter paper before drying them on the watch glass.

Macroscale Procedure

Once the crystals have been washed on a Hirsch funnel or a Büchner funnel, press them down with a clean cork or other flat object and allow air to pass through them until they are substantially dry. Final drying can be done under reduced pressure (Fig. 4.22). The crystals can then be turned out of the funnel and squeezed between sheets of filter paper to remove the last traces of solvent before the final drying on a watch glass.

EXPERIMENTS

1. SOLUBILITY TESTS

Video: *Picking a Solvent*

Test Compounds:

Resorcinol

Anthracene

Benzoic acid

4-Amino-1-naphthalenesulfonic acid, sodium salt

To test the solubility of a solid, transfer an amount roughly estimated to be about 10 mg (the amount that forms a symmetrical mound on the end of a stainless steel spatula) into a reaction tube and add about 0.25 mL of solvent from a calibrated dropper or pipette. Stir with a fire-polished stirring rod that is 4 mm in diameter, break up any lumps, and determine if the solid is readily soluble at room temperature (about 22°C). If the substance is readily soluble at about 22°C in methanol, ethanol, acetone, or acetic acid, add a few drops of water to the solution from a wash bottle to see if a solid precipitates. If so, heat the mixture, adjust the composition of the solvent pair to produce a hot solution saturated at the boiling point, let the solution stand undisturbed, and note the character of the crystals that form.

If the substance fails to dissolve in a given solvent at about 22°C, heat the suspension and observe if a solution occurs. If the solvent is flammable, heat the test tube on a steam bath or in a small beaker of water kept warm on a steam bath or a hot plate. If the solid dissolves completely, it can be declared readily soluble in the hot solvent; if some but not all dissolves, it is said to be moderately soluble, and further small amounts of solvent should then be added until dissolution is complete.

When a substance has been dissolved in hot solvent, cool the solution by holding the flask under the tap and, if necessary, induce recrystallization by rubbing the walls of the tube with a stirring rod to make sure that the concentration permits recrystallization. Then reheat to dissolve the solid, let the solution stand undisturbed, and inspect the character of the ultimate crystals.

Perform solubility tests on the test compounds that are shown in the margin, in each of the following solvents: water (hydroxylic and ionic), toluene (an aromatic hydrocarbon), and hexanes (a mixture of isomers of hexane). Note the degree of solubility in the solvents—cold and hot—and suggest suitable solvents, solvent pairs, or other expedients for the recrystallization of each substance. Record the crystal form, at least to the extent of distinguishing between needles (pointed crystals), plates (flat and thin), and prisms. How do your observations conform to the generalization that like dissolves like?

Cleaning Up. Place organic solvents and solutions of the compounds in the organic solvents waste container. Dilute the aqueous solutions with water and flush down the drain. (For this and all other "Cleaning Up" sections, refer to the complete discussion of waste disposal procedures in Chapter 2.)

---

2. RECRYSTALLIZATION OF PURE PHTHALIC ACID, NAPHTHALENE, AND ANTHRACENE

Phthalic acid

Naphthalene

Anthracene

The process of recrystallization can be readily observed using phthalic acid. In the *CRC Handbook of Chemistry and Physics*, in the table "Physical Constants of Organic Compounds," the entry for phthalic acid gives the following solubility data (in grams of solute per 100 mL of solvent). The superscripts refer to temperature in degrees Celsius:

Water	Alcohol	Ether, etc.
0.54^{14}	11.71^{18}	0.69^{15} eth., i. chl.
18^{99}		

The large difference in solubility in water as a function of temperature suggests that water is the solvent of choice. The solubility in alcohol is high at about 22°C. Ether is difficult to use because it is so volatile; the compound is insoluble in chloroform (i. chl.).

Microscale Procedure for Phthalic Acid

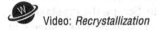
Video: *Recrystallization*

Recrystallize 60 mg (0.060 g) of phthalic acid from the minimum volume of water, using the previous data to calculate the required volume. First, turn on an electrically heated sand bath. Add the solid to a 10 × 100 mm reaction tube and add water dropwise with a Pasteur pipette. Use the calibration marks found in Chapter 1 (*see* Fig. 1.18 on page 19) to measure the volume of water in the pipette and the reaction tube. Add a boiling stick (a wood applicator stick) to facilitate even boiling and prevent bumping. After a portion of the water has been added, gently heat the solution to boiling on a hot sand bath in the electric heater. The deeper the tube is placed in the sand, the hotter it will be. As soon as boiling begins, continue to add water dropwise until the entire solid just dissolves. Remove the boiling stick. Cork the tube, clamp it as it cools, and observe the phenomenon of recrystallization.

Set the heater control to about 20% of the maximum.

After the tube reaches about 22°C, cool it in ice, stir the crystals that have formed with a Pasteur pipette, and expel the air from the pipette as the tip is pushed to the bottom of the tube. When the tip is firmly and squarely seated in the bottom of the tube, release the bulb and withdraw the water. Rap the tube sharply on a wood surface to compress the crystals and remove as much of the water as possible with the pipette. Then cool the tube in ice and add a few drops of ice-cold ethanol to the tube to remove water from the crystals. Connect the tube to a water aspirator and warm it in a beaker of hot water (*see* Fig. 4.13 on page 72). Once all the solvent is removed, use a stainless steel spatula to scrape the crystals onto a piece of filter paper, fold the paper over the crystals, and squeeze out excess water before allowing the crystals to dry to constant weight. Weigh the dry crystals and calculate the percent recovery of—the purified compound.

Alternate procedure: Dry the crystals under vacuum in a steam bath in the reaction tube.

Microscale Procedure for Naphthalene and Anthracene

Following the previous procedure, recrystallize 40 mg of naphthalene from 80% aqueous methanol or 10 mg of anthracene from ethanol. You may find it more convenient to use a hot water bath to heat these low-boiling alcohols. These are more typical of compounds to be recrystallized in later experiments because they are soluble in organic solvents. It will be much easier to remove these solvents from the crystals under vacuum than it is to remove water from phthalic acid. You will seldom encounter the need to recrystallize less than 30 mg of a solid in these experiments.

These compounds can also be isolated using a Wilfilter.

Cleaning Up. Dilute the aqueous filtrate with water and flush the solution down the drain. Phthalic acid is not considered toxic to the environment and if desired, can be recycled for future recrystallization experiments. Methanol and ethanol filtrates go into the organic solvents waste container.

Macroscale Procedure

Using the solubility data for phthalic acid to calculate the required volume, recrystallize 1.0 g of phthalic acid from the minimum volume of water. Add the solid to the smallest practical Erlenmeyer flask and then, using a Pasteur pipette, add water dropwise from a full 10-mL graduated cylinder. A boiling stick (a wood applicator stick) facilitates even boiling and will prevent bumping. After a portion of the water has been added, gently heat the solution to boiling on a hot plate. As soon as boiling begins, continue to add water dropwise until the entire solid dissolves. Remove the boiling stick. Place the flask on a cork ring or other insulator and allow it to cool undisturbed to about 22°C, during which time the recrystallization process can be observed. Slow cooling favors large crystals. Then cool the flask in an ice bath, decant (pour off) the mother liquor (the liquid remaining with the crystals), and remove the last traces of liquid with a Pasteur pipette. Scrape the crystals onto a filter paper using a stainless steel spatula, squeeze the crystals between sheets of filter paper to remove traces of moisture, and allow the crystals to dry. Alternatively, the crystals can be collected on a Hirsch funnel. Compare the calculated volume of water to the volume of water actually used to dissolve the acid. Calculate the percent recovery of dry, recrystallized phthalic acid.

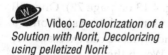

Video: *Macroscale Crystallization*

Cleaning Up. Dilute the filtrate with water and flush the solution down the drain. Phthalic acid is not considered toxic to the environment and if desired, can be recycled for future recrystallization experiments.

---

3. DECOLORIZING A SOLUTION WITH DECOLORIZING CHARCOAL

Into a reaction tube, place 1.0 mL of a solution of methylene blue dye that has a concentration of 10 mg per 100 mL of water. Add to the tube about 10 or 12 pieces of decolorizing charcoal, shake, and observe the color over a period of 1–2 minutes. Heat the contents of the tube to boiling (reflux) and observe the color by holding the tube in front of a piece of white paper from time to time. How rapidly is the color removed? If the color is not removed in a minute or so, add more charcoal pellets.

Video: *Decolorization of a Solution with Norit, Decolorizing using pelletized Norit*

Cleaning Up. Place the Norit charcoal pellets in the nonhazardous solid waste container.

---

4. DECOLORIZATION OF BROWN SUGAR (SUCROSE, $C_{12}H_{22}O_{11}$)

Raw sugar is refined commercially with the aid of decolorizing charcoal. The clarified solution is seeded generously with small sugar crystals, and excess water is removed under vacuum to facilitate recrystallization. The pure white crystalline product is collected by centrifugation. Brown sugar is partially refined sugar and can be easily decolorized using charcoal.

In a 50-mL Erlenmeyer flask, dissolve 15 g of dark brown sugar in 30 mL of water by heating and stirring. Pour half the solution into another 50-mL flask. Heat one of the solutions nearly to its boiling point, allow it to cool slightly, and add 250 mg (0.25 g) of decolorizing charcoal (Norit pellets) to it. Bring the solution back to near the boiling point for 2 minutes; then filter the hot solution into an Erlenmeyer flask through a fluted filter paper held in a previously heated funnel. Treat the other half of the sugar solution in exactly the same way but use only 50 mg of decolorizing charcoal. Collaborate with a fellow student who will heat the solution for only 15 seconds after adding the charcoal. Compare your results.

Cleaning Up. Decant (pour off) the aqueous layer. Place the Norit in the nonhazardous solid waste container. The sugar solution can be flushed down the drain.

5. RECRYSTALLIZATION OF BENZOIC ACID FROM WATER AND A SOLVENT PAIR

Benzoic acid

Recrystallize 50 mg of benzoic acid from water in the same way that phthalic acid was recrystallized. Then in a dry reaction tube, dissolve another 50-mg sample of benzoic acid in the minimum volume of hot methanol and add water to the hot solution dropwise. When the hot solution becomes cloudy and recrystallization has begun, allow the tube to cool slowly to about 22°C; then cool it in ice and collect the crystals. Compare recrystallization in water to that in the solvent pair.

Cleaning Up. The methanol-water solution can be disposed in the organic solvents waste container or, if regulations permit, diluted with water and flushed down the drain.

6. RECRYSTALLIZATION OF NAPHTHALENE FROM A MIXED SOLVENT

Naphthalene

Add 2.0 g of impure naphthalene (a mixture of 100 g of naphthalene, 0.3 g of a dye such as Congo Red, and another substance such as magnesium sulfate, or dust) to a 50-mL Erlenmeyer flask along with 3 mL of methanol and a boiling stick to promote even boiling. Heat the mixture to boiling over a steam bath or a hot plate, and then add methanol dropwise until the naphthalene just dissolves when the solvent is boiling. The total volume of methanol should be 4 mL. Remove the flask from the heat and cool it rapidly in an ice bath. Note that the contents of the flask set to a solid mass, which would be impossible to handle. Add enough methanol to bring the total volume to 25 mL, heat the solution to its boiling point, remove the flask from the heat, allow it to cool slightly, and add 30 mg of decolorizing charcoal pellets to remove the colored impurity in the solution. Heat the solution to its boiling point for 2 minutes; if the color is not gone, add more Norit and boil again, and then filter through a fluted filter paper in a previously warmed stemless funnel into a 50-mL Erlenmeyer flask. Sometimes filtration is slow because the funnel fits so snugly into the mouth of the flask that a back pressure develops. If you note that raising the funnel increases the flow of filtrate, fold a small strip of paper two or three times and insert it between the funnel and flask. Wash the used flask with 2 mL of hot methanol and use this liquid to wash the filter paper, transferring the

Do not try to grasp Erlenmeyer flasks with a test tube holder.

Support the funnel in a ring stand.

solvent with a Pasteur pipette in a succession of drops around the upper rim of the filter paper. When the filtration is complete, the volume of methanol should be 15 mL. If it is not, evaporate the excess methanol.

Because the filtrate is far from being saturated with naphthalene at this point, it will not yield crystals on cooling. However, the solubility of naphthalene in methanol can be greatly reduced by the addition of water. Heat the solution to its boiling point and add water dropwise from a 10-mL graduated cylinder using a Pasteur pipette (or a precalibrated pipette). After each drop of water, the solution will become cloudy for an instant. Swirl the contents of the flask and heat to redissolve any precipitated naphthalene. After the addition of 3.5 mL of water, the solution will almost be saturated with naphthalene at the boiling point of the solvent. Remove the flask from the heat and place it on a cork ring or other insulating surface to cool, without being disturbed, to about 22°C.

Immerse the flask in an ice bath along with another flask containing a 30:7 mixture of methanol and water. This cold solvent will be used for washing the crystals. The crystals will be separated from the cold recrystallization mixture using vacuum filtration on a small 50-mm Büchner funnel (Fig. 4.23). The water flowing through the aspirator should always be turned on full force. In collecting the product by suction filtration, use a spatula to dislodge crystals and ease them out of the flask. If crystals still remain in the flask, some filtrate can be poured back into the recrystallization flask as a rinse for washing as often as desired because it is saturated with solute. To further purify the crystals, break the suction, pour a few milliliters of the fresh cold solvent mixture into the Büchner funnel, and immediately reapply suction. Repeat this process until the crystals and the filtrate are free of color. Press the crystals with a clean cork to eliminate excess solvent, pull air through the filter cake for a few minutes, and then put the large, flat, platelike crystals out on a filter paper to dry. The yield of pure white crystalline naphthalene should be about 1.6 g. The mother liquor contains about 0.25 g, and about 0.15 g is retained in the charcoal and on the filter paper.

Cleaning Up. Place the Norit in the nonhazardous solid waste container. The methanol filtrate and washings are placed in the organic solvents waste container.

FIG. 4.23
A suction filter assembly clamped to provide firm support. The funnel must be pressed down on the Filtervac to establish reduced pressure in the flask.

Filtervac

7. PURIFICATION OF AN UNKNOWN

Recall the seven-step recrystallization procedure:

1. Choose the solvent.
2. Dissolve the solute.
3. Decolorize the solution (if necessary).
4. Filter suspended solids (if necessary).
5. Recrystallize the solute.
6. Collect and wash the crystals.
7. Dry the product.

You will purify an unknown provided by your instructor, 2.0 g if working on a macroscale and 100 mg if working on a microscale. Conduct tests for solubility and the ability to recrystallize in several organic solvents, solvent pairs, and water. Conserve your unknown by using very small quantities for the solubility tests. If only a drop or two of solvent is used, heating the test tube on a steam bath or a sand bath can evaporate the solvent, and the residue can be used for another test. If decolorization is necessary, dilute the solution before filtration. It is very difficult to filter a hot, saturated solution from decolorizing carbon without recrystallization occurring in the filtration apparatus. Evaporate the decolorized solution to the point of saturation and proceed with the recrystallization. Submit as much pure product as possible with evidence of its purity (i.e., the melting point). From the posted list, identify the unknown. If an authentic sample is available, your identification can be verified by a mixed melting point determination (see Chapter 3).

Cleaning Up. Place decolorizing charcoal, if used, and filter paper in the nonhazardous solid waste container. Put organic solvents in the organic solvents waste container and flush aqueous solutions down the drain.

RECRYSTALLIZATION PROBLEMS AND THEIR SOLUTIONS

INDUCTION OF CRYSTALLIZATION

Seeding

Scratching

Occasionally, a sample will not crystallize from solution on cooling, even though the solution is saturated with the solute at an elevated temperature. The easiest method for inducing crystallization is to add to the supersaturated solution a seed crystal that has been saved from the crude material (if it was crystalline before crystallization was attempted). In a probably apocryphal tale, the great sugar chemist Emil Fischer merely had to wave his beard over a recalcitrant solution, and the appropriate seed crystals would drop out, causing recrystallization to occur. In the absence of seed crystals, scratching the inside of the flask with a stirring rod at the liquid-air interface can often induce recrystallization. One theory holds that part of the freshly scratched glass surface has angles and planes corresponding to the crystal structure, and crystals start growing on these spots. Recrystallization is often very slow to begin. Placing the sample in a refrigerator overnight will bring success. Other expedients are to change the solvent (usually to a less soluble one) and to place the sample in an open container where slow evaporation and dust from the air may help induce recrystallization.

OILS AND "OILING OUT"

 Video: *Formation of an Oil Instead of Crystals*

Crystallize at a lower temperature

When cooled, some saturated solutions—especially those containing water—deposit not crystals but small droplets referred to as oils. "Oiling out" occurs when the temperature of the solution is above the melting point of the crystals. If these droplets solidify and are collected, they will be found to be quite impure. Similarly, the melting point of the desired compound may be depressed to a point such that a low-melting eutectic mixture of the solute and the solvent comes out of solution. The simplest remedy for this problem is to lower the temperature at which the solution becomes saturated with the solute by simply adding more room-temperature solvent. In extreme cases, it may be necessary to lower this temperature well below 22°C by cooling the solution with dry ice. If oiling out persists, use another solvent.

RECRYSTALLIZATION SUMMARY

Video: *Picking a Solvent*

Video: *Recrystallization*

Video: *Decolorization of a Solution with Norit*

Photo: *Preparation of a Filter Pipette*; Video: *Microscale Crystallization*

Photo: *Recrystallization*; Video: *Recrystallization*

Photos: *Use of the Wilfilter, Filtration Using a Pasteur Pipette*; Videos: *Microscale Filtration on the Hirsch Funnel, Filtration of Crystals Using the Pasteur Pipette*

Photo: *Drying Crystals Under Vacuum*; Video: *Recrystallization*

1. **Choosing the solvent.** "Like dissolves like." Some common solvents are water, methanol, ethanol, hexanes, and toluene. When you use a solvent pair, dissolve the solute in the better solvent and add the poorer solvent to the hot solution until saturation occurs. Some common solvent pairs are ethanol-water, ether-hexanes, and toluene—hexanes.

2. **Dissolving the solute.** In an Erlenmeyer flask or reaction tube, add solvent to the crushed or ground solute and heat the mixture to boiling. Add more solvent as necessary to obtain a hot, saturated solution.

3. **Decolorizing the solution.** If it is necessary to remove colored impurities, cool the solution to about 22°C and add more solvent to prevent recrystallization from occurring. Add decolorizing charcoal in the form of pelletized Norit to the cooled solution and then heat it to boiling for a few minutes, making sure to swirl the solution to prevent bumping. Remove the Norit by filtration and then concentrate the filtrate.

4. **Filtering suspended solids.** If it is necessary to remove suspended solids, dilute the hot solution slightly to prevent recrystallization from occurring during filtration. Filter the hot solution. Add solvent if recrystallization begins in the funnel. Concentrate the filtrate to obtain a saturated solution.

5. **Recrystallizing the solute.** Let the hot saturated solution cool to about 22°C spontaneously. Do not disturb the solution. Then cool it in ice. If recrystallization does not occur, scratch the inside of the container or add seed crystals.

6. **Collecting and washing the crystals.** Collect the crystals using the Pasteur pipette method, the Wilfilter, or by vacuum filtration on a Hirsch funnel or a Büchner funnel. If the latter technique is employed, wet the filter paper with solvent, apply vacuum to secure the paper, break vacuum, add crystals and liquid, apply vacuum until solvent just disappears, break vacuum, add cold wash solvent, apply vacuum, and repeat until crystals are clean and filtrate comes through clear.

7. **Drying the product.** Press the wet product on the filter to remove solvent. Then remove it from the filter, squeeze it between sheets of filter paper to remove more solvent, and spread it on a watch glass to dry.

QUESTIONS

1. A sample of naphthalene, which should be pure white, was found to have a grayish color after the usual purification procedure. The melting point was correct, and the melting point range was small. Explain the gray color.

2. How many milliliters of boiling water are required to dissolve 25 g of phthalic acid? If the solution were cooled to 14°C, how many grams of phthalic acid would recrystallize out?

3. Why should activated carbon be used during a recrystallization?

4. If a little activated charcoal does a good job removing impurities in a recrystallization, why not use a larger quantity?

5. Under which circumstances is it wise to use a mixture of solvents to carry out a recrystallization?

6. Why is gravity filtration rather than suction filtration used to remove suspended impurities and charcoal from a hot solution?

7. Why is a fluted filter paper used in gravity filtration?

8. Why are stemless funnels used instead of long-stem funnels to filter hot solutions through fluted filter paper?

9. Why is the final product from the recrystallization process isolated by vacuum filtration rather than gravity filtration?

10. Why should wood applicator sticks not be used when carrying out a chemical reaction?

11. Why should you never use a beaker for recrystallization?

5 CHAPTER

Distillation

PRELAB EXERCISE: Predict what a plot of temperature versus the volume of distillate will look like for the simple distillation and the fractional distillation of (a) a cyclohexane-toluene mixture and (b) an ethanol-water mixture.

Distillation is a common method for purifying liquids and can be used to determine their boiling points.

The origins of distillation are lost in antiquity, when humans in their thirst for more potent beverages found that dilute solutions of fermented alcohol could be separated into alcohol-rich and water-rich portions by heating the solution to boiling and condensing the vapors above the boiling liquid—the process of distillation.

Because ethyl alcohol (ethanol) boils at 78°C and water boils at 100°C, one might naïvely assume that heating a 50:50 mixture of ethanol and water to 78°C would cause the ethanol molecules to leave the solution as a vapor that could be condensed as pure ethanol. However, in such a mixture of ethanol and water, the water boils at about 87°C, and the vapor above the mixture is not 100% ethanol.

A liquid contains closely packed but mobile molecules of varying energy. When a molecule of the liquid approaches the vapor-liquid boundary and possesses sufficient energy, it may pass from the liquid phase into the gas phase. Some of the molecules present in the vapor phase above the liquid may, as they approach the surface of the liquid, reenter the liquid phase and thus become part of the condensed phase. In so doing, the molecules relinquish some of their kinetic energy (i.e., their motion is slowed). Heating the liquid causes more molecules to enter the vapor phase; cooling the vapor reverses this process.

When a closed system is at equilibrium, many molecules are escaping into the vapor phase from the liquid phase, and an equal number are returning from the vapor phase to the liquid phase. The extent of this equilibrium is measured as the vapor pressure. Even when energy is increased and more molecules in the liquid phase have sufficient energy to escape into the vapor phase, equilibrium is maintained because the number moving from the vapor phase into the liquid phase also increases. However, the number of molecules in the vapor phase increases, which increases the vapor pressure. The number of molecules in the vapor phase depends primarily on the volume of the system, the temperature, the combined pressure of all the gaseous components, and the strength of the intermolecular forces exerted in the liquid phase. Review the introduction to Chapter 3 about the types of intermolecular forces.

SIMPLE DISTILLATION

Simple distillation involves boiling a liquid in a vessel (a distilling flask) and directing the resulting vapors through a condenser, in which the vapors are cooled and converted to a liquid that flows down into a collection vessel (a receiving flask). (*See* Fig. 5.5 on page 93.) Simple distillation is used to purify liquid mixtures by separating one liquid component either from nonvolatile substances or from another liquid that differs in boiling point by at least 75°C. The initial condensate will have essentially the same mole ratio of liquids as the vapor just above the boiling liquid. The closer the boiling points of the components of a liquid mixture, the more difficult they are to completely separate by simple distillation.

FRACTIONAL DISTILLATION

Fractional distillation differs from simple distillation in that a fractionating column is placed between the distilling flask and the condenser. This fractionating column allows for successive condensations and distillations and produces a much better separation between liquids with boiling points closer than 75°C. The column is packed with material that provides a large surface area for heat exchange between the ascending vapor and the descending liquid. As a result, multiple condensations and vaporizations occur as the vapors ascend the column. Condensing of the higher-boiling vapor releases heat, which causes vaporization of the lower-boiling liquid on the packing so that the lower-boiling component moves up while the higher-boiling component moves down. Some of the lower-boiling component will run back into the distilling flask. Each successive condensation-vaporization cycle, also called a *theoretical plate*, produces a vapor that is richer in the more volatile fraction. As the temperature of the liquid mixture is increased, the lower-boiling fractions become enriched in the vapor.

Heat exchange between ascending vapor and descending liquid

A large surface area for the packing material is desirable, but the packing cannot be so dense that pressure changes take place within the column to cause nonequilibrium conditions. Also, if the column packing has a very large surface area, it will absorb (hold up) much of the material being distilled. Several different packings for distilling columns have been tried, including glass beads, glass helices, and carborundum chips. One of the best packings in our experience is a copper or steel sponge (brand name–Chore Boy). It is easy to insert into the column; it does not come out of the column as beads do; and it has a large surface area, good heat transfer characteristics, and low holdup. It can be used in both microscale and macroscale apparatus.

Column packing

Holdup (noun): unrecoverable distillate that wets the column packing

The ability of different column packings to separate two materials of differing boiling points is evaluated by calculating the number of theoretical plates. Each theoretical plate corresponds to one condensation-vaporization cycle. Other things being equal, the number of theoretical plates is proportional to the height of the column, so various packings are evaluated according to the *height equivalent to a theoretical plate (HETP)*; the smaller the HETP, the more plates the column will have and the more efficient it will be. The calculation is made by analyzing the proportion of lower- to higher-boiling material at the top of the column and in the distillation pot.[1]

---

[1]Weissberger, A. ed. *Techniques of Organic Chemistry*, Vol. IV; Wiley-Interscience: New York, 1951.

FIG. 5.1
A bubble plate distilling column.

Overflow pipe

Plate

Riser for vapor

Height equivalent to a theoretical plate (HETP)

Equilibration is slow.

Good fractional distillation takes a long time.

Although not obvious, the most important variable that contributes to good fractional distillation is the rate at which the distillation is carried out. When a series of simple distillations take place within a fractionating column, it is important that complete equilibrium be attained between the ascending vapors and the descending liquid. This process is not instantaneous. It should be an adiabatic process; that is, heat should be transferred from the ascending vapor to the descending liquid with no gain of heat or net heat loss to the surroundings. Advanced distillation systems use thermally insulated, vacuum-jacketed fractionating columns. They also allow the adjustment of the ratio between the amount of condensate that is directed to the receiving flask and the amount returned to the distillation column. A reflux ratio of 30:1 or 50:1 is not uncommon for a 40-plate column. Although a distillation of this type takes several hours, this is far less time than if one to had to do 40 distillations, one after the other, and yields much better separated compounds.

Perhaps it is easiest to understand the series of redistillations that occur in fractional distillation by examining the bubble plate column used to fractionally distill crude oil (Fig. 5.1). These columns dominate the skyline at oil refineries, with some being 150 ft high and capable of distilling 200,000 barrels of crude oil per day. The crude oil enters the column as a hot vapor. Some of this vapor with high-boiling components condenses on one of the plates. The more volatile substances travel through the bubble cap to the next higher plate, where some of the less-volatile components condense. As high-boiling liquid material accumulates on a plate, it descends through the overflow pipe to the next lower plate, and vapor rises through the bubble cap to the next higher plate. The temperature of the vapor that is rising through a cap is above the boiling point of the liquid on that plate. As bubbling takes place, heat is exchanged, and the less volatile components on that plate vaporize and go on to the next plate. The composition of the liquid on a plate is the same as that of the vapor coming from the plate below. So, on each plate, a simple distillation takes place. At equilibrium, vapor containing low-boiling material is ascending through the column, and high-boiling liquid is descending.

As a purification method, distillation, particularly fractional distillation, requires larger amounts of material than recrystallization, liquid/liquid extraction, or chromatography. Performing a fractional distillation on less than 1 g of material is virtually impossible. Fractional distillation can be carried out on a scale of about 3–4 g. As will be seen in Chapters 8, 9, and 10, various types of chromatography are employed for separations of milligram quantities of liquids.

LIQUID MIXTURES

If two different liquid compounds are mixed, the vapor above the mixture will contain some molecules of each component. Let us consider a mixture of cyclohexane and toluene. The vapor pressures, as a function of temperature, are plotted in Figure 5.2. When the vapor pressure of the liquid equals the applied pressure, the liquid boils. Figure 5.2 shows that at 760 mm Hg (standard atmospheric pressure), these pure liquids boil at about 81°C and 111°C, respectively. If one of these pure liquids were to be distilled, we would find that the boiling point of the liquid would equal the temperature of the vapor, and that the temperature of the vapor would remain constant throughout the distillation.

FIG. 5.2
Vapor pressure versus temperature plots for cyclohexane and toluene.

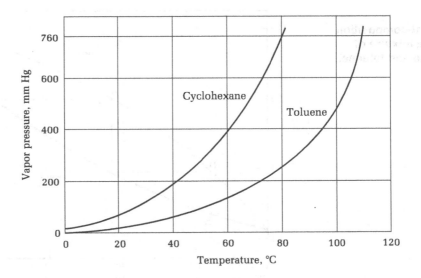

Figure 5.3 is a boiling point composition diagram for the cyclohexane-toluene system. If a mixture of 75 mole percent toluene and 25 mole percent cyclohexane is heated, we find that it boils at 100°C (point A). Above a binary mixture of cyclohexane and toluene, the vapor pressure has contributions from each component. Raoult's law states that the vapor pressure of the cyclohexane is equal to the product of the vapor pressure of pure cyclohexane and the mole fraction of cyclohexane in the liquid mixture:

Raoult's law of partial pressures

$$P_c = P_c^\circ N_c$$

The mole fraction of cyclohexane is equal to the moles of cyclohexane in the mixture divided by the total number of moles (cyclohexane plus toluene) in the mixture.

where P_c is the partial pressure of cyclohexane, P_c° is the vapor pressure of pure cyclohexane at the given temperature, and Nc is the mole fraction of cyclohexane in the mixture. Similarly, for toluene,

$$P_t = P_t^\circ N_t$$

The total vapor pressure above the solution (P_{Tot}) is given by the sum of the partial pressures due to cyclohexane and toluene:

$$P_{Tot} = P_c + P_t$$

Dalton's law states that the mole fraction of cyclohexane (X_c) in the vapor at a given temperature is equal to the partial pressure of the cyclohexane at that temperature divided by the total pressure:

$$X_c = \frac{P_c}{\text{total vapor pressure}}$$

At 100°C, cyclohexane has a partial pressure of 433 mm Hg, and toluene has a partial pressure of 327 mm Hg; the sum of the partial pressures is 760 mm Hg, so the liquid boils. If some of the liquid in equilibrium with this boiling mixture were condensed and analyzed, it would be found to be 433/760, or 57 mole percent cyclohexane (point B, Fig. 5.3). This is the best separation that can be achieved with a simple distillation of this mixture. As the simple distillation proceeds, the boiling point of the mixture moves toward 111°C along the line from point A, and the vapor

FIG. 5.3
Boiling point-composition curves for a mixture of cyclohexane and toluene.

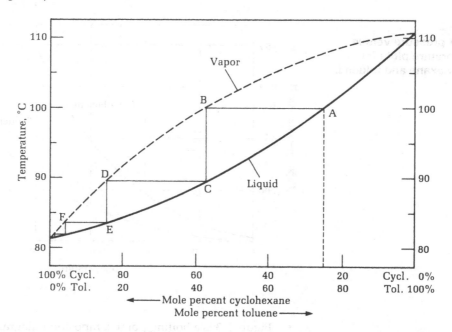

composition becomes richer in toluene as it moves from point B to 110°C. To obtain pure cyclohexane, it would be necessary to condense the liquid at point B and redistill it. When this is done, it is found that the liquid boils at 90°C (point C), and the vapor equilibrium with this liquid is about 85 mole percent cyclohexane (point D). Therefore, to separate a mixture of cyclohexane and toluene, a series of fractions would be collected, and each of these would be partially redistilled. If this fractional distillation were done enough times, the two components could be completely separated.

AZEOTROPES

The ethanol-water azeotrope.

Not all liquids form ideal solutions and conform to Raoult's law. Ethanol and water are two such liquids. Because of molecular interaction, a mixture of 95.5% (by weight) of ethanol and 4.5% of water boils *below* the boiling point of pure ethanol (78.15°C versus 78.3°C). Thus, no matter how efficient the distilling apparatus, 100% ethanol cannot be obtained by distillation of a mixture of, say, 75% water and 25% ethanol. A mixture of liquids of a certain definite composition that distills at a constant temperature without a change in composition is called an *azeotrope*; 95% ethanol is such an azeotrope. The boiling point-composition curve for the ethanol-water mixture is seen in Figure 5.4. To prepare 100% ethanol, the water can be removed chemically (by reaction with calcium oxide) or it can be removed as an azeotrope with still another liquid. An azeotropic mixture of 32.4% ethanol and 67.6% benzene (bp 80.1°C) boils at 68.2°C. A ternary azeotrope containing 74.1% benzene, 18.5% ethanol, and 7.4% water boils at 64.9°C. Absolute alcohol (100% ethanol) is made by adding benzene to 95% ethanol. The water is removed by distilling the ternary azeotrope of benzene, ethanol, and water, bp 64.9°C, followed by the distillation of 100% ethanol, bp 78.4°C

Ethanol and water form a minimum boiling azeotrope. Substances such as formic acid (bp 100.7°C) and water (bp 100°C) form maximum boiling azeotropes. The boiling point of a formic acid-water azeotrope is 107.3°C.

FIG. 5.4
Boiling point–composition curves for a mixture of ethanol and water.

BOILING POINTS AND DISTILLATION

A pure liquid has a constant boiling point. A change in boiling point during distillation is an indication of impurity. The converse proposition, however, is not always true; that is, constancy of a boiling point does not necessarily mean that the liquid consists of only one compound. For instance, two miscible liquids of similar chemical structure that boil at the same temperature individually will have nearly the same boiling point as a mixture. And, as noted previously, azeotropes have constant boiling points that can be either above or below the boiling points of the individual components.

A constant boiling point on distillation does not guarantee that the distillate is a single pure compound.

When a solution of sugar in water is distilled, the boiling point recorded on a thermometer located in the vapor phase is 100°C (at 760 torr) throughout the distillation, whereas the temperature of the boiling sugar solution itself is initially somewhat above 100°C and continues to rise as the concentration of sugar in the remaining solution increases. The vapor pressure of the solution is dependent on the number of water molecules present in a given volume; hence, with increasing concentration of nonvolatile sugar molecules and decreasing concentration of water, the vapor pressure at a given temperature decreases, and a higher temperature is required for boiling. However, sugar molecules do not leave the solution, and the drop clinging to the thermometer is pure water in equilibrium with pure water vapor.

Distilling a mixture of sugar and water.

Boiling point changes with pressure.

When a distillation is carried out in a system open to the air (the boiling point is thus dependent on existing air pressure), the prevailing barometric pressure should be noted and allowance made for appreciable deviations from the accepted boiling point temperature (Table 5.1). Distillation can also be done at the lower pressures that can be achieved using an oil pump or an aspirator, which produces a substantial reduction in the boiling point.

TABLE 5.1 *Variation in Boiling Point with Pressure*

	Boiling Point	
Pressure (mm Hg)	*Water (°C)*	*Benzene (°C)*
780	100.7	81.2
770	100.4	80.8
760	100.0	80.3
750	99.6	79.9
740	99.2	79.5
584*	92.8	71.2

*Instituto de Quimica, Mexico City, altitude 7700 ft (2310 m).

EXPERIMENTS

Before beginning any distillation, calibrate the thermometer to ensure accurate readings are made; refer to Part 3 of Chapter 3 for calibration instructions.

1. SIMPLE DISTILLATION

Apparatus for simple distillation.

IN THIS EXPERIMENT, the two liquids to be separated are placed in a 5-mL round-bottomed, long-necked flask that is fitted to a distilling head (Fig. 5.5). The flask has a larger surface area exposed to heat than does the reaction tube, so the necessary thermal energy can be put into the system to cause the materials to distill. The hot vapor rises and completely envelops the bulb of the thermometer before passing over it and down toward the receiver. The downward-sloping portion of the distilling head functions as an air condenser. The objective is to observe how the boiling point of the mixture changes during the course of its distillation. (Another simple distillation apparatus is shown in Figure 5.6. Here, the long air condenser will condense even low-boiling liquids, and the receiver is far from the heat.)

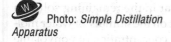

Photo: *Simple Distillation Apparatus*

The rate of distillation is determined by the heat input to the apparatus. This is most easily and effectively controlled by using a spatula to pile up or scrape away hot sand from around the flask.

(A) Simple Distillation of a Cyclohexane-Toluene Mixture

To a 5-mL long-necked, round-bottomed flask, add 2.0 mL of dry cyclohexane, 2.0 mL of dry toluene, and a boiling chip (*see* Fig. 5.5). This flask is joined by means of a Viton (black) connector to a distilling head fitted with a thermometer using a rubber connector. The thermometer bulb should be completely below the side arm of the Claisen head so that the mercury reaches the same temperature as the vapor that distills. The end of the distilling head dips well down into a receiving vial, which rests on the bottom of a 30-mL beaker filled with ice. The distillation is started by piling up hot sand to heat the flask. As soon as boiling begins, the vapors can be seen to rise up the

FIG. 5.5

A small-scale simple distillation apparatus. This apparatus can be adapted for fractional distillation by packing the long neck with a copper sponge. The temperature is regulated by either scraping sand away from or piling sand up around the flask.

FIG. 5.6

A simple distillation apparatus.

Distillation head with air condenser

Receiver vial

Long-necked 5-mL flask

Boiling chip

Distillation head

Air condenser

Boiling chip

Short-necked 5-mL flask

Viton is resistant to hot aromatic vapors.

The thermometer bulb must be *completely below* the side arm.

Cyclohexane
bp 81°C
MW 84.16
n_D^{20} 1.4260

Toluene
bp 111°C
MW 92.14
n_D^{20} 1.4960

Throughout this text, information regarding the physical properties of substances has been placed with each structure in the margin. MW is molecular weight, bp is boiling point, den. is density in g/mL, and *n*D 20 is the refractive index.

There are 21 ± 3 drops per milliliter.

neck of the flask. Adjust the rate of heating by piling up or scraping away sand from the flask so that it takes *several minutes* for the vapor to rise to the thermometer. **The rate of distillation should be no faster than 2 drops per minute.**

Record the temperature versus the number of drops during the entire distillation process. If the rate of distillation is as slow as it should be, there will be sufficient time between drops to read and record the temperature. Continue the distillation until only about 0.4 mL remains in the distilling flask. **Never distill to dryness.** On a larger scale, explosive peroxides can sometimes accumulate. At the end of the distillation, measure as accurately as possible, perhaps with a syringe, the volume of the distillate and, after it cools, the volume left in the pot (round-bottomed flask); the difference is the holdup of the column if none has been lost by evaporation. Note the barometric pressure, make any thermometer corrections necessary, and make a plot of milliliters (drop number) versus temperature for the distillation.

Cleaning Up. The pot residue should be placed in the organic solvents container. The distillate can also be placed there or recycled.

(B) Simple Distillation of an Ethanol-Water Mixture

In a 5-mL round-bottomed, long-necked flask, place 4 mL of a 10% to 20% ethanol-water mixture. Assemble the apparatus as described previously and carry out the distillation until you believe a representative sample of ethanol has collected in the receiver. In the hood, place 3 drops of this sample on a Pyrex watch glass and try to ignite it with the blue cone of a microburner flame. Does it burn? Is any unburned residue observed? There was a time when alcohol-water mixtures were mixed with gunpowder and ignited to give proof that the alcohol had not been diluted. One hundred proof alcohol is 50% ethanol by volume.

Cleaning Up. The distillate and pot residue can be disposed in the organic solvents waste container or, if regulations permit, diluted with water and flushed down the drain.

---

2 . FRACTIONAL DISTILLATION

Photos: *Column Packing with Chore Boy for Fractional Distillation, Fractional Distillation Apparatus*

IN THIS EXPERIMENT, just as in the last one, you will distill a mixture of two liquids and again record the boiling points as a function of the volume of distillate (drops). The necessity for a very slow rate of distillation cannot be overemphasized.

Apparatus

Assemble the apparatus shown in Figure 5.7. The 10-cm column is packed with 1.5 g of copper sponge and connected to the 5-mL short-necked flask using a black (Viton) connector. The column should be vertical and care should be taken to ensure that the bulb of the thermometer does not touch the side of the distilling head. The column, but not the distilling head, will be insulated with glass wool or cotton at the appropriate time to ensure that the process is adiabatic. Alternatively,

FIG. 5.7
A small-scale fractional distillation apparatus. The 10-cm column is packed with 1.5 g of copper sponge (Chore Boy).

Receiver vial

Distilling column packed with copper sponge

Temperature regulated by moving sand

Boiling chip

the column can be insulated with a 15-mL polyethylene centrifuge tube that has the conical bottom cut off.

(A) Fractional Distillation of a Cyclohexane-Toluene Mixture

To a short-necked flask, add 2.0 mL of cyclohexane, 2.0 mL of toluene, and a boiling chip. The distilling column is packed with 1.5 g of copper sponge (Fig. 5.7). The mixture is brought to a boil over a hot sand bath. Observe the ring of condensate that should rise slowly through the column; if you cannot at first see this ring, locate it by touching the column with your fingers. It will be cool above the ring and hot below. Reduce the heat by scraping sand away from the flask and wrap the column, but not the distilling head, with glass wool or cotton if it is not already insulated.

The distilling head and the thermometer function as a small reflux condenser. Again, apply the heat, and as soon as the vapor reaches the thermometer bulb, reduce the heat by scraping away sand. **Distill the mixture at a rate no faster than 2 drops per minute** and record the temperature as a function of the number of drops. If the heat input has been *very* carefully adjusted, the distillation will cease, and the temperature reading will drop after the cyclohexane has distilled. Increase the heat input by piling up the sand around the flask to cause the toluene to distill. Stop the distillation when only about 0.4 mL remains in the flask, and measure the volume of distillate and the pot residue as before. Make a plot of the boiling point versus the milliliters of distillate (drops) and compare it to the simple distillation carried out in the same apparatus. Compare your results with those in Figure 5.8.

Cleaning Up. The pot residue should be placed in the organic solvents container. The distillate can also be placed there or recycled.

(B) Fractional Distillation of an Ethanol-Water Mixture

Distill 4 mL of the same ethanol-water mixture used in the simple distillation experiment, following the procedure used for the cyclohexane-toluene mixture with either the short or the long distilling column. Remove what you regard to be the ethanol fraction and repeat the ignition test. Is any difference noted?

Cleaning Up. The pot residue and distillate can be disposed in the organic solvents waste container or, if regulations permit, diluted with water and flushed down the drain.

*Side notes (left margin):*

Never distill in an airtight system.

Adjust the heat input to the flask by piling up or scraping away sand around the flask.

Insulate the distilling column but not the Claisen head.

21 ± 3 drops = 1 mL

FIG. 5.8
Simple and fractional distillation curves for cyclohexane and toluene.

© 2011 Cengage Learning. All Rights Reserved. May not be scanned, copied or duplicated, or posted to a publicly accessible website, in whole or in part.

3. INSTANT MICROSCALE DISTILLATION

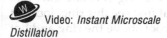
Video: *Instant Microscale Distillation*

Frequently, a very small quantity of freshly distilled material is needed in an experiment. For example, two compounds that need to be distilled freshly are aniline, which turns black because of the formation of oxidation products, and benzaldehyde, a liquid that easily oxides to solid benzoic acid. The impurities that arise in both of these compounds have much higher boiling points than the pure compounds, so a very simple distillation suffices to separate them. This can be accomplished as follows.

Place a few drops of the impure liquid in a reaction tube along with a boiling chip. Clamp the tube in a hot sand bath and adjust the heat so that the liquid refluxes about halfway up the tube. Expel the air from a Pasteur pipette, thrust it down into the hot vapor, and then pull the hot vapor into the cold upper portion of the pipette. The vapor will immediately condense and can then be expelled into another reaction tube that is held adjacent to the hot one (Fig. 5.9). In this way enough pure material can be distilled to determine a boiling point, run a spectrum, make a derivative, or carry out a reaction. Sometimes the first drop or two will be cloudy, which indicates the presence of water. This fraction should be discarded in order to obtain pure dry material.

4. SIMPLE DISTILLATION APPARATUS

In any distillation, the flask should be no more than two-thirds full at the start. Great care should be taken not to distill to dryness because, in some cases, high-boiling explosive peroxides can become concentrated.

Assemble the apparatus for macroscale simple distillation, as shown in Figure 5.10, starting with the support ring followed by the electric flask heater and then the flask. One or two boiling stones are put in the flask to promote even boiling. Each ground joint is greased by putting three or four stripes of grease lengthwise around the male joint and pressing the joint firmly into the other without twisting. The air is thus eliminated, and the joint will appear almost transparent. (Do not use excess grease because it will contaminate the product.) Water enters the condenser at the tubulature nearest the receiver. Because of the large heat capacity of water, only a very small stream (3 mm diameter) is needed; too much water pressure will cause the tubing to pop off. A heavy rubber band, or better, a Keck clamp, can be used to hold the condenser to the distillation head. Note that the bulb of the thermometer is below the opening into the side arm of the distillation head.

(A) Simple Distillation of a Cyclohexane-Toluene Mixture

Place a mixture of 30 mL cyclohexane and 30 mL toluene, and a boiling chip in a dry 100-mL round-bottomed flask and assemble the apparatus for simple distillation. After assuring that all connections are tight, heat the flask strongly until boiling begins. Then adjust the heat until the distillate drops at a regular rate of about 1 drop per second. Record both the temperature and the volume of distillate at regular intervals. After 50 mL of distillate is collected, discontinue the distillation. Record the barometric pressure, make any thermometer correction necessary, and plot the boiling point versus the volume of distillate. Save the distillate for fractional distillation.

FIG. 5.9
An apparatus for instant microscale distillation.

FIG. 5.10
An apparatus for macroscale simple distillation.

Refluxing vapor

Boiling liquid

Boiling chip

⚠️
Cyclohexane and toluene are flammable; make sure the distilling apparatus is tight.

Do not add a boiling chip to a hot liquid. It may boil over.

Dispose of cyclohexane and toluene in the waste container provided. Do not pour them down the drain.

Cleaning Up. The pot residue should be placed in the organic solvents container. The distillate can also be placed there or recycled.

(B) Simple Distillation of an Ethanol-Water Mixture

In a 500-mL round-bottomed flask, place 200 mL of a 20% aqueous solution of ethanol. Follow the previous procedure for the distillation of a cyclohexane-toluene mixture. Discontinue the distillation after 50 mL of distillate has been collected. Working in the hood, place 3 drops of distillate on a Pyrex watch glass and try to ignite it with the blue cone of a microburner flame. Does it burn? Is any unburned residue observed?

Cleaning Up. The pot residue and distillate can be disposed in the organic solvents waste container or, if regulations permit, diluted with water and flushed down the drain.

5. FRACTIONAL DISTILLATION

Apparatus

Assemble the apparatus shown in Figures 5.11 and 5.12. The fractionating column is packed with one-fourth to one-third of a metal sponge. The column should be perfectly vertical and be insulated with glass wool covered with aluminum foil (shiny side in). However, insulation is omitted for this experiment so that you can observe what is taking place in the column.

FIG. 5.11

An apparatus for macroscale fractional distillation. The position of the thermometer bulb is critical.

FIG. 5.12

A fractionating column and its packing. Use one-third of a copper sponge (Chore Boy).

(A) Fractional Distillation of a Cyclohexane-Toluene Mixture

After the flask from the simple macroscale distillation experiment has cooled, pour the 50 mL of distillate back into the distilling flask, add one or two new boiling chips, and assemble the apparatus for fractional distillation. The stillhead delivers into a short condenser fitted with a bent adapter leading into a 10-mL graduated cylinder. Gradually turn up the heat to the electric flask heater until the mixture of cyclohexane and toluene just begins to boil. As soon as boiling starts, turn down the power. Heat slowly at first. A ring of condensate will rise slowly through the column; if you cannot at first see this ring, locate it by cautiously touching the column with your fingers. The rise in temperature should be very gradual so that the column can acquire a uniform temperature gradient. Do not apply more heat until you are sure that the ring of condensate has stopped rising; then increase the heat gradually. In a properly conducted operation, the vapor-condensate mixture reaches the top of the column only after several minutes. Once distillation has commenced, it should continue steadily without any drop in temperature at a rate no greater than 1 mL in 1.5–2 min. Observe the flow and keep it steady by slight increases in heat as required. Protect the column from drafts by wrapping it with aluminum foil, glass wool, or even a towel. This insulation will help prevent flooding of the column, as will slow and steady distillation.

Record the temperature as each milliliter of distillate collects and take more frequent readings when the temperature starts to rise abruptly. Each time the graduated cylinder fills, quickly empty it into a series of labeled 25-mL Erlenmeyer flasks. Stop the distillation when a second constant temperature is reached. Plot a distillation curve and record what you observed inside the column in the course of the fractionation. Combine the fractions that you think are pure, and turn in the product in a bottle labeled with your name, desk number, the name of the product, the boiling point range, and the weight.

Cleaning Up. The pot residue should be placed in the organic solvents waste container. The cyclohexane and toluene fractions can also be placed there or recycled.

(B) Fractional Distillation of Ethanol-Water Mixture

Place the 50 mL of distillate from the simple distillation experiment into a 100-mL round-bottomed flask, add one or two boiling chips, and assemble the apparatus for fractional distillation. Follow the previous procedure for the fractional distillation of a cyclohexane-toluene mixture. Repeat the ignition test. Is any difference noted? Alternatively, distill 60 mL of the 10%–20% ethanol-water mixture that results from the fermentation of sucrose (*see* Chapter 64).

Cleaning Up. The pot residue and distillate can be disposed in the organic solvents waste container or, if regulations permit, diluted with water and flushed down the drain.

6. FRACTIONAL DISTILLATION OF UNKNOWNS

You will be supplied with an unknown, prepared by your instructor, that is a mixture of two solvents listed in Table 5.2, only two of which form azeotropes. The solvents in the mixture will be mutually soluble and differ in boiling point by more than 20°C. The composition of the mixture (in percentages of the two components) will be either 20:80, 30:70, 40:60, 50:50, 60:40, 70:30, or 80:20. Identify the two compounds and determine the percent composition of each. Perform a fractional distillation on

TABLE 5.2 *Some Properties of Common Solvents*

Solvent	Boiling Point (°C)
Acetone	56.5
Methanol	64.7
Hexane	68.8
1-Butanol	117.2
2-Methyl-2-propanol	82.2
Water	100.0
Toluene*	110.6

*Methanol and toluene form an azeotrope with a boiling point of 63.8°C (69% methanol).

4 mL of the unknown for microscale; use at least 50 mL of unknown for macroscale. Fractionate the unknown and identify the components from the boiling points. Prepare a distillation curve. You may be directed to analyze your distillate by gas chromatography (*see* Chapter 10) or refractive index (*see* Chapter 14).

Cleaning Up. Organic material goes in the organic solvents waste container. Water and aqueous solutions can be flushed down the drain.

QUESTIONS

1. In either of the simple distillation experiments, can you account for the boiling point of your product in terms of the known boiling points of the pure components of your mixture? If so, how? If not, why not?

2. From the plots of the boiling point versus the volume of distillate in the simple distillation experiments, what can you conclude about the purity of your product?

3. From the plots of the boiling point versus the volume of distillate in either of the fractional distillations of the cyclohexane-toluene mixture, what conclusion can you draw about the homogeneity of the distillate?

4. From the plots of the boiling point versus the volume of distillate in either of the fractional distillations of the ethanol-water mixture, what conclusion can you draw about the homogeneity of the distillate? Does it have a constant boiling point? If constant, is it a pure substance?

5. What is the effect on the boiling point of a solution (e.g., water) produced by a soluble nonvolatile substance (e.g., sodium chloride)? What is the effect of an insoluble substance such as sand or charcoal? What is the temperature of the vapor above these two boiling solutions?

6. In the distillation of a pure substance (e.g., water), why does all of the water not vaporize at once when the boiling point is reached?

7. In fractional distillation, liquid can be seen running from the bottom of the distillation column back into the distilling flask. What effect does this returning condensate have on the fractional distillation?

8. Why is it extremely dangerous to attempt to carry out a distillation in a completely closed apparatus (one with no vent to the atmosphere)?

9. Why is better separation of two liquids achieved by slow rather than fast distillation?

10. Explain why a packed fractionating column is more efficient than an unpacked one.

11. In the distillation of the cyclohexane-toluene mixture, the first few drops of distillate may be cloudy. Explain this occurrence.

12. What effect does the reduction of atmospheric pressure have on the boiling point? Can cyclohexane and toluene be separated if the external pressure is 350 mm Hg instead of 760 mm Hg?

13. When water-cooled condensers are used for distillation or for refluxing a liquid, the water enters the condenser at the lowest point and leaves at the highest. Why?

 See *Web Links*

REFERENCE

An excellent review of distillation at the level of this textbook is *Distillation, an Introduction* by M.T. Tham, http://lorien.ncl.ac.uk/ming/distil/distilop.htm

Steam Distillation, Vacuum Distillation, and Sublimation

PRELAB EXERCISE: If a mixture of toluene and water is distilled at 97°C, what weight of water would be necessary to carry over 1 g of toluene? Compare the operation of a barometer, which is used to measure atmospheric pressure, with that of a mercury manometer, which is used to measure the pressure in an evacuated system.

PART 1: STEAM DISTILLATION

The boiling point of a pair of immiscible liquids is below the boiling point of either pure liquid.

Each liquid exerts its own vapor pressure.

When a mixture of cyclohexane and toluene is distilled (see Chapter 5), the boiling point of these two miscible liquids is between the boiling points of each of the pure components. By contrast, if a mixture of benzene and water (immiscible liquids) is distilled, the boiling point of the mixture will be below the boiling point of each pure component. Because benzene and water are essentially insoluble in each other, the molecules in a droplet of benzene are not diluted by water molecules from nearby water droplets; thus, the vapor pressure exerted by benzene in the mixture is the same as that of benzene alone at the existing temperature. The same is true for water. These two immiscible liquids exert pressures against the common external pressure independently, and when the sum of the two partial pressures equals the external pressure, boiling occurs. Benzene has a vapor pressure of 760 torr at 80.1°C, and if it is mixed with water, the combined vapor pressure must equal 760 torr at some temperature below 80.1°C. This temperature, the boiling point of the mixture, can be calculated from known values of the vapor pressures of the separate liquids at that temperature. Vapor pressures for water and benzene in the range 50–80°C are plotted in Figure 6.1. The dashed line cuts the two curves at points where the sum of the vapor pressures is 760 torr; hence the boiling point of the mixture is 69.3°C.

Practical use can sometimes be made of the fact that many water-insoluble liquids and solids behave as benzene does when mixed with water, volatilizing at temperatures below their boiling points. Naphthalene, a solid, boils at 218°C but distills with water at a temperature below 100°C. Because naphthalene is not very

FIG. 6.1
Vapor pressure versus temperature curves for water and benzene.

volatile, considerable water is required to entrain it, and the conventional way of conducting the distillation is to pass steam into a boiling flask containing naphthalene and water, a process called *steam distillation*. With more volatile compounds, or with a small amount of material, the substance can be heated with water in a simple distillation flask, with the steam generated in situ.

Some high-boiling substances decompose before the boiling point is reached and, if impure, cannot be purified by ordinary distillation. However, these substances can be freed from contaminating substances by steam distillation at a lower temperature, at which they are stable. Steam distillation also offers the advantage of selectivity because some water-insoluble substances are volatile with steam while others are not; some volatilize so slowly that sharp separation is possible.

> **Used for the isolation of perfume and flavor oils.**

This technique is useful in processing natural oils and resins, which can be separated into steam-volatile and non-steam-volatile fractions. It is useful for the recovery of a non-steam-volatile solid from its solution in a high-boiling solvent such as nitrobenzene (bp 210°C); all traces of the solvent can be eliminated, and the temperature can be kept low.

The boiling point remains constant during a steam distillation as long as adequate amounts of both water and the organic component are present to saturate the vapor space. Determination of the boiling point and correction for any deviation from normal atmospheric pressure permits calculation of the amount of water required for the distillation of a given amount of organic substance. According to

> **Dalton's law**

Dalton's law, the molecular proportion of the two components in the distillate is equal to the ratio of their vapor pressures (p) in the boiling mixture; the more volatile component contributes the greater number of molecules to the vapor phase. Thus,

$$\frac{\text{moles of water}}{\text{moles of substance}} = \frac{p_{\text{water}}}{p_{\text{substance}}}$$

TABLE 6.1 *The Vapor Pressure of Water at Different Temperatures*

t (°C)	p (mm Hg)	t (°C)	p (mm Hg)	t (°C)	p (mm Hg)	t (°C)	p (mm Hg)
0	4.58	20	17.41	24	22.18	28	28.10
5	6.53	21	18.50	25	23.54	29	29.78
10	9.18	22	19.66	26	24.99	30	31.55
15	12.73	23	20.88	27	26.50	35	41.85
60	149.3	70	233.7	80	355.1	90	525.8
61	156.4	71	243.9	81	369.7	91	546.0
62	163.8	72	254.6	82	384.9	92	567.0
63	171.4	73	265.7	83	400.6	93	588.6
64	179.3	74	277.2	84	416.8	94	610.9
65	187.5	75	289.1	85	433.6	95	633.9
66	196.1	76	301.4	86	450.9	96	657.6
67	205.0	77	314.1	87	468.7	97	682.1
68	214.2	78	327.3	88	487.1	98	707.3
69	223.7	79	341.0	89	506.1	99	733.2

The vapor pressure of water (p_{water}) at the boiling temperature in question can be found by interpolating the data in Table 6.1. For the organic substance, the vapor pressure is equal to $760 - p_{water}$. Hence, the weight of water required per gram of substance is given by the expression:

$$\text{wt of water per g of substance} = \frac{18 \times p_{water}}{\text{MW of substance} \times (760 - p_{water})}$$

From the data given in Figure 6.1 for benzene and water, the fact that the mixture boils at 69.3°C, and the molecular weight of benzene is 78.11, the water required for the steam distillation of 1 g of benzene is only $227 \times 18/533 \times 1/78 = 0.10$ g. Nitrobenzene (bp 210°C, MW 123.11) steam distills at 99°C and requires 4.0 g of water per gram of nitrobenzene. The low molecular weight of water makes water a favorable liquid for the two-phase distillation of organic compounds.

Steam distillation is employed in several experiments in this text. On a small scale, steam is generated in the flask that contains the substance to be steam distilled by simply boiling a mixture of water and the immiscible substance.

ISOLATION OF CITRAL

Terpenes

Citral is an example of a very large group of natural products called terpenes. They are responsible for the characteristic odors of plants such as eucalyptus, pine, mint, peppermint, and lemon. The odors of camphor, menthol, lavender, rose, and hundreds of other fragrances are due to terpenes, which have 10 carbon atoms with double bonds along with aldehyde, ketone, or alcohol functional groups (Fig. 6.2).

FIG. 6.2
Structures of some terpenes.

Geranial

Isopentenyl pyrophosphate

Isoprene
(2-Methyl-1,3-butadiene)

Neral

Limonene
(lemons)

Myrcene
(bayberry)

α-Pinene
(turpentine)

Menthol
(mint)

Carvone
(caraway seeds)

Camphor

1,8-Cineole
(eucalyptus)

Pulegone
(pennyroyal oil)

Anethole
(anise seed)

The isoprene rule.

Geranial and neral are geometric isomers.

Steam distillation: the isolation of heat-sensitive compounds.

These natural terpenes all arise from a common precursor: isopentenyl pyrophosphate. At one time, these were thought to come from the simple diene, isoprene (2-methyl-1,3-butadiene), because the skeletons of terpenes can be dissected into isoprene units, each having five carbon atoms arranged as in 2-methylbutane. These isoprene units are almost always arranged in a "head-to-tail" fashion.

In the present experiment, citral, a mixture of geranial and neral, is isolated by steam distillation of lemongrass oil, which is used to make lemongrass tea, a popular drink in Mexico. The distillate contains 90% geranial and 10% neral, with the isomer about the 2,3-bond. Citral is used in a commercial synthesis of vitamin A.

Lemongrass oil contains a number of substances; simple or fractional distillation would not be a practical method for obtaining pure citral. And because lemongrass oil boils at 229°C, it has a tendency to polymerize, oxidize, and decompose during distillation. For example, heating with potassium bisulfate, an acidic compound, converts citral to 1-methyl-4-isopropylbenzene (*p*-cymene).

Steam distillation is thus a very gentle method for isolating citral. The distillation takes place below the boiling point of water. The distillate consists of a mixture of citral (and some neral) and water. It is isolated by shaking the mixture with *t*-butyl methyl ether. The citral dissolves in the *t*-butyl methyl ether, which is immiscible with water, and the two layers are separated. The *t*-butyl methyl ether is dried (it dissolves some water) and evaporated to leave citral.

Store the citral in the smallest possible container in the dark for later characterization. The homogeneity of the substance can be investigated using thin-layer chromatography (TLC; *see* Chapter 8) or gas chromatography (*see* Chapter 10). An infrared spectrum (*see* Chapter 11) would confirm the presence of the aldehyde; an ultraviolet spectrum (*see* Chapter 14) would indicate it is a conjugated aldehyde; and a nuclear magnetic resonance (NMR) spectrum (*see* Chapter 12) would clearly show the aldehyde proton, the three methyl groups, and the two olefinic protons. Chemically, the molecule can be characterized by reaction with bromine and also permanganate, which shows it contains double bonds; the Tollens test confirms the presence of an aldehyde (*see* Chapter 36).

EXPERIMENTS

1. ISOLATION OF CITRAL

Video: *Steam Distillation Apparatus*

Wrap the vertical part of the apparatus in cotton or glass wool to speed the distillation.

Into a 5-mL short-necked, round-bottomed flask place a boiling chip, 0.5 mL of lemongrass oil (*not* lemon oil)[1], and 3 mL of water. Assemble the apparatus as depicted in Figure 6.3 and distill as rapidly as possible, taking care that all the distillate condenses. Using a syringe, inject water dropwise through the septum to keep the volume in the flask constant. Distill into an ice-cooled vial, as shown, or better, into a 15-mL centrifuge tube, until no more oily drops can be detected, about 10 to 12 mL. Use this citral and water mixture for the next experiment.

---

[1]Lemongrass oil can be obtained from Pfaitz and Bauer, 172 E. Aurora St., Waterbury, CT 06708.

FIG. 6.3
A small-scale steam distillation apparatus. Add water via syringe at A.

Citral (mixture of geranial and neral)
MW 152.24
bp 229°C, den. 0.888
n_D^{20} 1.4880

Ice

Hot sand bath

Boiling chip

A

---

2. EXTRACTION OF CITRAL

IN THIS EXPERIMENT, you will extract the pleasant-smelling liquid citral from water (from the previous experiment) using ether as the solvent. The ether solution is dried, and the ether is evaporated to leave pure citral. Extraction is a common isolation technique (*see* Chapter 7 for information on the theory and practice of extraction).

In a centrifuge tube, add 2.5 mL of *t*-butyl methyl ether to the cold distillate. Shake, let the layers separate, draw off the aqueous layer with a Pasteur pipette, and transfer it to another centrifuge tube. Continue this extraction process by again adding 1.5 mL of ether to the aqueous layer, shaking, and separating to extract the citral from the steam distillate. (*See* Chapter 7 for the many advantages of *t*-butyl methyl ether as an extraction solvent.)

In Sweden they say, "Add anhydrous drying agent until it begins to snow."

Place the ether in a reaction tube and then add about 2 mL of saturated sodium chloride solution to the ether. Stopper the tube, flick the tube or shake it, and then remove and discard the aqueous layer. Add anhydrous calcium chloride pellets to the ether until these no longer clump together, stopper the tube, and shake it over a period of 5–10 minutes. This removes water adhering to the reaction tube and dissolved in the ether. Force a Pasteur pipette to the bottom of the reaction tube, expel the air from the pipette, draw up the ether, and expel it into another tared reaction tube. Add fresh ether, which will serve to wash off the drying agent, and add that ether to the tared reaction tube. Add a boiling stick or boiling chip to the ether in

See **Chapter 7 for the removal of water from ether solutions.**

the reaction tube, place it in a beaker of hot water, and evaporate the ether by boiling and drawing the ether vapors into a water aspirator or, better, by blowing a gentle stream of air or nitrogen into the tube (in the hood). The last traces of ether may be removed by connecting the reaction tube directly to a water aspirator. The residue should be a clear, fragrant oil. If it is cloudy, it is wet.

Determine the weight of the citral and calculate the percentage of citral recovered from the lemongrass oil, assuming that the density of the lemongrass oil is the same as that of citral (0.89). Transfer the product to the smallest possible airtight container and store it in the dark for later analysis to confirm the presence of double bonds (alkenes) and the aldehyde group (*see* Chapters 18 and 36). Analyze the infrared spectrum in detail.

Cleaning Up. The aqueous layer can be flushed down the drain. Any ether goes into the organic solvents waste container. Allow ether to evaporate from the calcium chloride in the hood and then place the calcium chloride in the nonhazardous solid waste container. However, be aware of the regulations in your area, as they may not allow evaporation of small amounts of organic solvents in a hood. If this is the case, special containers should be available for the disposal of these wet solids.

---

3. ISOLATION OF CITRAL

Citral, a fragrant terpene aldehyde made up of two isoprene units, is the main component of the steam-volatile fraction of lemongrass oil and is used in a commercial synthesis of vitamin A.

Steam Distillation Apparatus

In the assembly shown in Figure 6.4, steam is passed into a 250-mL round-bottomed flask through a section of 6-mm glass tubing fitted into a stillhead with a piece of 5-mm rubber tubing connected to a trap, which in turn is connected to a steam line.

FIG. 6.4
A steam distillation apparatus.

CAUTION: Live steam causes severe burns. If the apparatus leaks steam, immediately turn off the steam valve.

Perform steam distillations within fume hoods.

The trap serves two purposes: (1) it allows water, which is in the steam line, to be removed before it reaches the round-bottomed flask; and (2) adjustment of the clamp on the hose at the bottom of the trap allows precise control of the steam flow. As shown, the stopper in the trap should be wired on as a precaution. A bent adapter attached to a long condenser delivers the condensate into a 250-mL Erlenmeyer flask.

Alternative Steam Distillation Setup

If a steam line is not available, the steam distillation setup shown in Figure 6.5 may be used. A 100-mL or 250-mL boiling flask containing the mixture to be distilled is equipped with a boiling chip or better a magnetic stirring bar and magnetic stirrer and is heated on a heating mantle. Equip the boiling flask with a distillation adapter to which is attached a thermometer adapter and a separatory funnel, which serves to add water to the boiling flask during the distillation. A condenser is attached to the thermometer adapter and is equipped with a vacuum adapter, which is attached to the receiving flask. The receiving flask can be cooled by placing it in an ice-water bath. Make sure you securely clamp the distillation flask and condenser. Also make sure to use a rubber band or a Keck clip to hold the vacuum adapter on the end of the condenser.

Steam Distillation

Using a graduated cylinder, measure out 10 mL of lemongrass oil (not lemon oil) into a 250-mL boiling flask. Rinse the remaining contents of the graduated cylinder into the flask with a small amount of t-butyl methyl ether. Add 100 mL of water, make the connections as in Figure 6.4, heat the flask with a low flame, and pass in the steam.

FIG. 6.5

An alternative macroscale steam distillation setup. Water is to be added through the separatory funnel.

Separatory funnel

Keck clamp

Water out

Boiling chip

Keck clamp

Thermowell

Water in

To start the steam distillation, heat the flask containing the mixture on a Thermowell to prevent water from condensing in the flask to the point where water and product splash over into the receiver. Then turn on the steam valve, being sure that the screw clamp on the bottom of the trap is open. Slowly close the clamp and allow steam to pass into the flask. Try to adjust the rate of steam addition and the rate of heating so that the water level in the flask remains constant. Unlike ordinary distillations, steam distillations are usually run as fast as possible, with proper care to avoid splashing of material into the receiver and the escape of uncondensed steam. Distill as rapidly as the cooling facilities allow and continue until droplets of oil no longer appear at the tip of the condenser (about 250 mL of distillate).

Extraction

Pour 50 mL of t-butyl methyl ether into a 125-mL separatory funnel, cool the distillate if necessary, and pour a part of it into the funnel. Shake, let the layers separate, discard the lower layer, add another portion of distillate, and repeat. When the last portion of distillate has been added, rinse the flask with a small amount of t-butyl methyl ether to recover adhering citral. Use the techniques described in Chapter 7 for drying, filtering, and evaporating the t-butyl methyl ether. Take the tare of a 1-g tincture bottle, transfer the citral to it with a Pasteur pipette, and determine the weight and the yield from the lemongrass oil. Label the bottle and store (in the dark) for later testing for the presence of double bonds (alkenes) and the aldehyde group (*see* Chapters 18 and 36).

Cleaning Up. The aqueous layer can be flushed down the drain. Any t-butyl methyl ether goes in the organic solvents waste container. Allow t-butyl methyl ether to evaporate from the calcium chloride pellets in the hood and then place the calcium chloride in the nonhazardous solid waste container. However, be aware of the regulations in your area, as they may not allow evaporation of small amounts of organic solvents in a hood. If this is the case, special containers should be available for the disposal of these wet solids.

---

4. RECOVERY OF A DISSOLVED SUBSTANCE

Anthracene
mp 216°C

Toluene
bp 110.8°C
den. 0.866

Measure 50 mL of a 0.2% solution of anthracene in toluene into a 250-mL round-bottomed flask and add 100 mL of water (see Fig. 6.4 on page 108). For an initial distillation to determine the boiling point and composition of the toluene-water azeotrope, fit the stillhead with a thermometer instead of a steam-inlet tube (see Fig. 5.4 on page 91). Heat the mixture with a hot plate, a sand bath, or an electric flask heater; distill about 50 mL of the azeotrope and record a value for the boiling point. After removing the heat source, pour the distillate into a graduated cylinder and measure the volumes of toluene and water. Calculate the weight of water per gram of toluene and compare the result to the theoretical value calculated from the vapor pressure of water at the observed boiling point (see Table 6.1 on page 104).

Replace the thermometer with the steam-inlet tube. To start the steam distillation, heat the flask containing the mixture with a Thermowell to prevent water from condensing, which may cause water and product to splash over into the receiver. Then turn on the steam valve, being sure that the screw clamp on the bottom of the trap is open. Slowly close the clamp and allow steam to pass into the flask. Try to adjust the rate of steam addition and the rate of heating so that the water level in the flask remains constant. Unlike ordinary distillations, steam distillations are usually run as fast as possible, with proper care to avoid splashing of material into the receiver and the escape of uncondensed steam.

Continue the distillation by passing in steam until the distillate is clear and then until fluorescence appearing in the stillhead indicates that a trace of anthracene is beginning to distill. Stop the steam distillation by first opening the clamp at the bottom of the trap and then turning off the steam valve. Grasp the round-bottomed flask with a towel when disconnecting it and, using the clamp to support it, cool it under the tap. The bulk of the anthracene can be dislodged from the flask walls and collected on a small suction filter. To recover any remaining anthracene, add a small amount of acetone to the flask, warm the flask on a steam bath to dissolve the material, add water to precipitate it, and then collect the precipitate on the same suction filter. About 80% of the hydrocarbon in the original toluene solution should be recoverable. When dry, recrystallize the material from about 1 mL of toluene and note that the crystals are more intensely fluorescent than the solution or the amorphous solid. The characteristic fluorescence is quenched by mere traces of impurities.

Cleaning Up. Place the toluene and the anthracene in the organic solvents waste container. The aqueous layer can be flushed down the drain.

---

5. ISOLATION AND BIOASSAY OF EUGENOL FROM CLOVES

In the 15th century, Philippus Aureolus Theophrastus Bombast von Hohenheim, otherwise known as Paracelsus, urged all chemists to make extractives for medicinal purposes rather than try to transmute base metals into gold. He believed every extractive possessed a quintessence that was the most effective part in effecting cures. There was then an upsurge in the isolation of essential oils from plant materials, which are highly concentrated extracts that may consist of one or two to hundreds of chemical compounds. Some of the essential oils that were isolated centuries ago are still used today for medicinal purposes. Among these are camphor, quinine, oil of cloves, cedarwood, turpentine, cinnamon, gum benzoin, and myrrh. Clove oil, which consists almost entirely of eugenol and its acetate, is a food flavoring agent as well as a dental anesthetic. The Food and Drug Administration has declared clove oil to be the most effective nonprescription remedy for toothache.

The biggest market for essential oils is for perfumes, and prices for these oils reflect their rarity. Recently, worldwide production of orange oil was 1500 tons and sold for $2 per oz, whereas 400 tons of clove oil sold for $4 per oz, and 10 tons of jasmine oil sold for $150 per oz. These three oils represent the most common extractive processes. Orange oil is obtained by expression (squeezing) of the peel in presses; clove oil is obtained by steam distillation, as performed in this experiment; and jasmine oil is obtained by the extraction of the flower petals using ethanol. An even more gentle method of extraction is to use supercritical carbon dioxide. At a pressure of 73 atmospheres and temperatures above 32°C, carbon dioxide becomes a supercritical fluid. It is like a gas, but will dissolve many non-polar organic substances. It evaporates below room temperature when the pressure is released, so delicate perfumes such as rose oil can be extracted with virtually no chemical change. The resulting oil costs several hundred dollars per ounce.

Eugenol

Acetyleugenol

Cloves are the dried flower buds from a tropical tree that can grow to 50 ft in height. The buds are handpicked in the Moluccas (the Spice Islands) of Indonesia, the East Indies, and the islands of the Indian Ocean, where a single tree can yield up to 75 lb of the sun-dried buds we know as cloves.

Cloves contain between 14% and 20% by weight of essential oil, of which only about 50% can be isolated. The principal constituent of clove oil is eugenol and its acetyl derivative. Eugenol boils at 255°C, but because it is insoluble in water, it will form an azeotrope with water and steam distill at a temperature slightly below the boiling point of water. Being a phenol, eugenol will dissolve in aqueous alkali to form the phenolate anion, which forms the basis for its separation from its acetyl derivative. The relative amounts of eugenol and acetyleugenol, and the effectiveness of the alkali extraction in separating them can be analyzed by thin-layer chromatography.

Procedure

IN THIS EXPERIMENT the essential oil—a mixture of eugenol and cetyleugenol—is steam distilled from cloves. These compounds are isolated from the aqueous distillate by extraction into dichloromethane. The dichloromethane solution is shaken with aqueous sodium hydroxide, which reacts with the acidic eugenol. The dichloromethane layer is dried and evaporated to give acetyleugenol. The basic layer is acidified, and the eugenol is extracted into dichloromethane, which is in turn dried and evaporated to give pure eugenol. The isolated crude oil, eugenol, and acetyleugenol can then be evaluated for antibacterial properties.

Steam Distillation

Place 25 g of whole cloves in a 250-mL round-bottomed flask, add 100 mL of water, and set up an apparatus for steam distillation (*see* Fig. 6.4 on page 108 or Fig. 6.5 on page 109) or simple distillation (*see* Fig. 5.10 on page 97). In the latter procedure, steam is generated in situ. Heat the flask strongly until boiling begins, and then reduce the heat just enough to prevent foam from being carried over into the receiver. Instead of using a graduated cylinder as a receiver, use an Erlenmeyer flask and transfer the distillate periodically to the graduated cylinder; then, if any material does foam over, the entire distillate will not be contaminated. Collect 60 mL of distillate, remove the flame, and add 60 mL of water to the flask. Resume the distillation and collect an additional 60 mL of distillate.

Extraction

The eugenol is sparingly soluble in water and is extracted easily from the distillate with dichloromethane. Place the 120 mL of distillate in a 250-mL separatory funnel and extract with three 15-mL portions of dichloromethane. In this extraction, very gentle shaking will fail to remove all of the product, and long and vigorous shaking will produce an emulsion of the organic layer and water. The separatory funnel will appear to have three layers in it. It is better to err on the side of vigorous shaking and draw off the clear lower layer to the emulsion line for the first two extractions. For the third extraction, shake the mixture less vigorously and allow a longer period of time for the two layers to separate.

Combine the dichloromethane extracts (the aqueous layer can be discarded) and add just enough anhydrous calcium chloride pellets so that the drying agent no longer clumps together but appears to be a dry powder as it settles in the solution. This may require as little as 2 g of drying agent. Swirl the flask for 1–2 minutes to complete the drying process and then decant the solvents into an Erlenmeyer flask. It is quite easy to decant the dichloromethane from the drying agent, so it is not necessary to set up a filtration apparatus to accomplish this separation.

Measure the volume of the dichloromethane in a dry graduated cylinder, place exactly one-fifth of the solution in a tared Erlenmeyer flask, add a wood boiling stick (easier to remove than a boiling chip), and evaporate the solution on a steam bath or a hot plate in a hood. The residue of crude clove oil will be used in a TLC (thin-layer chromatography) analysis and/or in a bioassay. From its weight, the total yield can be calculated. This residue can then be dissolved in acetone (a 5%–10% solution) for TLC analysis and/or for a bioassay.

See Chapter 7 for the theory of acid/base extractions.

To separate eugenol from acetyleugenol, extract the remaining four-fifths of the dichloromethane solution (about 30 mL) with 5% aqueous sodium hydroxide solution. Carry out this extraction three times, using 10-mL portions of sodium hydroxide each time. Dry the dichloromethane layer over anhydrous calcium chloride pellets, decant the solution into a tared Erlenmeyer flask, and evaporate the solvent. The residue should consist of acetyleugenol and other steam-volatile neutral compounds from cloves.

Acidify the combined aqueous extracts to pH 1 with concentrated hydrochloric acid (use Congo Red or litmus paper to test) and then extract the liberated eugenol with three 8-mL portions of dichloromethane. Dry the combined extracts, decant into a tared Erlenmeyer flask, and evaporate the solution on a steam bath or a hot plate. Calculate the weight percent yields of eugenol and acetyleugenol on the basis of the weight of cloves used.

Chapter 11: Infrared Spectroscopy

Analyze your products using infrared spectroscopy and thin-layer chromatography. Obtain an infrared spectrum of eugenol or acetyleugenol using the thin-film method. Compare your spectrum to the spectrum of a fellow student who has examined the other compound.

Chapter 8: Thin-Layer Chromatography

Use plastic sheets precoated with silica gel for thin-layer chromatography. One piece the size of a microscope slide should suffice. Spot crude clove oil, eugenol, and acetyleugenol (1% solutions) side by side about 5 mm from one end of the plate. The spots should be very small. Immerse the end of the slide in a dichloromethane–hexane mixture (1:2 or 2:1) about 3 mm deep in a covered beaker. After running the chromatogram, observe the spots under an ultraviolet lamp or by developing them in an iodine chamber.

Antibiotic Behavior of Spice Essential Oils

You will bioassay your isolated clove oil with Bacillus cereus to test for its antibiotic behavior. Many bacterial cultures are available commercially, but Bacillus cereus is preferred because it is nonpathogenic, requires no special medium for growth, and grows at room temperature in a short time. Cultures of E. coli have to be handled with care because of their potential pathogenicity, depending on the strain. Their optimal growth is at 37°C, which means that an incubator is needed to work with these cultures.

Wash hands after handling bacteria.

Agar culture plates are prepared in sterile Petri dishes or can be purchased.[2] These plates are stored in the refrigerator. Whenever you handle the sterile agar

[2]Agar plates and bacteria can be purchased from Carolina Biological Supply Co. www.carolina.com. Nutrient Agar Plates: part number CE-82–1862 (packages of 10); *Bacillus cereus*: part number CE-15–4869.

FIG. 6.6

Two sets of test disks (clockwise from top left) showing the control, 2 mg of clove oil, control, 2 mg of clove oil. The clove oil disks show inhibition of bacterial growth; there is no bacterial growth in the immediate area of the disks.

Petri dishes (bottom dish and top cover), try to minimize any exposure to random forms of bacteria or dirt in the laboratory. Always wear gloves when handling the plates and the *Bacillus cereus* because your hands can easily contaminate the agar. Open the cover of the dish a few inches so that you have just enough room to streak the plate with the bacteria or insert a testing disk that is impregnated with the essential oil. Immediately cover the agar again with the Petri dish lid to reduce the risk of outside contamination. You will use a pair of sterile tweezers to handle the test disk, and sterile swabs to streak the plates with the *Bacillus cereus*. After preparing your assay, you will observe the growth of bacteria on the plate after 1–2 days of growth. If the bacteria do not grow in the area surrounding the disk treated with your essential oil, then one or more of the compounds in this isolated mixture is exhibiting antibiotic behavior.

Bioassay Using Agar Medium Bacterial Growth Plates

Two students can use one agar plate (typically a plastic disposable Petri plate). Draw a line down the middle of the plate to separate each student's disks from the other's. Label the bottom of the culture plate with your name and each disk's identity so that you will know which disk is which. See Figure 6.6 for an example of an agar plate.

Procedure for the transfer of sterile cultures:

(All students must be wearing gloves during this entire procedure.)

1. Obtain a prepared, sterile agar plate.

2. Label the nutrient agar plate with your last name. The plate is to be divided into 4 equal quadrants. Each student/group will have two of these quadrants, one for the control and one for the clove oil. Use a marking pen to delineate these quadrants and use this area as a guide when preparing the plates. **Be very careful not to remove the cover of the plate during this step.**

3. Next, the bacteria will be transferred to the plate:

   a. Insert a sterile swab into the culture tube containing the bacteria.

   b. Remove the swab from the culture tube and then tilt the cover of the agar plate at an angle to keep exposure to unwanted bacteria in the air to a minimum. Do not lay the top of the plate on the benchtop and do not allow anyone to breathe on or come in close contact with the plate.

   c. The moist swab is brought in contact with the agar using a rubbing motion. Start at the center of the plate and very gently rub back and forth, moving toward the edge of the plate. Turn the plate 90 degrees and repeat the rubbing of the swab. Turn the plate 135 degrees and rub the remaining section of the plate so that the entire surface area of the plate has been covered. The plate should now be evenly coated with the bacterial culture.

   d. Replace the cover on the culture dish.

   e. Dispose of the used sterile swab in the appropriate biohazard waste container.

4. Next, the isolated clove oil will be placed in contact with the inoculated culture.

   a. Add the required volume of acetone to your oil sample to make a 5 to 10% (wt/vol) solution of your isolated clove oil in acetone.

   b. Dip the tweezers into alcohol to sterilize.

   c. Remove tweezers from the alcohol and fan back and forth to evaporate the alcohol.

5. Pick up one sterile sample disk using the sterile tweezers and hold it in contact with the solution of your isolated clove oil so that it is absorbed into the disk. Allow the solvent to evaporate and then transfer the disk to the culture dish by lifting the lid slightly and placing it in the center of one of the 4 quadrants.

6. Next, transfer a control disk to the culture dish. The control disk is made sterile by dipping it in ethanol and then allowing the ethanol to evaporate.

7. Wrap the edges of the dish with Parafilm to keep the agar from drying out or to prevent contamination.

8. Allow the dish to sit on the benchtop for about 10 minutes to seat the disks in the agar.

9. Invert the culture dish so that the bottom is facing up.

10. Place the dish either at room temperature in a secure location or in an incubator oven. The results of the assay can be assessed after 24 hours or longer.

Bioassays of the isolated eugenol and acetyleugenol may also be performed and compared.

Cleaning Up. Combine all of the aqueous layers, neutralize with sodium carbonate, dilute with water, and flush down the drain. Any solutions containing dichloromethane should be placed in the halogenated organic solvents waste container. Allow the solvent to evaporate from the calcium chloride pellets in the hood and then place the drying agent in the nonhazardous solid waste container. If local regulations do not allow for the evaporation of solvent from the pellets in a hood, dispose of the wet pellets in a special container. The acetone solution of oil can be placed in the nonhalogenated solvent waste container. The plastic, disposable agar plate can be taped shut with masking tape and placed into a biohazard waste bin. If an autoclave is not available, soak the agar plates and contaminated materials in bleach for several days. The bleach solution can then be flushed down the drain with lots of water.

PART 2: VACUUM DISTILLATION

Many substances cannot be satisfactorily distilled in the ordinary way, either because they boil at such high temperatures that decomposition occurs or because they are sensitive to oxidation. Steam distillation will work only if the compound is volatile. When neither ordinary distillation nor steam distillation is practical, purification can be accomplished by distillation at reduced pressure.

VACUUM DISTILLATION ASSEMBLIES

Macroscale Vacuum Distillation

⚠️

Carry out vacuum distillation behind a safety shield. Before using, check the apparatus for scratches and cracks.

A typical macroscale vacuum distillation apparatus is illustrated in Figure 6.7. It is constructed of a round-bottomed flask (often called the pot) containing the material to be distilled, a Claisen distilling head fitted with a hair-fine capillary mounted through a rubber tubing sleeve, and a thermometer with the bulb extending below the side-arm opening. The condenser fits into a vacuum adapter that is connected to the receiver and, via heavy-walled rubber tubing, to a mercury manometer and then to the trap and water aspirator.

Liquids usually bump vigorously when boiled at reduced pressure, and most boiling stones lose their activity in an evacuated system; it is therefore essential to make special provision to control bumping. This is done by allowing a fine stream of air bubbles to be drawn into the boiling liquid through a glass tube drawn to a

FIG. 6.7
A macroscale vacuum distillation apparatus.

Thermometer bulb below side arm of Claisen distilling head

Keck clamp

Water out

Capillary

Claisen distilling head

Pot

Condenser

Keck clamp

Vacuum adapter

Water in

To trap and aspirator

Keck clamp

Receiver

Manometer

hair-fine capillary. The capillary should be so fine that even under vacuum only a few bubbles of air are drawn in each second; smooth boiling will be promoted, and the pressure will remain low. The capillary should extend to the very bottom of the flask and should be slender and flexible so that it will whip back and forth in the boiling liquid. Another method used to prevent bumping when small quantities of material are being distilled is to introduce sufficient glass wool into the flask to fill a part of the space above the liquid. Rapid magnetic stirring will also prevent bumping.

A hair-fine capillary is made as follows. A 6-in. length of 6-mm glass tubing is rotated and heated in a small area over a *very hot* flame to collapse the glass and thicken the side walls, as shown in Figure 6.8a. The tube is removed from the flame, allowed to cool slightly, and then drawn into a thick-walled, coarse-diameter capillary (Fig. 6.8b). This coarse capillary is heated at point X over the wing top of a Bunsen burner turned 90°. When the glass is very soft, but not soft enough to collapse the tube entirely, the coarse capillary is lifted from the flame and without hesitation drawn smoothly and rapidly into a hair-fine capillary by stretching the hands as far as they will reach (about 2 m; Fig. 6.8c). The two capillaries so produced can be snapped off to the desired length. To ascertain that there is indeed a continuous opening inside the hair-fine capillary, place the fine end into a low-viscosity liquid such as acetone or *t*-butyl methyl ether and blow in the large end. A stream of very small bubbles should be seen. If the stream of bubbles is not extremely small, make a new capillary. The flow of air through the capillary *cannot* be controlled by attaching a rubber tube and clamp to the top of the capillary tube. Should the right-hand capillary of Figure 6.8c break when in use, it can be fused to a scrap of glass (for use as a handle) and heated again at point Y (Fig. 6.8c). In this way a capillary can be redrawn many times.

The pot is heated via a heating bath rather than a Thermowell to promote even boiling and make accurate determination of the boiling point possible. The bath is filled with a suitable heat-transfer liquid (water, cottonseed oil, silicone oil, or molten metal) and heated to a temperature about 20°C higher than that at which the substance in the flask distills. The bath temperature is kept constant throughout the distillation. The surface of the liquid in the flask should be below that of the heating medium so as to lessen the tendency to bump. Heating of the flask is begun only

Prevention of bumping.

Making a hair-fine capillary.

Handle flames in the organic laboratory with great care.
Heating baths

FIG. 6.8
A capillary for vacuum distillation.

(a)

(b)

(c)

after the system has been evacuated to the desired pressure; otherwise, the liquid might boil too suddenly on reduction of the pressure.

Changing fractions

To change fractions, the following must be done in sequence: Remove the source of heat, release the vacuum, change the receiver, restore the vacuum to its former pressure, and resume heating.

A fractional vacuum distillation apparatus is shown in Figure 6.9. The distillation neck of the Claisen adapter is longer than that of other adapters, and it has a series of indentations intruding from four directions such that the points nearly meet in the center. These indentations increase the surface area over which rising vapor can come to equilibrium with descending liquid, and the distillation neck then serves as a fractionating column (a Vigreux column). A column packed with a metal sponge has a high tendency to become filled with liquid (flood) at reduced pressure. The apparatus illustrated in Figure 6.9 also has a fraction collector, which allows the removal of a fraction without disturbing the vacuum in the system. While the receiver is being changed, the distillate collects in small reservoir A. The clean receiver is evacuated by another aspirator at tube B before being reconnected to the system.

Semi-microscale and Microscale Vacuum Distillation

If only a few milliliters of a liquid are to be distilled, the apparatus shown in Figure 6.10 has the advantage of low holdup—that is, not much liquid is lost to wetting the surface area of the apparatus. The fraction collector illustrated is known as a cow. Rotation of the cow about the lightly greased standard taper joint will allow four fractions to be collected without interrupting the vacuum.

A distillation head of the type shown in Figure 6.11 allows fractions to be removed without disturbing the vacuum and control of the reflux ratio (*see* Chapter 5) by manipulation of the condenser and stopcock A. These can be adjusted to remove all the material that condenses or only a small fraction, with

FIG. 6.9
A vacuum distillation apparatus with a Vigreux column and fraction collector.

FIG. 6.10
A semi-microscale vacuum distillation apparatus.

Condensing water
Out
In
To vacuum
Air in
Capillary
Cow

FIG. 6.11
A vacuum distillation head.

FIG. 6.12
A microscale apparatus for simple vacuum distillation.

the bulk of the liquid being returned to the distilling column to establish equilibrium between the descending liquid and the ascending vapor. Thus liquids with small boiling-point differences can be separated.

On a truly micro scale (<10 mg), simple distillation is not practical because of mechanical losses. Fractional distillation of small quantities of liquids is also difficult. The necessity for maintaining an equilibrium between ascending vapors and descending liquid means that there will inevitably be large mechanical losses. The best apparatus for the fractional distillation of 0.5 mL to 20 mL of liquid under reduced pressure is the *micro spinning band column*, which has a holdup of about 0.1 mL. In research, preparative-scale gas chromatography (*see* Chapter 10) and high-performance liquid chromatography (HPLC) have supplanted vacuum distillation of very small quantities of material.

It is possible, however, to assemble several pieces of apparatus that can be used for simple vacuum distillation using components from the microscale kit that accompanies this text. One such assembly is shown in Figure 6.12. The material to be distilled is placed in a 5-mL short-necked flask packed loosely with glass wool, which will help prevent bumping. The thermometer bulb extends entirely below the side arm, and the distillate is collected in a reaction tube, which can be cooled in a beaker of ice. The vacuum source is connected to a syringe needle; alternatively, the rubber tubing from the aspirator, if of the proper diameter, can be connected directly to the adapter, dispensing with the septum and needle.

THE KUGELROHR

The Kugelrohr (German, meaning "bulb-tube") is a widely used piece of research apparatus that consists of a series of bulbs that can be rotated and heated under vacuum. Bulb-to-bulb distillation frees the desired compound of very low-boiling and very high-boiling or nonvolatile impurities. The crude mixture is placed in

FIG. 6.13
A Kugelrohr bulb-to-bulb distillation apparatus.

FIG. 6.14
A closed-end mercury manometer.

bulb A (Fig. 6.13) in the heated glass chamber. At bulb C is a shutter mechanism that holds in the heat but allows the bulbs to be moved out of the heated chamber one by one as distillation proceeds. The lowest boiling material collects in bulb D; then bulb C is moved out of the heated chamber, the temperature increased, and the next fraction is collected in bulb C. Finally, this process is repeated for bulb B. The bulbs rotate under vacuum via a mechanism similar to the one used on rotary evaporators. The same apparatus is used for bulb-to-bulb fractional sublimation (see Part 3 for sublimation).

MANOMETERS

The pressure of the system is measured with a closed-end mercury manometer. The manometer (Fig. 6.14) is connected to the system by turning the stopcock until its V-groove is aligned with the side arm. To avoid contamination of the manometer, it should be connected to the system only when a reading is being made. The pressure (in mm Hg) is given by the height (in mm) of the central mercury column above the reservoir of mercury, and represents the difference in pressure between the nearly perfect vacuum in the center tube (closed at the top, open at the bottom) and the large volume of the manometer, which is at the pressure of the system.

Another common type of closed-end mercury manometer is shown in Figure 6.15. At atmospheric pressure the manometer is completely full of mercury, as shown in Figure 6.15a. When the open end is connected to a vacuum, the pressure is measured as the distance in millimeters between the mercury in the right and left legs. Note that the pressure in the left leg is essentially zero (mercury has a low vapor pressure). If the applied vacuum were perfect (0 mm Hg), then the two columns would have the same height.

FIG. 6.15
Another type of closed-end mercury manometer.

THE WATER ASPIRATOR IN VACUUM DISTILLATION

A water aspirator in good order produces a vacuum nearly corresponding to the vapor pressure of the water flowing through it. Polypropylene aspirators perform well and are not subject to corrosion, which does affect brass aspirators. If a manometer is not available, the assembly is free of leaks, and the trap and lines are clean and dry, an approximate estimate of the pressure can be made by measuring the water temperature and reading the pressure from Table 6.1 (on page 104).

THE ROTARY OIL PUMP

To obtain pressures below 10 mm Hg, a mechanical vacuum pump of the type illustrated in Figure 6.16a is used. A pump of this type in good condition can attain pressures as low as 0.1 mm Hg. These low pressures are measured with a tilting-type McLeod gauge (Fig. 6.16b). When a reading is being made, the gauge is tilted to the vertical position shown, and the pressure is read as the difference between the heights of the two columns of mercury. Between readings, the gauge is rotated clockwise 90°.

⚠️
The Dewar flask should be wrapped with tape or otherwise protected from implosion.

Never use a mechanical vacuum pump before placing a mixture of dry ice and isopropyl alcohol in a Dewar flask (Fig. 6.16c) around the trap, and never pump corrosive vapors (e.g., hydrogen chloride gas) into the pump. Should this happen, change the pump oil immediately. With care, the pump will give many years of good service. The dry-ice trap condenses organic vapors and water vapor, both of which would otherwise contaminate the vacuum pump oil and exert enough vapor pressure to destroy a good vacuum.

For an exceedingly high vacuum (5×10^{-8} mm Hg), a high-speed, three-stage mercury diffusion pump is used (Fig. 6.17).

RELATIONSHIP BETWEEN BOILING POINT AND PRESSURE

It is not possible to calculate the boiling point of a substance at some reduced pressure from a knowledge of the boiling temperature at 760 mm Hg because the relationship between boiling point and pressure varies from compound to compound

FIG. 6.16
(a) A rotary oil pump.
(b) A tilting McLeod gauge.
(c) A vacuum system.

(a)

(b)

(c)

Dewar flask

Dry ice/isopropyl alcohol

Trap

To McLeod gauge

Oil pump

FIG. 6.17
A high-speed, three-stage mercury diffusion pump that is capable of producing a vacuum of 5×10^{-8} mm Hg. Mercury is boiled in the flask; the vapor rises in the center tube, is deflected downward in the inverted cups and entrains gas molecules, which diffuse in from the space to be evacuated, A. The mercury condenses to a liquid and is returned to the flask; the gas molecules are removed at B by an ordinary rotary vacuum pump.

A

H_2O

B

$H_2O \rightarrow$

Hg

FIG. 6.18
Boiling point curves.

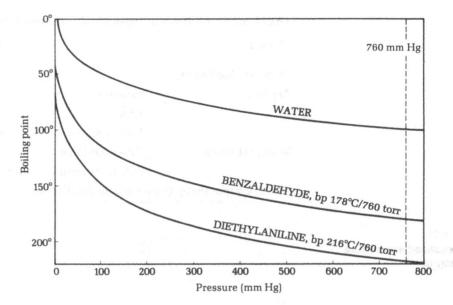

and is somewhat unpredictable. It is true, however, that boiling point curves for organic substances have much the same general disposition, as illustrated by the two lower curves in Figure 6.18. These are similar and do not differ greatly from the curve for water. For substances boiling in the range of 150°C to 250°C at 760 mm Hg, the boiling point at 20 mm Hg is 100–120°C lower than that at 760 mm Hg. Benzaldehyde, which is very sensitive to air oxidation at the normal boiling point of 178°C, distills at 76°C at 20 mm Hg, and the concentration of oxygen in the rarefied atmosphere is just 3% of what it would be in an ordinary distillation.

The curves all show a sharp upward inclination in the region of very low pressure. The lowering of the boiling point that accompanies a reduction in pressure is far more pronounced at low pressures rather than at high pressures. A drop in atmospheric pressure of 10 mm Hg lowers the normal boiling point of an ordinary liquid by less than 1°C, but a reduction of pressure from 20 mm Hg to 10 mm Hg causes a drop of about 15°C in the boiling point. The effect at pressures below 1 mm is still more striking, and with the development of highly efficient oil vapor or mercury vapor diffusion pumps, distillation at a pressure of a few thousandths or ten-thousandths of a millimeter has become a standard operation in many research laboratories. High-vacuum distillation—that is, at a pressure below 1 mm Hg— affords a useful means of purifying extremely sensitive or very slightly volatile substances. Table 6.2 indicates the order of magnitude of the reduction in boiling point attainable by operating at various pressures with different methods, and illustrates the importance of keeping vacuum pumps in good repair.

The boiling point of a substance at varying pressures can be estimated from a pressure-temperature nomograph, such as the one shown in Figure 6.19. If the boiling point of a nonpolar substance at 760 mm Hg is known, for example, 145°C (column B), and the new pressure measured, for example, 28 mm Hg (column C), then a straight line connecting these values on columns B and C when extended intersects column A to give the observed boiling point of 50°C. Conversely, a substance observed to boil at 50°C (column A) at 1.0 mm Hg (column C) will boil at approximately 212°C at atmospheric pressure (column B). If the material being

TABLE 6.2 *Distillation of a (Hypothetical) Substance at Various Pressures*

Method		Pressure (mm Hg)	bp (°C)
Ordinary distillation		760	250
Aspirator	summer	25	144
	winter	15	134
	Poor condition	10	124
Rotary oil pump	Good condition	3	99
	excellent condition	1	89
Mercury vapor pump (high vacuum distillation)		0.01	30

FIG. 6.19
A pressure-temperature nomograph.

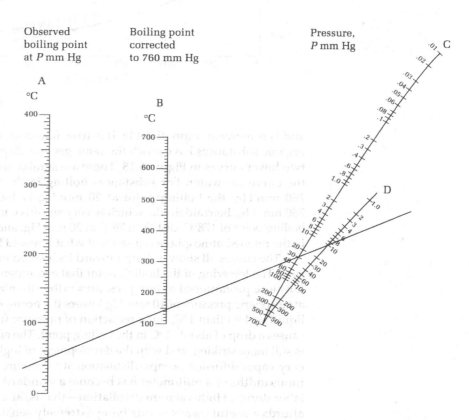

Observed boiling point at *P* mm Hg	Boiling point corrected to 760 mm Hg	Pressure, *P* mm Hg

distilled is polar, such as a carboxylic acid, column D is used. Thus, a substance that boils at 145°C at atmospheric pressure (column B) will boil at 28 mm Hg (column C) if it is nonpolar, and at a pressure of 10 mm Hg (column D) if it is polar. The boiling point will be 50°C (column A).

Vacuum distillation is not confined to the purification of substances that are liquid at ordinary temperatures; it can often be used to advantage for solid substances. This operation is conducted for a different purpose and by a different technique. A solid is seldom distilled in order to separate constituents of differing degrees of volatility; distillation is intended to purify the solid. Often, one vacuum distillation can remove foreign coloring matter and tar without any appreciable loss of product, whereas several wasteful recrystallizations might be required to

FIG. 6.20
A molecular distillation apparatus.

Water →

To high vacuum

Distillate

Material to be distilled

attain the same purity. It is often good practice to distill a crude product and then to recrystallize it. Time is saved in the recrystallization process because the hot solution usually requires neither filtration nor clarification. The solid must be dry, and a test should be made to determine if it will distill without decomposition at the pressure of the available pump. A compound lacking the required stability at high temperatures is sometimes indicated by its structure, but a high melting point should not be taken as an indication that distillation will fail. Substances melting as high as 300°C have been distilled with success at the pressure of an ordinary rotary vacuum pump.

MOLECULAR DISTILLATION

At 1×10^{-3} mm Hg, the mean free path of nitrogen molecules is 56 mm at 25°C. This means that an average N_2 molecule can travel 56 mm before bumping into another N_2 molecule. Specially designed apparatus makes it possible to distill almost any volatile molecule by operating at a very low pressure and having the condensing surface close to the material being distilled. The thermally energized molecule escapes from the liquid, moves about 10 mm without encountering any other molecules, and condenses on a cold surface. A simple apparatus for molecular distillation is illustrated in Figure 6.20. The bottom of the apparatus is placed on a hot surface, and the distillate moves a very short distance before condensing. If it is not too viscous, it will drip from the point on the glass condensing surface and run down to the receiver.

The efficiency of this molecular distillation apparatus is less than one theoretical plate (*see* Chapter 5). It is used to remove very volatile substances such as solvents and to separate volatile, high-boiling substances at low temperatures from nonvolatile impurities.

In more sophisticated apparatus of quite different design, the liquid to be distilled falls down on a heated surface, which is again close to the condenser. This movement of a film prevents a buildup of nonvolatile material on the surface of the material to be distilled, which would cause the distillation to cease. Vitamin A is distilled commercially in this manner.

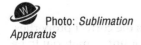

Photo: *Sublimation Apparatus*

PART 3: SUBLIMATION

Sublimation is the process whereby a solid evaporates from a warm surface and condenses on a cold surface, again as a solid (Fig. 6.21 and Fig. 6.22). This technique is particularly useful for the small-scale purification of solids because there is

FIG. 6.21
A small-scale vacuum sublimation apparatus.

15-mL Centrifuge tube, to be filled with ice

Adapter (Pluro stopper)

Pipette bulb

25-mL Filter flask

Material to be sublimed

Sublimate

Heat source

FIG. 6.22
(a) A Mallory sublimator.
(b) A large vacuum sublimator.

Vacuum

Sublimate

Water in

Rubber O-ring

Material to be sublimed

Heat here

(a)

Vacuum

Rubber O-ring

Ice

Sublimate goes to here
Material to be sublimed
Heat this surface

(b)

so little loss of material in transfer. If the substance possesses the correct properties, sublimation is preferred over recrystallization when the amount of material to be purified weighs less than 100 mg.

As demonstrated in the experiment that follows, sublimation can occur readily at atmospheric pressure. For substances with lower vapor pressures, vacuum sublimation is used. At very low pressures, sublimation becomes very similar to molecular distillation, where the molecule leaves the warm solid and passes unobstructed to a cold condensing surface and condenses in the form of a solid.

Because sublimation occurs from the surface of the warm solid, impurities can accumulate and slow down or even stop the sublimation, in which case it is necessary to open the apparatus, grind the impure solid to a fine powder, and restart the sublimation.

Sublimation is much easier to carry out on a small scale than on a large one. It would be unusual for a research chemist to sublime more than about 10 g of material because the sublimate tends to fall back to the bottom of the apparatus. In an apparatus such as that illustrated in Figure 6.22a, the solid to be sublimed is placed in the lower flask and connected via a lubricant-free rubber O-ring to the condenser, which in turn is connected to a vacuum pump. The lower flask is immersed in an oil bath at the appropriate temperature, and the product is sublimed and condensed onto the cool walls of the condenser. The parts of the apparatus are gently separated, and the condenser is inverted; the vacuum connection serves as a convenient funnel for product removal. For large-scale work, the sublimator in Figure 6.22b is used. The inner well is filled with a coolant (ice or dry ice). The sublimate clings to this cool surface, from which it can be removed by scraping and dissolving in an appropriate solvent.

A very simple sublimation apparatus: an inverted stemless funnel on a watch glass.

LYOPHILIZATION

Lyophilization, also called freeze-drying, is the process of subliming a solvent, usually water, with the object of recovering the solid that remains after the solvent is removed. This technique is used extensively to recover heat- and oxygen-sensitive substances of natural origin, such as proteins, vitamins, nucleic acids, and other biochemicals, from a dilute aqueous solution. The aqueous solution of the substance to be lyophilized is usually frozen to prevent bumping and then subjected to a vacuum of about 1×10^{-3} mm Hg. The water sublimes and condenses as ice on the surface of a large and very cold condenser. The sample remains frozen during this entire process, without any external cooling being supplied, because of the very high heat of vaporization of water; thus the temperature of the sample never exceeds 0°C. Freeze-drying on a large scale is employed to make "instant" coffee, tea, soup, and rice and all sorts of dehydrated foods.

EXPERIMENT

SUBLIMATION OF AN UNKNOWN SUBSTANCE

Apparatus and Technique

The apparatus consists of a 15-mL centrifuge tube thrust through an adapter (use a drop of glycerol to lubricate the adapter) fitted in a 25-mL filter flask. Once the adapter is properly positioned on the centrifuge tube, it should remain there permanently. This tube is used only for sublimation.

The sample is either ground to a fine powder and uniformly distributed on the bottom of the flask or introduced into the flask as a solution, and then the solvent evaporated to deposit the substance on the bottom of the filter flask. If the compound sublimes easily, care must be exercised using the latter technique to ensure that the sample does not evaporate as the last of the solvent is being removed.

TABLE 6.3 *Sublimation Unknowns*

Substance	mp (°C)	Substance	mp (°C)
1,4-Dichlorobenzene	55	Benzoic acid	122
Naphthalene	82	Salicylic acid	159
1-Naphthol	96	Camphor	177
Acetanilide	114	Caffeine	235

Sublimation: Add sample to flask, close flask openings, add ice, sublime sample, remove ice, add room-temperature water, open apparatus, and scrape off product.

The 15-mL centrifuge tube and adapter are placed in the flask so that the tip of the centrifuge tube is about 3–8 mm above the bottom of the flask (*see* Fig. 6.21). The flask is clamped with a three-prong clamp. Many substances sublime at atmospheric pressure, including the unknowns listed in Table 6.3. For vacuum sublimation, the side arm of the flask leads to an aspirator or vacuum pump for reduced pressure sublimation. The centrifuge tube is filled with ice and water. The ice is not added before closing the apparatus, so atmospheric moisture will not condense on the tube.

Roll the filter flask in the sand bath or heat it with a heat gun to drive material from the upper walls of the flask.

The filter flask is warmed cautiously on a hot sand bath until the product just begins to sublime. The heat is maintained at that temperature until sublimation is complete. Because some product will collect on the cool upper parts of the flask, it should be fitted with a loose cone of aluminum foil to direct heat there and cause the material to collect on the surface of the centrifuge tube. Alternatively, tilt the flask and rotate it in the hot sand, or remove the flask from the sand bath, and then use a heat gun to warm the flask.

Once sublimation is judged complete, the ice water is removed from the centrifuge tube with a pipette and replaced with water at room temperature. This will prevent moisture from condensing on the product once the vacuum is turned off and the tube is removed from the flask. The product is scraped from the centrifuge tube with a metal spatula onto a piece of glazed paper. It is much easier to scrape the product from a centrifuge tube than from a round-bottomed test tube. The last traces can be removed by washing off the tube with a few drops of an appropriate solvent, if that is deemed necessary.

Procedure

Into the bottom of a 25-mL filter flask, place 50 mg of an impure unknown taken from the list in Table 6.3. These substances can be sublimed at atmospheric pressure, although some will sublime more rapidly at reduced pressure. Slip a rubber pipette bulb over the flask's side arm to close off the flask, and then place ice water in the centrifuge tube. Cautiously warm the flask until sublimation starts, and then maintain that temperature throughout the sublimation. Fit the flask with a loose cone of aluminum foil to direct heat up the sides of the flask, which causes the product to collect on the tube. Once sublimation is complete, remove the ice water from the centrifuge tube and replace it with water at room temperature. Collect the product, determine its weight and the percent recovery, and from the melting point identify the unknown. Hand in the product in a neatly labeled vial.

Cleaning Up. Wash material from the apparatus with a minimum quantity of acetone, which, except for the chloro compound, can be placed in the organic solvents waste container. The 1,4-dichlorobenzene solution must be placed in the halogenated organic waste container.

FIG. 6.23
The ¹H NMR spectrum of eugenol (250 MHz).

PPM (δ)

FOR FURTHER INVESTIGATION

Room deodorants, for example, the Renuzit Long Last adjustable air freshener, appear to sublime. Place about 150 mg, carefully weighed, of the green solid in the filter flask and sublime it with very little heat applied to the flask. Identify the substance that sublimes. Weigh the residue. As an advanced experiment, run the IR spectrum (see Chapter 11) of the residue (not of the substance that sublimes). Comment on the economics of air fresheners.

QUESTIONS

1. Assign the peaks in the ¹H NMR spectrum of eugenol (Fig. 6.23) to specific protons in the molecule. The OH peak is at 5.1 ppm.

2. A mixture of ethyl iodide (C_2H_5I, bp 72.3°C) and water boils at 63.7°C. What weight of ethyl iodide would be carried over by 1 g of steam during steam distillation?

3. Iodobenzene (C_6H_5I, bp 188°C) steam distills at 98.2°C. How many molecules of water are required to carry over 1 molecule of iodobenzene? How many grams of water per gram of iodobenzene?

4. The condensate from a steam distillation contains 8 g of an unknown compound and 18 g of water. The mixture steam distilled at 98°C. What is the molecular weight of the unknown?

5. Bearing in mind that a sealed container filled with steam will develop a vacuum if the container is cooled, explain what would occur if a steam distillation was stopped by turning off the steam valve before opening the screw clamp on the adapter trap.

6. A mixture of toluene (bp 110.8°C) and water is steam distilled. Visual inspection of the distillate reveals that there is a greater volume of toluene than water present, yet water (bp 100°C) has the higher vapor pressure. Explain this observation.

7. Did sublimation aid in the purification of the unknown in part 3? Justify your answer.

8. From your experience and knowledge of the process of sublimation, cite some examples of substances that sublime.

9. How might freeze-dried foods be prepared?

10. Describe the mercury level in a manometer like that shown in Figure 6.15a if the left arm is 1000 cm tall.

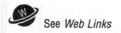

See *Web Links*

11. What criteria would you use to decide whether distillation is an appropriate technique for the purification of a reaction product? What type of distillation method—simple, fractional, vacuum, or steam—should be used?

CHAPTER 7

Extraction

PRELAB EXERCISE: Describe how to separate a mixture of 3-toluic acid and 4'-aminoacetophenone using acid-base liquid/liquid extraction. What species will end up in the aqueous layer if you mix a solution of benzoic acid and aniline in ether with a solution of $NaHCO_3$ (aq)? Draw the structure of this species.

Extraction is one of the oldest chemical operations known to humankind. The preparation of a cup of coffee or tea involves the extraction of flavor and odor components from dried vegetable matter with hot water. Aqueous extracts of bay leaves, stick cinnamon, peppercorns, and cloves, along with alcoholic extracts of vanilla and almond, are used as food flavorings. For the past 150 years or so, organic chemists have extracted, isolated, purified, and characterized the myriad compounds produced by plants that for centuries have been used as drugs and perfumes—substances such as quinine from cinchona bark, morphine from the opium poppy, cocaine from coca leaves, and menthol from peppermint oil. The extraction of compounds from these natural products is an example of solid/liquid extraction—the solid being the natural product and the liquid being the solvent into which the compounds are extracted. In research, a Soxhlet extractor (Fig. 7.1) is often used for solid/liquid extraction.

Although solid/liquid extraction is the most common technique for brewing beverages and isolating compounds from natural products, liquid/liquid extraction is a very common method used in the organic laboratory, specifically when isolating reaction products. Reactions are typically homogeneous liquid mixtures and can therefore be extracted with either an organic or aqueous solvent. Organic reactions often yield a number of byproducts—some inorganic and some organic. Also, because some organic reactions do not go to 100% completion, a small amount of starting material is present at the end of the reaction. When a reaction is complete, it is necessary to do a *workup*, that is, separate and purify the desired product from the mixture of byproducts and residual starting material. Liquid/liquid extraction is a common separation step in this workup, which is then followed by purification of the product. There are two types of liquid/liquid extraction: neutral and acid/base. The experiments in this chapter demonstrate solid/liquid extraction and the two types of liquid/liquid extraction.

FIG. 7.1
The Soxhlet extractor for the extraction of solids such as dried leaves or seeds. The solid is put in a filter paper thimble. Solvent vapor rises in the tube on the right; condensate drops onto the solid in the thimble, leaches out soluble material, and, after initiating an automatic siphon, carries it to the flask where nonvolatile extracted material accumulates. Substances of low solubility can be extracted by prolonged operation.

Condenser

Paper thimble — Soxhlet

Organic products are often separated from inorganic substances in a reaction mixture by liquid/liquid extraction with an organic solvent. For example, in the synthesis of 1-bromobutane (*see* Chapter 16), 1-butanol, also a liquid, is heated with an aqueous solution of sodium bromide and sulfuric acid to produce the product and sodium sulfate.

$$2 \ CH_3CH_2CH_2CH_2OH + 2 \ NaBr + H_2SO_4 \rightarrow$$
$$2 \ CH_3CH_2CH_2CH_2Br + 2 \ H_2O + Na_2SO_4$$

The 1-bromobutane is isolated from the reaction mixture by extraction with *t*-butyl methyl ether, an organic solvent in which 1-bromobutane is soluble and in which water and sodium sulfate are insoluble. The extraction is accomplished by simply adding *t*-butyl methyl ether to the aqueous mixture and shaking it. Two layers will result: an organic layer and an aqueous layer. The *t*-butyl methyl ether is less dense than water and floats on top; it is easily removed/drained away from the water layer and evaporated to leave the bromo product free of inorganic substances, which reside in the aqueous layer.

PARTITION COEFFICIENT

The extraction of a compound such as 1-butanol, which is slightly soluble in water as well as very soluble in ether, is an equilibrium process governed by the solubilities of the alcohol in the two solvents. The ratio of the solubilities is known as the *distribution coefficient*, also called the *partition coefficient* (*k*), and is an equilibrium constant with a certain value for a given substance, pair of solvents, and temperature.

The *concentration* of the solute in each solvent can be well correlated with the *solubility* of the solute in the pure solvent, a figure that is readily found in solubility tables in reference books. For substance C:

$$k = \frac{\text{concentration of C in } t\text{-butyl methyl ether}}{\text{concentration of C in water}}$$

$$\cong \frac{\text{solubility of C in } t\text{-butyl methyl ether (g/100 mL)}}{\text{concentration of C in water (g/100 mL)}}$$

Consider compound A that dissolves in *t*-butyl methyl ether to the extent of 12 g/100 mL and dissolves in water to the extent of 6 g/100 mL.

$$k = \frac{12 \text{g/100mL } t\text{-butyl methyl ether (g/100 mL)}}{6 \text{g/100mL water}} = 2$$

If a solution of 6 g of A in 100 mL of water is shaken with 100 mL of *t*-butyl methyl ether, then:

$$k = \frac{x \text{g of A/100mL } t\text{-butyl methyl ether}}{6 - x \text{g of A/100mL water}}$$

from which

$$x = 4.0 \text{ g of A in the ether layer}$$

$$6 - x = 2.0 \text{ g of A left in the water layer.}$$

It is, however, more efficient to extract the 100 mL of aqueous solution twice with 50-mL portions of *t*-butyl methyl ether rather than once with a 100-mL portion.

$$k = \frac{x\text{g of A}/50\text{mL}}{6 - x\text{g of A}/100\text{mL}} = 2$$

from which

$x = 3.0$ g of A in the *t*-butyl methyl ether layer
$6 - x = 3.0$ g of A in the water layer.

If this 3.0 g/100 mL of water is extracted again with 50 mL of *t*-butyl methyl ether, we can calculate that 1.5 g of A will be in the ether layer, leaving 1.5 g in the water layer. So two extractions with 50-mL portions of ether will extract 3.0 g + 1.5 g = 4.5 g of A, whereas one extraction with a 100-mL portion of *t*-butyl methyl ether removes only 4.0 g of A. Three extractions with 33-mL portions of *t*-butyl methyl ether would extract 4.7 g. Obviously, there is a point at which the increased amount of A extracted does not repay the effort of multiple extractions, but remember that several small-scale extractions are more effective than one large-scale extraction.

PROPERTIES OF EXTRACTION SOLVENTS

Liquid/liquid extraction involves two layers: the organic layer and the aqueous layer. The solvent used for extraction should possess many properties, including the following:

- It should readily dissolve the substance to be extracted at room temperature.
- It should have a low boiling point so that it can be removed readily.
- It should not react with the solute or the other solvent.
- It should not be highly flammable or toxic.
- It should be relatively inexpensive.

In addition, it should not be miscible with water (the usual second phase). No solvent meets every criterion, but several come close. Some common liquid/liquid extraction solvent pairs are water-ether, water-dichloromethane, and water-hexane. Notice that each combination includes water because most organic compounds are immiscible in water, and therefore can be separated from inorganic compounds. Organic solvents such as methanol and ethanol are not good extraction solvents because they are soluble in water.

Identifying the Layers

One common mistake when performing an extraction is to misidentify the layers and discard the wrong one. It is good practice to save all layers until the desired product is in hand. The densities of the solvents will predict the identities of the top and bottom layers. In general, the densities of nonhalogenated organic solvents are less than 1.0 g/mL and those of halogenated solvents are greater than 1.0 g/mL. Table 7.1 lists the densities of common solvents used in extraction.

Although density is the physical property that determines which layer is on top or on bottom, a very concentrated amount of solute dissolved in either layer can reverse the order. The best method to avoid a misidentification is to perform a drop test. Add a few drops of water to the layer in question and watch the drop

TABLE 7.1 *Common Solvents Listed by Density*

Solvent	Density (g/mL)
Hexane	0.695
Diethyl ether	0.708
t-Butyl methyl ether	0.740
Toluene	0.867
Water	1.000
Dichloromethane	1.325
Chloroform	1.492

Identify layers by a drop test.

$$CH_3CH_2\text{—}O\text{—}CH_2CH_3$$

Diethyl ether
"Ether"
MW 74.12, den. 0.708
bp 34.6°C, n_D^{20} 1.3530

tert-**Butyl methyl ether**
MW 88.14, den. 0.741
bp 55.2°C, n_D^{20} 1.369

carefully. If the layer is water, then the drop will mix with the solution. If the solvent is the organic layer, then the water drop will create a second layer.

Ethereal Extraction Solvents

In the past, diethyl ether was the most common solvent for extraction in the laboratory. It has high solvent power for hydrocarbons and oxygen-containing compounds. It is highly volatile (bp 34.6°C) and is therefore easily removed from an extract. However, diethyl ether has two big disadvantages: it is highly flammable and poses a great fire threat, and it easily forms peroxides. The reaction of diethyl ether with air is catalyzed by light. The resulting peroxides are higher boiling than the ether and are left as a residue when the ether evaporates. If the residue is heated, it will explode because ether peroxides are volatile and treacherously explosive. In recent years, a new solvent has come on the scene—*tert*-butyl methyl ether.

tert-Butyl methyl ether, called methyl *tert*-butyl ether (MTBE) in industry, has many advantages over diethyl ether as an extraction solvent. Most important, it does not easily form peroxides, so it can be stored for much longer periods than diethyl ether. And, in the United States, it is less than half the price of diethyl ether. It is slightly less volatile (bp 55°C), so it does not pose the same fire threat as diethyl ether, although one must be as careful in handling this solvent as in handling any other highly volatile, flammable substance. The explosion limits for *t*-butyl methyl ether mixed with air are much narrower than for diethyl ether, the toxicity is less, the solvent power is the same, and the ignition temperature is higher (224°C versus 180°C).

The weight percent solubility of diethyl ether dissolved in water is 7.2%, whereas that of *t*-butyl methyl ether is 4.8%. The solubility of water in diethyl ether is 1.2%, while in *t*-butyl methyl ether it is 1.5%. Unlike diethyl ether, *t*-butyl methyl ether forms an azeotrope with water (4% water) that boils at 52.6°C. This means that evaporation of any *t*-butyl methyl ether solution that is saturated with water should leave no water residue, unlike diethyl ether.

The low price and ready availability of *t*-butyl methyl ether came about because it replaced tetraethyl lead as the antiknock additive for high-octane gasoline and as a fuel oxygenate, which helps reduce air pollution, but its water solubility has allowed it to contaminate drinking water supplies in states where leaking underground fuel storage tanks are not well regulated. Consequently, it has been replaced with the much more expensive ethanol. In this text, *t*-butyl methyl ether is *strongly* suggested wherever diethyl ether formerly would have been used in an

FIG. 7.2
A separatory funnel with a Teflon stopcock.

FIG. 7.3
The correct position for holding a separatory funnel when shaking. Point outlet away from yourself and your neighbors.

extraction. It will not, however, work as the only solvent in the Grignard reaction, probably because of steric hindrance. So whenever the word *ether* appears in this text as an extraction solvent, it is suggested that *t*-butyl methyl ether be used and not diethyl ether.

MIXING AND SEPARATING THE LAYERS

For microscale separations, mixing and separating the layers with a pipette normally incurs very little product loss. Because the two solvents are typically in a reaction tube for microscale extraction, the two layers can be mixed by drawing up and rapidly expelling them with a pipette. Then the layers are allowed to separate, and the bottom layer is separated by drawing it up into a pipette and transferring it to a different container.

For macroscale separations, a separatory funnel (Fig. 7.2) is used to mix and separate the organic and aqueous layers. In macroscale experiments, a frequently used method of working up a reaction mixture is to dilute the mixture with water and extract it with an organic solvent, such as ether, in a separatory funnel. When the stoppered funnel is shaken to distribute the components between the immiscible solvents *t*-butyl methyl ether and water, pressure always develops through volatilization of ether from the heat of the hands, and liberation of a gas (CO_2) (in acid/base extractions) can increase the pressure. Consequently, the funnel is grasped so that the stopper is held in place by one hand and the stopcock by the other, as illustrated in Figure 7.3. After a brief shake or two, the funnel is held in the inverted position shown, and the stopcock is opened cautiously (with the funnel stem pointed away from nearby persons) to release pressure. The mixture can then be shaken more vigorously, with pressure released as necessary. When equilibration is judged to be complete, the slight, constant terminal pressure due to ether is released, the stopper is rinsed with a few drops of ether delivered by a Pasteur pipette, and the layers are allowed to separate. The organic reaction product is distributed wholly or largely into the upper ether layer, whereas inorganic salts, acids or bases pass into the water layer, which can be drawn off. If the reaction was conducted in alcohol or some other water-soluble solvent, the bulk of the solvent is removed in the water layer, and the remainder can be eliminated in two or three washings with 1–2 volumes of water conducted with the techniques used in the first equilibration. The separatory funnel should be supported in a ring stand, as shown in Figure 7.2.

Before adding a liquid to the separatory funnel, check the stopcock. If it is glass, see that it is properly greased, bearing in mind that too much grease will clog the hole in the stopcock and also contaminate the extract. If the stopcock is Teflon, see that it is adjusted to a tight fit in the bore. Store the separatory funnel with the Teflon stopcock loosened to prevent sticking. Because Teflon has a much larger temperature coefficient of expansion than glass, a stuck stopcock can be loosened by cooling the stopcock in ice or dry ice. Do not store liquids in the separatory funnel; they often leak or cause the stopper or stopcock to freeze. To have sufficient room for mixing the layers, fill the separatory funnel no more than three-fourths full. Withdraw the lower layer from the separatory funnel through the stopcock, and pour the upper layer out through the neck.

All too often, the inexperienced chemist discards the wrong layer when using a separatory funnel. Through incomplete neutralization, a desired component may still remain in the aqueous layer, or the densities of the layers may change. Cautious workers save all layers until the desired product has been isolated.

The organic layer is not always the top layer. If in doubt, perform a drop test by adding a few drops of each to water in a test tube.

Practical Considerations When Mixing Layers

Pressure Buildup

The heat of one's hand or heat from acid/base reactions will cause pressure buildup in an extraction mixture that contains a very volatile solvent such as dichloromethane. The extraction container—whether a test tube or a separatory funnel—must be opened carefully to vent this pressure.

Sodium bicarbonate solution is often used to neutralize acids when carrying out acid/base extractions. The result is the formation of carbon dioxide, which can cause foaming and high pressure buildup. Whenever bicarbonate is used, add it very gradually with thorough mixing and frequent venting of the extraction device. If a large amount of acid is to be neutralized with bicarbonate, the process should be carried out in a beaker.

Emulsions

Imagine trying to extract a soap solution (e.g., a nonfoaming dishwashing detergent) into an organic solvent. After a few shakes with an organic solvent, you would have an absolutely intractable emulsion. An emulsion is a suspension of one liquid as droplets in another. Detergents stabilize emulsions, and so any time a detergent-like molecule is in the material being extracted, there is the danger that emulsions will form. Substances of this type are commonly found in nature, so one must be particularly wary of emulsion formation when creating organic extracts of aqueous plant material, such as caffeine from tea. Emulsions, once formed, can be quite stable. You would be quite surprised to open your refrigerator one morning and see a layer of clarified butter floating on the top of a perfectly clear aqueous solution that had once been milk, but milk is the classic example of an emulsion.

Prevention is the best cure for emulsions. This means shaking the solution to be extracted *very gently* until you see that the two layers will separate readily. If a bit of emulsion forms, it may break simply on standing for a sufficient length of time. Making the aqueous layer highly ionic will help. Add as much sodium chloride as will dissolve and shake the mixture gently. Vacuum filtration sometimes works and, when the organic layer is the lower layer, filtration through silicone-impregnated filter paper is helpful. Centrifugation works very well for breaking emulsions. This is easy on a small scale, but often the equipment is not available for large-scale centrifugation of organic liquids.

Shake gently to avoid emulsions.

DRYING AGENTS

The organic solvents used for extraction dissolve not only the compound being extracted but also water. Evaporation of the solvent then leaves the desired compound contaminated with water. At room temperature, water dissolves 4.8% of *t*-butyl methyl ether by weight, and the ether dissolves 1.5% of water. But ether is virtually insoluble in water saturated with sodium chloride (36.7 g/100 mL). If ether that contains dissolved water is shaken with a saturated aqueous solution of sodium chloride, water will be transferred from the *t*-butyl methyl ether to the aqueous layer. So, strange as it may seem, ethereal extracts are routinely dried by shaking them with an aqueous saturated sodium chloride solution.

Solvents such as dichloromethane do not dissolve nearly as much water and are therefore dried over a chemical drying agent. Many choices of chemical drying agents are available for this purpose, and the choice of which one to use is governed by four factors: (1) the possibility of reaction with the substance being extracted, (2) the speed with which it removes water from the solvent, (3) the efficiency of the process, and (4) the ease of recovery from the drying agent.

Some very good but specialized and reactive drying agents are potassium hydroxide, anhydrous potassium carbonate, sodium metal, calcium hydride, lithium aluminum hydride, and phosphorus pentoxide. Substances that are essentially neutral and unreactive and are widely used as drying agents include anhydrous calcium sulfate (Drierite), magnesium sulfate, molecular sieves, calcium chloride, and sodium sulfate.

Drierite, CaSO₄

Drierite, a specially prepared form of calcium sulfate, is a fast and effective drying agent. However, it is difficult to ascertain whether enough has been used. An indicating type of Drierite is impregnated with cobalt chloride, which turns from blue to red when it is saturated with water. This works well when gases are being dried, but it should not be used for liquid extractions because the cobalt chloride dissolves in many protic solvents.

Magnesium sulfate, MgSO₄

Magnesium sulfate is also a fast and fairly effective drying agent, but it is so finely powdered that it always requires careful filtration for removal.

Molecular sieves, zeolites

Molecular sieves are sodium alumino-silicates (zeolites) that have well-defined pore sizes. The 4 Å size adsorbs water to the exclusion of almost all organic substances, making them a fast and effective drying agent. Like Drierite, however, it is impossible to ascertain by appearance whether enough has been used. Molecular sieves in the form of 1/16-in. pellets are often used to dry solvents by simply adding them to the container.

Calcium chloride (CaCl₂) pellets are the drying agent of choice for small-scale experiments.

Calcium chloride, recently available in the preferred form of pellets (4 to 80 mesh[1]), is a very fast and effective drying agent. It has the advantage that it clumps together when excess water is present, which makes it possible to know how much to add by observing its behavior. Unlike the older granular form, the pellets do not disintegrate into a fine powder. These pellets are admirably suited to microscale experiments where the solvent is removed from the drying agent with a Pasteur pipette. Calcium chloride is much faster and far more effective than anhydrous sodium sulfate; after much experimentation, we have decided that this is the agent of choice, particularly for microscale experiments. These pellets are used for most of the drying operations in this text. Note, however, that calcium chloride reacts with some alcohols, phenols, amides, and some carbonyl-containing compounds. Advantage is sometimes taken of this property to remove not only water from a solvent but also, for example, a contaminating alcohol (*see* Chapter 16—the synthesis of 1-bromobutane from 1-butanol). Because *t*-butyl methyl ether forms an azeotrope with water, its solutions should, theoretically, not need to be dried because evaporation carries away the water. Drying these ether solutions with calcium chloride pellets removes water droplets that get carried into the ether solution.

Sodium sulfate, Na₂SO₄

Sodium sulfate is a very poor drying agent. It has a very high capacity for water but is slow and not very efficient in the removal of water. Like calcium chloride pellets, it clumps together when wet, and solutions are easily removed from it using a Pasteur pipette. Sodium sulfate has been used extensively in the past and should still be used for compounds that react with calcium chloride.

[1]These drying pellets are available from Fisher Scientific, Cat. No. C614–3.

PART 1: THE TECHNIQUE OF NEUTRAL LIQUID/LIQUID EXTRACTION

The workup technique of liquid/liquid extraction has four steps: (1) mixing the layers, (2) separating the layers, (3) drying the organic layer, and (4) removing the solvent. The microscale neutral liquid/liquid extraction technique is described in the following sections.

STEP 1. MIXING THE LAYERS

FIG. 7.4
Mixing the contents of a reaction tube by flicking it. Grasp the tube firmly at the very top and flick it vigorously at the bottom. The contents will mix without coming out of the tube.

Once the organic and aqueous layers are in contact with one another, mixing is required to ensure that the desired compound(s) get extracted into the desired layer. First, place 1–2 mL of an aqueous solution of the compound to be extracted in a reaction tube. Add about 1 mL of extraction solvent, for example, dichloromethane. Note, as you add the dichloromethane, whether it is the top or the bottom layer. (Since dichloromethane is more dense than water, predict what layer it will be.) An effective way to mix the two layers is to flick the tube with a finger. Grasp the tube firmly at the very top between the thumb and forefinger and flick it vigorously at the bottom (Fig. 7.4). You will find that this violent motion mixes the two layers well, but nothing will spill out the top. Another good mixing technique is to pull the contents of the reaction tube into a Pasteur pipette and then expel the mixture back into the tube with force. Doing this several times will effect good mixing of the two layers. A stopper can be placed in the top of the tube, and the contents can be mixed by shaking the tube, but the problem with this technique is that the high vapor pressure of the solvent will often force liquid out around the cork or stopper.

STEP 2. SEPARATING THE LAYERS

After thoroughly mixing the two layers, allow them to separate. Tap the tube if droplets of one layer are in the other layer, or on the side of the tube. After the layers separate completely, draw up the lower dichloromethane layer into a Pasteur pipette. Leave behind any middle emulsion layer. The easiest way to do this is to attach the pipette to a pipette pump (Fig. 7.5). This allows very precise control of the liquid being removed. It takes more skill and practice to remove the lower layer cleanly with a 2-mL rubber bulb attached to a pipette because the high vapor pressure of the solvent tends to make it dribble out. To avoid losing any of the solution, it is best to hold a clean, dry, empty tube in the same hand as the full tube to receive the organic layer (Fig. 7.6).

Always draw out the lower layer and place it in another container.

From the discussion of the partition coefficient, you know that several small extractions are better than one large one, so repeat the extraction process with two further 1-mL portions of dichloromethane. An experienced chemist might summarize all the preceding with the following notebook entry, "Aqueous layer extracted 3×1-mL portions CH$_2$Cl$_2$," and in a formal report would write, "The aqueous layer was extracted three times with 1-mL portions of dichloromethane."

If you are working on a larger microscale, a microscale separatory funnel (Fig. 7.7) should be used. A separatory funnel, regardless of size, should be filled to only about two-thirds of its capacity so the layers can be mixed by shaking. The microscale separatory funnel has a capacity of 8.5 mL when full, so it is useful for an extraction with a total volume of about 6 mL.

FIG. 7.5
The removal of a solvent from a reaction tube with a pipette and pipette pump.

2-mL Pipette pump

1-mL Pipette graduated to ± 0.01 mL

Reaction tube

FIG. 7.6
Grasp both reaction tubes in one hand when transferring material from one tube to another with a Pasteur pipette.

FIG. 7.7
A microscale separatory funnel. Remove the polyethylene frit from the micro Büchner funnel before using.

Polyethylene cap

Glass column

Micro Büchner funnel

Use a wood boiling stick to poke out the polyethylene frit from the bottom part of the separatory funnel. Store it for later replacement. Close the valve, add up to 5 mL of the solution to be extracted to the separatory funnel, then add the extraction solvent so that the total volume does not exceed 6 mL.

Cap the separatory funnel and mix the contents by inverting the funnel several times. If the two layers separate fairly easily, then the contents can be shaken more thoroughly. If the layers do not separate easily, be careful not to shake the funnel too vigorously because intractable emulsions could form.

Remove the stopper from the funnel, clamp it, and then, grasping the valve with two hands, empty the bottom layer into an Erlenmeyer flask or other container. If the top layer is desired, pour it out through the top of the separatory funnel—don't drain it through the valve, which may have a drop of the lower layer remaining in it.

STEP 3. DRYING THE ORGANIC LAYER

Dichloromethane dissolves a very small quantity of water, and microscopic droplets of water are suspended in the organic layer, often making it cloudy. To remove the water, a drying agent, for example, anhydrous calcium chloride pellets, is added to the dichloromethane solution.

FIG. 7.8

An aspirator tube being used to remove solvent vapors.

To water aspirator or to nitrogen or air supply

Pasteur pipette

Record the tare of the final container.

How Much Drying Agent Should Be Used?

When a small quantity of the drying agent is added, the crystals or pellets become sticky with water, clump together, and fall rapidly as a lump to the bottom of the reaction tube. There will come a point when a new small quantity of drying agent no longer clumps together, but the individual particles settle slowly throughout the solution. As they say in Sweden, "Add drying agent until it begins to snow." The drying process takes about 10–15 minutes, during which time the tube contents should be mixed occasionally by flicking the tube. The solution should no longer be cloudy, but clear (although it may be colored).

Once drying is judged complete, the solvent is removed by forcing a Pasteur pipette to the bottom of the reaction tube and pulling the solvent in. Air is expelled from the pipette as it is being pushed through the crystals or pellets so that no drying agent will enter the pipette. It is very important to wash the drying agent left in the reaction tube with several small quantities of pure solvent to transfer all the extract.

STEP 4. REMOVING THE SOLVENT

If the quantity of extract is relatively small, say 3 mL or less, then the easiest way to remove the solvent is to blow a stream of air (or nitrogen) onto the surface of the solution from a Pasteur pipette (Fig. 7.8). Be sure that the stream of air is very gentle before inserting it into the reaction tube. The heat of vaporization of the solvent will cause the tube to become rather cold during the evaporation and, of course, slow down the process. The easiest way to add heat is to hold the tube in your hand.

Another way to remove the solvent is to attach the Pasteur pipette to an aspirator and pull air over the surface of the liquid. This is not quite as fast as blowing air onto the surface of the liquid, and runs the danger of sucking up the liquid into the aspirator.

If the volume of liquid is more than about 3 mL, put it into a 25-mL filter flask, put a plastic Hirsch funnel in place, and attach the flask to the aspirator. By placing your thumb in the Hirsch funnel, the vacuum can be controlled, and heat can be applied by holding the flask in the other hand while swirling the contents (Fig. 7.9).

The reaction tube or filter flask in which the solvent is evaporated should be tared (weighed empty), and this weight recorded in your notebook. In this way, the weight of material extracted can be determined by again weighing the container that contains the extract.

EXPERIMENT

PARTITION COEFFICIENT OF BENZOIC ACID

IN THIS EXPERIMENT, you will shake a solution of benzoic acid in water with the immiscible solvent dichloromethane. The benzoic acid will distribute (partition) itself between the two layers. By removing the organic layer, drying, and evaporating it, the weight of benzoic acid in the dichloromethane can be determined and thus the ratio in the two layers. This ratio is a constant known as the partition coefficient.

FIG. 7.9
The apparatus for removing a solvent under vacuum.

To
aspirator

In a reaction tube, place about 100 mg of benzoic acid (weighed to the nearest milligram) and add exactly equal volumes of water followed by dichloromethane (about 1.6 mL each). While making this addition, note which layer is organic and which is aqueous. Put a septum on the tube and shake the contents vigorously for at least 2 minutes. Allow the tube to stand undisturbed until the layers separate and then carefully draw off, using a Pasteur pipette, *all* of the aqueous layer without removing any of the organic layer. It may be helpful to draw out the tip of the pipette to a finer point in a flame and, using this, to tilt the reaction tube at a 45° angle to make this separation as clean as possible.

Add anhydrous calcium chloride pellets to the dichloromethane in very small quantities until they no longer clump together. Mix the contents of the tube by flicking it, and allow it to stand for about 5 minutes to complete the drying process. Using a dry Pasteur pipette, transfer the dichloromethane to a tared dry reaction tube or a 10-mL Erlenmeyer flask containing a boiling chip. Complete the transfer by washing the drying agent with two more portions of solvent that are added to the original solution, and then evaporate the solvent. This can be done by boiling off the solvent while removing solvent vapors with an aspirator tube, or by blowing a stream of air or nitrogen into the container while warming it in one's hand (*see* Fig. 7.8). This operation should be performed in a hood.

From the weight of the benzoic acid in the dichloromethane layer, the weight in the water layer can be obtained by difference. The ratio of the weight in dichloromethane to the weight in water is the distribution coefficient because the volumes of the two solvents were equal. Report the value of the distribution coefficient in your notebook.

Cleaning Up. The aqueous layer can be flushed down the drain. Dichloromethane goes into the halogenated organic solvents waste container. After allowing the solvent to evaporate from the sodium sulfate in the hood, place the sodium sulfate in the non-hazardous solid waste container. If local regulations do not allow for the evaporation of solvents in a hood, dispose of the wet sodium sulfate in a special waste container.

PART 2: ACID/BASE LIQUID/LIQUID EXTRACTION

Acid/base liquid/liquid extraction involves carrying out simple acid/base reactions to separate strong organic acids, weak organic acids, neutral organic compounds, and basic organic substances. The chemistry involved is given in the following equations, using benzoic acid, phenol, naphthalene, and aniline as examples of the four types of compounds.

Here is the strategy (refer to the flow sheet in Fig. 7.10): The four organic compounds are dissolved in *t*-butyl methyl ether. The ether solution is shaken with a saturated aqueous solution of sodium bicarbonate, a weak base. This will react only with the strong acid, benzoic acid (**1**), to form the ionic salt, sodium benzoate (**5**), which dissolves in the aqueous layer and is removed. The ether solution now contains just phenol (**2**), naphthalene (**4**), and aniline (**3**). A 3 *M* aqueous solution of sodium hydroxide is added, and the mixture is shaken. The hydroxide, a strong base, will react only with the phenol (**2**), a weak acid, to form sodium phenoxide (**6**), an ionic compound that dissolves in the aqueous layer and is removed. The ether now contains only naphthalene (**4**) and aniline (**3**). Shaking it with dilute

FIG. 7.10

A flow sheet for the separation of a strong acid, a weak acid, a neutral compound, and a base: benzoic acid, phenol, naphthalene, and aniline (this page). Acid/base reactions of the acidic and basic compounds (opposite page).

In reaction tube A,
1) Dissolve all four compounds in *t*-butyl methyl ether.
2) Mix with HCO_3^-, remove lower aqueous layer, and place it in tube B.

1) Add OH^-, mix, remove lower aqueous layer, and place it in tube C.

1) Add HCl, mix, remove lower aqueous layer, and place it in tube D.

1) Dry solution over anhydrous calcium chloride pellets, remove solvent, and evaporate it to dryness in a clean, dry, tared reaction tube.

1
Benzoic acid
Forms a white, crystalline precipitate that can be removed by filtration

2
Phenol

3
Aniline

4
Naphthalene

Phenol and aniline each form oily layers on top of the aqueous layer. Extract each with *t*-butyl methyl ether: Add ether to the tube, mix, separate layers, dry the ether layer over anhydrous calcium chloride pellets, remove solution from drying agent, and evaporate the solvent.

1
Benzoic acid
$pK_a = 4.17$
Covalent, sol. in org. solvents

$+ \ Na^+HCO_3^-$ ⟶

5
Sodium benzoate
Ionic, sol. in water

$+ \ H_2O + CO_2$

5

$+ \ H^+Cl^-$ ⟶

1

$+ \ Na^+Cl^-$

2
Phenol
$pK_a = 10$
Covalent, sol. in org. solvents

$+ \ Na^+OH^-$ ⟶

6
Sodium phenoxide
Ionic, sol. in water

$+ \ H_2O$

6

$+ \ H^+Cl^-$ ⟶

2

$+ \ Na^+Cl^-$

3
Aniline
$pK_b = 9.30$
Covalent, sol. in org. solvents

$+ \ H^+Cl^-$ ⟶

7
Anilinium chloride
Ionic, sol. in water

7

$+ \ Na^+OH^-$ ⟶

3

$+ \ H_2O + Na^+Cl^-$

hydrochloric acid removes the aniline, a base, as the ionic anilinium chloride (**7**). The aqueous layer is removed. Evaporation of the *t*-butyl methyl ether now leaves naphthalene (**4**), the neutral compound. The other three compounds are recovered by adding acid to the sodium benzoate (**5**) and sodium phenoxide (**6**) and base to the anilinium chloride (**7**) to regenerate the covalent compounds benzoic acid (**1**), phenol (**2**), and aniline (**3**).

The pK$_a$ of carbonic acid, H$_2$CO$_3$, is 6.35.

The ability to separate strong acids from weak acids depends on the acidity constants of the acids and the basicity constants of the bases. In the first equation, consider the ionization of benzoic acid, which has an equilibrium constant (K_a) of 6.8×10^2. The conversion of benzoic acid to the benzoate anion in equation 4 is governed by the equilibrium constant, K (equation 5), obtained by combining equations 3 and 4.

$$C_6H_5COOH \; + \; H_2O \; \rightleftharpoons \; C_6H_5COO^- \; + \; H_3O^+ \tag{1}$$

$$K_a \; = \; \frac{[C_6H_5COO^-][H_3O^+]}{[C_6H_5COOH]} = 6.8 \times 10^{-5}, \, pK_a = 4.17 \tag{2}$$

$$K_w = [H_3O^+][OH^-] = 10^{-14} \tag{3}$$

$$C_6H_5COOH \; + \; OH^- \; \rightleftharpoons \; C_6H_5COO^- \; + \; H_2O \tag{4}$$

$$K = \frac{[C_6H_5COO^-]}{[C_6H_5COOH][OH^-]} = \frac{K_a}{K_w} = \frac{6.8 \times 10^{-5}}{10^{-14}} = 3.2 \times 10^8 \tag{5}$$

If 99% of the benzoic acid is converted to $C_6H_5COO^-$,

$$\frac{[C_6H_5COO^-]}{[C_6H_5COOH]} = \frac{99}{1} \tag{6}$$

then from equation 5 the hydroxide ion concentration would need to be $6.8 \times 10^{-7} \, M$. Because saturated NaHCO$_3$ has [OH$^-$] = $3 \times 10^{-4} \, M$, the hydroxide ion concentration is high enough to convert benzoic acid completely to sodium benzoate.

For phenol, with a K_a of 10^{-10}, the minimum hydroxide ion concentration that will produce the phenoxide anion in 99% conversion is $10^{-2} \, M$. The concentration of hydroxide in 10% sodium hydroxide solution is $10^{-1} \, M$, and so phenol in a strong base is entirely converted to the water-soluble salt.

GENERAL CONSIDERATIONS

If acetic acid was used as the reaction solvent, it would also be distributed largely into the aqueous phase. If the reaction product is a neutral substance, however, the residual acetic acid in the ether can be removed by one washing with excess 5% sodium bicarbonate solution. If the reaction product is a higher molecular weight acid, for example, benzoic acid (C$_6$H$_5$COOH), it will stay in the ether layer, while acetic acid is being removed by repeated washing with water. The benzoic acid can then be separated from neutral byproducts by extraction with sodium bicarbonate or sodium hydroxide solution and acidification of the extract. Acids of high molecular weight are extracted only slowly by sodium bicarbonate, so sodium carbonate is used in its place; however, carbonate is more prone than bicarbonate to produce emulsions. Sometimes an emulsion in the lower layer can be settled by twirling the separatory funnel by its stem. An emulsion in the upper layer can be broken by grasping the funnel at the neck and swirling it. Because the tendency to emulsify increases with the removal of electrolytes and solvents, a little sodium chloride solution is added with each portion of wash water. If the layers are largely clear but an emulsion persists at the interface, the clear part of the water layer can be drawn off, and the emulsion run into a second funnel and shaken with fresh ether.

Liquid/liquid extraction and acid/base extraction are employed in the majority of organic reactions because it is unusual to have the product crystallize from the reaction mixture or to be able to distill the reaction product directly from the reaction mixture. In the research literature, one will often see the statement "the reaction mixture was worked up in the usual way," which implies an extraction process of the type described here. Good laboratory practice dictates, however, that the details of the process be written out.

EXPERIMENTS

1. SEPARATION OF A CARBOXYLIC ACID, A PHENOL, AND A NEUTRAL SUBSTANCE

Benzoic acid
mp 123°C, pK_a 4.17

OCH₃

OCH₃

1,4-Dimethoxybenzene
(Hydroquinone dimethyl ether)
mp 57°C

Photos: *Extraction with Ether*
Video: *Extraction with Ether*

A mixture of equal parts of a carboxylic acid, a phenol, and a neutral substance is to be separated by extraction from an ether solvent. Note carefully the procedure for this extraction. In the next experiment, you are to work out your own extraction procedure. Your unknown will consist of either benzoic acid or 2-chlorobenzoic acid (the carboxylic acid), 4-*t*-butyl phenol or 4-bromophenol, and biphenyl or 1,4-dimethoxybenzene (the neutral substance). The object of this experiment is to identify the three substances in the mixture and to determine the percent recovery of each from the mixture.

Procedure

> IN THIS EXPERIMENT, three organic solids are separated by reaction with base followed by extraction. Bicarbonate converts carboxylic acids (but not phenols) to ions. Hydroxide ion converts phenols (as well as carboxylic acids) to ions. Ionic substances are soluble in water. The addition of hydrochloric acid to the aqueous ionic solutions regenerates nonionic substances. At each step you should ask yourself, "Have I converted a nonionic substance to an ionic one?" (or vice versa). The ionic substances will be in the aqueous layer; the nonionic ones will be in the organic layer.

Dissolve about 0.18 g of the mixture (record the exact weight) in 2 mL of *t*-butyl methyl ether or diethyl ether in a reaction tube (tube 1). Then add 1 mL of a saturated aqueous solution of sodium bicarbonate to the tube. Use the graduations on the side of the tube to measure the amounts, since they do not need to be exact. Mix the contents of the tube thoroughly by pulling the two layers into a Pasteur pipette and expelling them forcefully into the reaction tube. Do this for about 3 minutes. Allow the layers to separate completely and then draw off the lower layer into another reaction tube (tube 2). Add another 0.15 mL of sodium bicarbonate solution to the tube, mix the contents as before, and add the lower layer to tube 2.

OH

H₃C — C — CH₃
|
CH₃

4-*tert*-Butylphenol
mp 101°C, pK_a 10.17

⚠️
Add HCl with care; CO_2 is released.

🌐 Videos: *Filtration of Crystals Using the Pasteur Pipette, Microscale Filtration on the Hirsch Funnel*

OH

Br

4-Bromophenol
mp 66°C, pK_a 10.2

Biphenyl
mp 71°C

COOH
Cl

2-Chlorobenzoic acid
mp 141°C, pK_a 2.92

The best way to remove the solvent: under a gentle stream of air or nitrogen.

Exactly which chemical species is in tube 2? Add 0.2 mL of ether to tube 2, mix it thoroughly, remove the ether layer, and discard it. This is called *back-washing* and serves to remove any organic material that might contaminate the contents of tube 2.

Add 1.0 mL of 3 *M* aqueous sodium hydroxide to tube 1, shake the mixture thoroughly, allow the layers to separate, draw off the lower layer using a clean Pasteur pipette, and place it in tube 3. Extract tube 1 with two 0.15-mL portions of water, and add these to tube 3. Backwash the contents of tube 3 with 0.15 mL of ether and discard the ether wash just as was done for tube 2. Exactly which chemical species is in tube 3?

To tube 1, add saturated sodium chloride solution, mix, remove the aqueous layer, and then add to the ether anhydrous calcium chloride pellets until the drying agent no longer clumps together. Wash it off with ether after the drying process is finished. Allow 5–10 minutes for the drying of the ether solution.

Using the concentration information given in the inside back cover of this book, calculate exactly how much concentrated hydrochloric acid is needed to neutralize the contents of tube 2. Then, by dropwise addition of concentrated hydrochloric acid, carry out this neutralization while testing the solution with litmus paper. An excess of hydrochloric acid does no harm. This reaction must be carried out with *extreme care* because much carbon dioxide is released in the neutralization. Add a boiling stick to the tube and very cautiously heat the tube to bring most of the solid carboxylic acid into solution. Allow the tube to cool slowly to room temperature, and then cool it in ice. Remove the solvent with a Pasteur pipette and recrystallize the residue from boiling water. Again, allow the tube to cool slowly to room temperature and then cool it in ice. At the appropriate time, stir the crystals and collect them on a Hirsch funnel using the procedures detailed in Chapter 4. The crystals can be transferred and washed on the funnel using a small quantity of ice water. The solubility of benzoic acid in water is 1.9 g/L at 0°C and 68 g/L at 95°C. The solubility of chlorobenzoic acid is similar. Spread the crystals out onto a tared piece of paper, allow them to dry thoroughly, and determine the percent recovery of the acid. Assess the purity of the product by checking its melting point.

In exactly the same way, neutralize the contents of tube 3 with concentrated hydrochloric acid. This time, of course, there will be no carbon dioxide evolution. Again, heat the tube to bring most of the material into solution, allow it to cool slowly, remove the solvent, and recrystallize the phenol from boiling water. At the appropriate time, after the product has cooled slowly to room temperature and then in ice, it is also collected on a Hirsch funnel, washed with a very small quantity of ice water, and allowed to dry. The percent recovery and melting point are determined.

The neutral compound is recovered using a Pasteur pipette to remove the ether from the drying agent and to transfer it to a tared reaction tube. The drying agent is washed two or three times with additional ether to ensure complete transfer of the product.

Evaporate the solvent by placing the tube in a warm water bath and directing a stream of nitrogen or air onto the surface of the ether in the hood (*see* Fig. 7.8 on page 140). An aspirator tube can also be used for this purpose. Determine the weight of the crude product and then recrystallize it from methanol-water if it is the low-melting compound. Reread Chapter 4 for detailed instructions on carrying out the process of recrystallization from a mixed solvent. The product is dissolved in about 0.5–1 mL of methanol, and water is added until the solution gets cloudy, which indicates that the solution is saturated. This process is best carried out while heating the tube in a hot water bath at 50°C. Allow the tube to cool slowly to room temperature, and then cool it thoroughly in ice. If you have the high-melting compound, recrystallize it from ethanol (8 mL/g).

The products are best isolated by collection on a Hirsch funnel using an ice-cold alcohol-water mixture to transfer and wash the compounds. Determine the percent recovery and the melting point. Turn in the products in neatly labeled $1\frac{1}{2}$-in. $\times$ $1\frac{1}{2}$-in. (4 cm $\times$ 4 cm) ziplock plastic bags attached to the laboratory report. If the yield on recrystallization is low, concentrate the filtrate (the mother liquor) and obtain a second crop of crystals.

2. SEPARATION OF NEUTRAL AND BASIC SUBSTANCES

IN THIS EXPERIMENT, remember that hydrochloric acid will convert a nonionic amine to an ionic substance and that base will regenerate the nonionic substance from the ionic form. The nonionic and neutral substances are ether soluble, and the ionic substances will be found in the aqueous layer.

A mixture of equal parts of a neutral substance (naphthalene or 1,4-dichlorobenzene) and a basic substance (4-chloroaniline or ethyl 4-aminobenzoate) is to be separated by extraction from an ether solution. Naphthalene and 1,4-dichlorobenzene are completely insoluble in water. The bases will dissolve in hydrochloric acid, while the neutral compounds will remain in the ether solution. The bases are insoluble in cold water, but will dissolve to some extent in hot water and are soluble in ethanol. Naphthalene and 1,4-dichlorobenzene can be purified as described in Chapter 4. They also sublime very easily. Keep the samples covered.

Naphthalene
mp 82°C

1,4-Dichlorobenzene
mp 56°C

4-Chloroaniline
mp 68–71°C, pK_b 4.15

Ethyl 4-aminobenzoate
mp 90°C, pK_b 4.92

⚠ Ether vapors are heavier than air and can travel along bench tops, run down drain troughs, and collect in sinks. Be extremely careful to avoid flames when working with volatile ethers.

Plan a step-by-step procedure for separating 200 mg of the mixture into its components and have the plan checked by your instructor before proceeding. A flow sheet is a convenient way to present the plan. Select the correct solvent or mixture of solvents for the recrystallization of the bases on the basis of solubility tests. Determine the weights and melting points of the isolated and purified products and calculate the percent recovery of each. Turn in the products in neatly labeled vials or 1-1/2-in. $\times$ 1-1/2-in. ziplock plastic bags attached to the report.

Cleaning Up. Combine all aqueous filtrates and solutions, neutralize them, and flush the resulting solution down the drain. Used ether should be placed in the organic solvents waste container, and the drying agent, once the solvent has evaporated from it, can be placed in the nonhazardous solid waste container. If local regulations do not allow for the evaporation of solvents in a hood, dispose of the wet sodium sulfate in a special waste container. Any 4-chloroaniline or 1,4-dichlorobenzene should be placed in the halogenated waste container.

3. SEPARATION OF ACIDIC AND NEUTRAL SUBSTANCES

A mixture of equal proportions of benzoic acid, 4-*t*-butylphenol, and 1,4-dimethoxybenzene is to be separated by extraction from *t*-butyl methyl ether. Note the detailed directions for extraction carefully. Prepare a flow sheet (*see* Fig. 7.10 on page 142) for this sequence of operations. In the next experiment you will work out your own extraction procedure.

pH = −log [H⁺]

pK_a = acidity constant

pK_b = basicity constant

Procedure

Dissolve 3 g of the mixture in 30 mL of *t*-butyl methyl ether and transfer the mixture to a 125-mL separatory funnel (*see* Fig. 7.2 on page 135) using a little *t*-butyl methyl ether to complete the transfer. Add 10 mL of water and take note of which layer is organic and which is aqueous. Add 10 mL of a saturated aqueous solution of sodium bicarbonate to the funnel. Swirl or stir the mixture to allow carbon dioxide to escape. Stopper the funnel and cautiously mix the contents. Vent the liberated carbon dioxide and then shake the mixture thoroughly with frequent venting of the funnel. Repeat the process with another 10 mL of bicarbonate solution. Allow the layers to separate completely and then draw off the lower layer into a 50-mL Erlenmeyer flask (labeled flask 1). What does this layer contain?

Add 10 mL of a 1.5 *M* aqueous sodium hydroxide solution to the separatory funnel, shake the mixture thoroughly, allow the layers to separate, and draw off the lower layer into a 50-mL Erlenmeyer flask (labeled flask 2). Repeat the process with another 10 mL of base. Then add an additional 5 mL of water to the separatory funnel, shake the mixture as before, and add this to flask 2. What does flask 2 contain?

Add 15 mL of a saturated aqueous solution of sodium chloride to the separatory funnel, shake the mixture thoroughly, allow the layers to separate, and draw off the lower layer, which can be discarded. What is the purpose of adding a saturated sodium chloride solution? Carefully pour the ether layer into a 50-mL Erlenmeyer flask (labeled flask 3) from the top of the separatory funnel, taking great care not to allow any water droplets to be transferred. Add about 4 g of anhydrous calcium chloride pellets to the ether extract and set it aside.

Acidify the contents of flask 2 by dropwise addition of concentrated hydrochloric acid while testing with litmus paper. Cool the flask in an ice bath.

Cautiously add concentrated hydrochloric acid dropwise to flask 1 until the contents are acidic to litmus, and then cool the flask in ice.

Decant (pour off) the ether from flask 3 into a tared flask, making sure to leave all the drying agent behind. Wash the drying agent with additional ether to ensure complete transfer of the product. If decantation is difficult, then remove the drying agent by gravity filtration (*see* Fig. 4.6 on page 68). Put a boiling stick in the flask and evaporate the ether in the hood. An aspirator tube can be used for this purpose (Fig. 7.11). Determine the weight of the crude *p*-dimethoxybenzene and then recrystallize it from methanol. See Chapter 4 for detailed instructions on how to carry out recrystallization.

Isolate the *t*-butylphenol from flask 2, employing vacuum filtration on a Hirsch funnel, and wash it on the filter with a small quantity of ice water. Determine the weight of the crude product and then recrystallize it from ethanol. Similarly isolate, weigh, and recrystallize from boiling water the benzoic acid in flask 1. The solubility of benzoic acid in water is 1.9 g/L at 0°C and 68 g/L at 95°C.

Benzoic acid
mp 123°C, pK_a 4.17

4-*tert*-Butylphenol
mp 101°C, pK_a 10.17

Video: *Macroscale Crystallization*

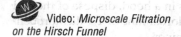

Video: *Microscale Filtration on the Hirsch Funnel*

Extinguish all flames when working with *t*-butyl methyl ether! The best method for removing the ether is by simple distillation. Dispose of waste ether in the container provided.

FIG. 7.11
An aspirator tube in use.

Dry the purified products, determine their melting points and weights, and calculate the percent recovery of each substance, bearing in mind that the original mixture contained 1 g of each compound. Hand in the three products in neatly labeled vials.

Cleaning Up. Combine all aqueous layers, washes, and filtrates. Dilute with water, neutralize using either sodium carbonate or dilute hydrochloric acid. This material can then be flushed down the drain with excess water. Methanol filtrate and any ether go in the organic solvents waste container. Allow ether to evaporate from the calcium chloride in the hood. Then place the calcium chloride in the nonhazardous solid waste container. If local regulations do not allow for the evaporation of solvents in a hood, dispose of the wet sodium sulfate in a special waste container.

1,4-Dimethoxybenzene
(Hydroquinone dimethyl ether)
mp 57°C

Naphthalene
mp 82°C

4-Chloroaniline
mp 68–71°C, pK_b 10.0

4. SEPARATION OF NEUTRAL AND BASIC SUBSTANCES

A mixture of equal parts of a neutral substance (naphthalene) and a basic substance (4-chloroaniline) is to be separated by extraction from *t*-butyl methyl ether solution. The base will dissolve in hydrochloric acid, whereas the neutral naphthalene will remain in the *t*-butyl methyl ether solution. 4-Chloroaniline is insoluble in cold water, but will dissolve to some extent in hot water and is soluble in ethanol. Naphthalene can be purified as described in Chapter 4.

Plan a procedure for separating 2.0 g of the mixture into its components and have the plan checked by your instructor before proceeding. A flow sheet is a convenient way to present the plan. Using solubility tests, select the correct solvent or mixture of solvents to recrystallize 4-chloroaniline. Determine the weights and melting points of the isolated and purified products, and calculate the percent recovery of each. Turn in the products in neatly labeled vials.

Handle aromatic amines with care. Most are toxic, and some are carcinogenic. Avoid breathing the dust and vapor from the solid and keep the compounds off the skin, which is best done by wearing nitrile gloves.

Cleaning Up. Combine all aqueous filtrates and solutions, neutralize them, and flush the resulting solution down the drain with a large excess of water. Used *t*-butyl methyl ether should be placed in the organic solvents waste container, and the drying agent, once the solvent has evaporated from it, can be placed in the nonhazardous solid waste container. If local regulations do not allow for the evaporation of solvents in a hood, dispose of the wet sodium sulfate in a special waste container. Any 4-chloroaniline should be placed in the chlorinated organic compounds waste container.

5. EXTRACTION AND PURIFICATION OF COMPONENTS IN AN ANALGESIC TABLET

IN THIS EXPERIMENT, a powdered analgesic tablet, Excedrin, is boiled with dichloromethane and filtered. The solid on the filter is boiled with ethanol, which dissolves everything but the binder. The ethanol is evaporated and from the hot solution, acetaminophen recrystallizes. The dichloromethane solution is shaken with base that converts aspirin to the water-soluble carboxylate anion. The dichloromethane is then evaporated to give caffeine that is purified by sublimation. The aqueous carboxylate anion solution is made acidic, which frees aspirin; warming the mixture and allowing it to cool allows aspirin to recrystallize. It is isolated by filtration.

Excedrin contains aspirin, caffeine, and acetaminophen as determined by thin-layer chromatography (TLC; *see* Chapter 8) or high performance liquid chromatography. A tablet is held together with a binder to prevent the components from crumbling when stored or while being swallowed. A close reading of the contents on the package will disclose the nature of the binder. Starch is commonly used, as is microcrystalline cellulose or silica gel. All of these have one property in common: They are insoluble in water and common organic solvents.

Aspirin
(Acetylsalicylic acid)
mp 135°C

Acetaminophen
(*p*-Hydroxyacetanilide)
mp 169–170.5°C

Caffeine
mp 238°C

Inspection of the structures of caffeine, acetylsalicylic acid, and acetaminophen reveals that one is a base, one is a strong organic acid, and one is a weak organic acid. It might be tempting to separate this mixture using exactly the same procedure employed in separating benzoic acid, 4-*t*-butylphenol, and 1,4-dimethoxybenzene (experiment 3)—that is, dissolve the mixture in dichloromethane; separate the strongly acidic component by reaction with bicarbonate ion, a weak base; then remove the weakly acidic component by reaction with hydroxide, a strong base. This process would leave the neutral compound in the dichloromethane solution.

In the present experiment, the solubility data (see Table 7.2) reveal that the weak acid, acetaminophen, is not soluble in ether, chloroform, or dichloromethane, so it cannot be extracted by a strong base. We can take advantage of this lack of solubility by dissolving the other two components, caffeine and aspirin, in dichloromethane

TABLE 7.2 *Solubilities*

	Water	Ethanol	Chloroform	Diethyl ether	Hexanes
Aspirin	0.33 g/100 mL at 25°C; 1 g/100 mL at 37°C	1 g/5 mL	1 g/17 mL	1 g/13 mL	
Acetaminophen	v. sl. sol. cold; sol. hot	sol.	ins.	sl. sol.	ins.
Caffeine	1 g/46 mL at 25°C; 1 g/5.5 mL at 80°C; 1 g/1.5 mL at 100°C	1 g/66 mL at 25°C; 1 g/22 mL at 60°C	1 g/5.5 mL	1 g/530 mL	sl. sol.

and removing the acetaminophen by filtration. The binder is also insoluble in dichloromethane, so the solid mixture can be treated with ethanol to dissolve the acetaminophen and not the binder. These can then be separated by filtration, with the acetaminophen isolated by evaporation of the ethanol.

This experiment is a test of technique. It is not easy to separate and recrystallize a few milligrams of a compound that occurs in a mixture.

Microscale Procedure

⚠ Handle dichloromethane in the hood. It is a suspected carcinogen.

 Photos: *Micro Büchner Funnel, Vacuum Filtration into Reaction Tube through Hirsch Funnel, Use of the Wilfilter*

In a mortar, grind an Extra Strength Excedrin tablet to a very fine powder. The label states that this analgesic contains 250 mg of aspirin, 250 mg of acetaminophen, and 65 mg of caffeine per tablet. Place 300 mg of this powder in a reaction tube and add 2 mL of dichloromethane. Warm the mixture briefly and note that a large part of the material does not dissolve. Filter the mixture on a microscale Büchner funnel (the base of the chromatography column in the kit; Fig. 7.12) into another reaction tube. This is done by transferring the slurry to the funnel with a Pasteur pipette, and completing the transfer with a small portion of dichloromethane which will also wash the material on the funnel. This filtrate is solution 1. A Hirsch funnel (Fig. 7.13) or a Wilfilter (Fig. 7.14) can also be used for this procedure. Pressure filtration is another alternative.

The binder can be starch, microcrystalline cellulose, or silica gel.

Transfer the powder on the filter to a reaction tube, add 1 mL of ethanol, and heat the mixture to boiling on a sand bath (with a boiling stick). Not all the material will go into solution. That which does not is the binder. Filter the mixture on the same previously used microscale Büchner funnel into a tared reaction tube, and complete the transfer and washing using a few drops of hot ethanol.

Acetaminophen

Photos: *Vacuum Filtration into a Reaction Tube through a Hirsch Funnel, Micro Büchner Funnel,* Video: *Filtration of Crystals Using the Pasteur Pipette*

Evaporate about two-thirds of the filtrate by boiling off the ethanol or, better, by warming the solution and blowing a stream of air into the reaction tube. Heat the residue to boiling (add a boiling stick to prevent bumping) and, if necessary, add more ethanol to bring the solid into solution. Allow the saturated solution to cool slowly to room temperature to deposit crystals of acetaminophen, which are reported to melt at 169°C–170.5°C. After the mixture has cooled to room temperature, cool it in ice for several minutes, remove the solvent with a Pasteur pipette, wash the crystals once with 2 drops of ice-cold ethanol, remove the ethanol, and dry the crystals under aspirator vacuum while heating the tube on a steam or sand bath.

Check product purity by TLC (Chapter 8) using 25:1 ethyl acetate–acetic acid to elute the silica gel plates.

Alternatively, the original ethanol solution can be evaporated to dryness, and the residue recrystallized from boiling water. The crystals can be collected on a Hirsch funnel (Fig. 7.13) or by use of a Wilfilter (Fig. 7.14). Once the crystals are dry, determine their weight and melting point. TLC analysis (see Chapter 8) and a determination of the melting points of these crystals and the two other components of this mixture will indicate their purity.

FIG. 7.12

A microscale Büchner funnel assembly.

Thermometer adapter

Micro Büchner funnel with fritted disk

To aspirator

Vacuum-tight connector

Reaction tube with filtrate

FIG. 7.13

A Hirsch funnel with an integral adapter, a polyethylene frit, and a 25-mL filter flask.

Filter paper, 12 mm dia.

Polyethylene filter disk (frit), 10 mm dia.

Hirsch funnel

To aspirator

25-mL Filter flask

FIG. 7.14

The Wilfilter filtration apparatus. *See* **Chapter 4 for usage information.**

Crystals

Wilfilter

Filtrate

Videos: *Recrystallization, Extraction with Dichloromethane*; Photos: *Vacuum Filtration into Reaction Tube through Hirsch Funnel, Use of the Wilfilter*

Photos: *Sublimation Apparatus, Filtration Using a Pasteur Pipette*; Videos: *Recrystallization, Filtration Using a Pasteur Pipette*

Caffeine
See Figure 4.13 on page 72 for drying crystals under vacuum.

The dichloromethane filtered from the binder and acetaminophen mixture (solution 1) should contain caffeine and aspirin. These can be separated by extraction either with acid (which will remove the caffeine as a water-soluble salt) or with base (which will remove the aspirin as a water-soluble salt). We shall use the latter procedure.

To the dichloromethane solution in a reaction tube, add 1 mL of 3 M sodium hydroxide solution and shake the mixture thoroughly. Remove the aqueous layer, add 0.2 mL more water, shake the mixture thoroughly, and again remove the aqueous layer, which is combined with the first aqueous extract.

To the dichloromethane, add calcium chloride pellets until the drying agent no longer clumps together. Shake the mixture over a 5-minute to 10-minute period to complete the drying process. Then remove the solvent, wash the drying agent with more solvent, and evaporate the combined extracts to dryness under a stream of air to leave crude caffeine.

The caffeine can be purified by sublimation (Fig. 7.15) or by recrystallization. Recrystallize the caffeine by dissolving it in the minimum quantity of 30% ethanol in tetrahydrofuran. It also can be recrystallized by dissolving the product in a minimum quantity of hot toluene or acetone, and adding to this solution hexanes until the solution is cloudy while at the boiling point. In any case, allow the solution to cool slowly to room temperature; then cool the mixture in ice and remove the solvent from the crystals with a Pasteur pipette. Remove the remainder of the solvent under aspirator vacuum and determine the weight of the caffeine and its melting point.

The aqueous hydroxide extract contains aspirin as the sodium salt of the carboxylic acid. To the aqueous solution, add 3 M hydrochloric acid dropwise until the solution tests strongly acid with indicator paper; then add 2 more drops of acid. This will give a suspension of white acetylsalicylic acid in the aqueous solution. It

FIG. 7.15
A sublimation apparatus.

15-mL Centrifuge tube, to be filled with ice

Adapter (Pluro stopper)

Pipette bulb

25-mL Filter flask

Material to be sublimed

Sublimate

Heat source

FIG. 7.16
Recrystallization in a reaction tube.

Boiling stick ——

Cool at this poin

Air condenser –

Boiling solvent –

Temperature controlled by depth in sand ——

Photos: *Filtration Using a Pasteur Pipette, Use of the Wilfilter*, Video: *Recrystallization, Filtration of Crystals Using the Pasteur Pipette*

Aspirin

Alternative procedure: Use a Hirsch funnel or a Wilfilter to isolate the aspirin.

could be filtered off and recrystallized from boiling water, but this would cause transfer losses. An easier procedure is to heat the aqueous solution that contains the precipitated aspirin.

Add a boiling stick and heat the mixture to boiling (Fig. 7.16), at which time the aspirin should dissolve completely. If it does not, add more water. Long boiling will hydrolyze the aspirin to salicylic acid (mp 157–159°C). Once completely dissolved, the aspirin should be allowed to recrystallize slowly as the solution cools to room temperature in an insulated container. Once the tube has reached room temperature, it should be cooled in ice for several minutes, and then the solvent is removed with a Pasteur pipette. Wash the crystals with a few drops of ice-cold water and isolate them with a Wilfilter or scrape them out onto a piece of filter paper. Squeezing the crystals between sheets of filter paper will hasten drying. Once these crystals are completely dry, determine the weight of the acetylsalicylic acid and its melting point.

Cleaning Up. Place any dichloromethane-containing solutions in the halogenated organic waste container and the other organic liquids in the organic solvents waste container. The aqueous layers should be diluted and neutralized with sodium carbonate before being flushed down the drain. After it is free of solvent, the calcium chloride can be placed in the nonhazardous solid waste container. If local regulations do not allow for the evaporation of solvents in a hood, dispose of the wet sodium sulfate in a special container.

Macroscale Procedure

⚠ Handle dichloromethane in the hood. It is a suspected carcinogen.

In a mortar, grind two Extra Strength Excedrin tablets to a very fine powder. The label states that this analgesic contains 250 mg of aspirin, 250 mg of acetaminophen, and 65 mg of caffeine per tablet. Place this powder in a test tube and add 7.5 mL of dichloromethane. Warm the mixture briefly and note that a large part of the material does not dissolve. Filter the mixture into another test tube by using a Hirsch funnel equipped with a piece of filter paper. Use a Pasteur pipette and complete the transfer with a small portion of dichloromethane. This filtrate is solution 1.

Acetaminophen

Photo: *Filtration Using a Pasteur Pipette*; Video: *Filtration of Crystals Using the Pasteur Pipette*

Check product purity by TLC (*Chapter 8*) using 25:1 ethyl acetate–acetic acid to elute the silica gel plates.

Video: *Extraction with Dichloromethane*

An alternative to shaking is pipette mixing or using a vortex stirrer, if available.

Photo: *Sublimation Apparatus*

Caffeine

Sodium acetylsalicylate
(soluble in water)

Aspirin

Alternative procedure: Use a Hirsch funnel (*see* Fig. 4.15 on page 73) to isolate the aspirin.

Transfer the powder on the filter to a test tube, add 4 mL of ethanol, and heat the mixture to boiling (with a boiling stick). Not all of the material will go into solution. That which does not is the binder. Filter the mixture into a tared test tube and complete the transfer and washing by using a few drops of hot ethanol. This is solution 2.

Evaporate about two-thirds of solution 2 by boiling off the ethanol (with a boiling stick) or, better, by warming the solution and blowing a stream of air into the test tube. Heat the residue to boiling (add a boiling stick to prevent bumping) and add more ethanol, if necessary, to bring the solid into solution. Allow the saturated solution to cool slowly to room temperature to deposit crystals of acetaminophen, which is reported to melt at 169–170.5°C. After the mixture has cooled to room temperature, cool it in ice for several minutes, remove the solvent with a Pasteur pipette, wash the crystals once with 2 drops of ice-cold ethanol, remove the ethanol, and dry the crystals under aspirator vacuum while heating the tube on a steam or sand bath.

Alternatively, the original ethanol solution is evaporated to dryness, and the residue is recrystallized from boiling water. The crystals are best collected and dried on a Hirsch funnel (*see* Fig. 7.13 on page 152). Once the crystals are dry, determine their weight and melting point. TLC analysis (*see* Chapter 8) and a determination of the melting points of these crystals and the two other components of this mixture will indicate their purity.

The dichloromethane filtered from the binder and acetaminophen mixture (solution 1) should contain caffeine and aspirin. These can be separated by extraction either with acid (which will remove the caffeine as a water-soluble salt) or with base (which will remove the aspirin as a water-soluble salt). We shall use the latter procedure.

To the dichloromethane solution in a test tube, add 4 mL of 3 M sodium hydroxide solution and shake the mixture thoroughly. Remove the aqueous layer, add 1 mL more water, shake the mixture thoroughly, and again remove the aqueous layer, which is combined with the first aqueous extract.

To the dichloromethane, add anhydrous calcium chloride pellets until the drying agent no longer clumps together. Shake the mixture over a 5–10-minute period to complete the drying process, then remove the solvent, wash the drying agent with more solvent, and evaporate the combined extracts to dryness under a stream of air to leave crude caffeine.

The caffeine can be purified by sublimation or by recrystallization. Recrystallize the caffeine by dissolving it in the minimum quantity of 30% ethanol in tetrahydrofuran. It can also be recrystallized by dissolving the product in a minimum quantity of hot toluene or acetone, and adding hexanes to this solution until the solution is cloudy while at the boiling point. In any case, allow the solution to cool slowly to room temperature; then cool the mixture in ice and remove the solvent from the crystals with a Pasteur pipette. Remove the remainder of the solvent under aspirator vacuum and determine the weight of the caffeine and its melting point.

The aqueous hydroxide extract contains aspirin as the sodium salt of the carboxylic acid. To the aqueous solution, add 3 M hydrochloric acid dropwise until the solution tests strongly acid with indicator paper; then add 2 more drops of acid. This will give a suspension of white acetylsalicylic acid in the aqueous solution. It could be filtered off and recrystallized from boiling water, but this would cause transfer losses. An easier procedure is to simply heat the aqueous solution that contains the precipitated aspirin and allow it to recrystallize on slow cooling.

Add a boiling stick and heat the mixture to boiling, at which time the aspirin should dissolve completely. If it does not, add more water. Long boiling will

Photo: *Filtration Using a Pasteur Pipette*; Video: *Filtration of Crystals Using the Pasteur Pipette*

hydrolyze the aspirin to salicylic acid (mp 157–159°C). Once completely dissolved, the aspirin should be allowed to recrystallize slowly as the solution cools to room temperature in an insulated container. Once the tube has reached room temperature, it should be cooled in ice for several minutes, and then the solvent is removed with a Pasteur pipette. The crystals are to be washed with a few drops of ice-cold water and then scraped out onto a piece of filter paper. Squeezing the crystals between sheets of the filter paper will hasten drying. Once these crystals are completely dry, determine the weight of the acetylsalicylic acid and its melting point.

Cleaning Up. Place any dichloromethane-containing solutions in the halogenated organic waste container and the other organic liquids in the organic solvents waste container. The aqueous layers should be diluted and neutralized with sodium carbonate before being flushed down the drain. After it is free of solvent, the calcium chloride can be placed in the nonhazardous solid waste container. If local regulations do not allow for the evaporation of solvents in a hood, dispose of the wet sodium sulfate in a special waste container.

EXTRACTIONS FROM COMMON ITEMS

6. Extraction of Caffeine from Tea

Tea and coffee have been popular beverages for centuries, primarily because they contain caffeine, a stimulant. Caffeine stimulates respiration, the heart, and the central nervous system, and it is a diuretic (i.e., it promotes urination). It can cause nervousness and insomnia and, like many drugs, can be addictive, making it difficult to reduce the daily dose. A regular coffee drinker who consumes just 4 cups per day can experience headache, insomnia, and even nausea upon withdrawal from the drug. On the other hand, it helps people to pay attention and can sharpen moderately complex mental skills as well as prolong the ability to exercise.

Caffeine may be the most widely abused drug in the United States. During the course of a day, an average person may unwittingly consume up to 1 g of caffeine. The caffeine content of some common foods and drugs is given in Table 7.3.

Caffeine belongs to a large class of compounds known as alkaloids. These are of plant origin, contain basic nitrogen, often have a bitter taste and a complex structure, and usually have physiological activity. Their names usually end in *-ine*; many are quite familiar by name if not chemical structure—for example, nicotine, cocaine, morphine, and strychnine.

Tea leaves contain tannins, which are acidic, as well as a number of colored compounds and a small amount of undecomposed chlorophyll (soluble in dichloromethane). To ensure that the acidic substances remain water soluble and that the caffeine will be present as the free base, sodium carbonate is added to the extraction medium.

The solubility of caffeine in water is 2.2 mg/mL at 25°C, 180 mg/mL at 80°C, and 670 mg/mL at 100°C. It is quite soluble in dichloromethane, the solvent used in this experiment to extract the caffeine from water.

Caffeine can be easily extracted from tea bags. The procedure one would use to make a cup of tea—simply "steeping" the tea with very hot water for about 7 minutes—extracts most of the caffeine. There is no advantage to boiling the tea leaves with water for 20 minutes. Because caffeine is a white, slightly bitter, odorless, crystalline solid, it is obvious that water extracts more than just

TABLE 7.3 *Caffeine Content of Common Foods and Drugs*

Espresso	120 mg per 2 oz
Coffee, regular, brewed	103 mg per cup
Instant coffee	57 mg per cup
Coffee, decaffeinated	2–4 mg per cup
Tea, black (fermented)	40–75 mg per cup
Tea, green	15–30 mg per cup
Tea, white	10–15 mg per cup
Cocoa	5–40 mg per cup
Milk chocolate	6 mg per oz
Baking chocolate	35 mg per oz
Coca-Cola, Classic	46 mg per 12 oz
Anacin, Bromo-Seltzer, Midol	32 mg per pill
Excedrin, Extra Strength	65 mg per pill
Dexatrim, Dietac, Vivarin	200 mg per pill
Dristan	16 mg per pill
No-Doz	100 mg per pill

caffeine. When the brown aqueous solution is subsequently extracted with dichloromethane, caffeine primarily dissolves in the organic solvent. Evaporation of the solvent leaves crude caffeine, which on sublimation yields a relatively pure product. When the concentrated tea solution is extracted with dichloromethane, emulsions can form very easily. There are substances in tea that cause small droplets of the organic layer to remain suspended in the aqueous layer. This emulsion formation results from vigorous shaking. To avoid this problem, it might seem that one could boil the tea leaves with dichloromethane first and then extract the caffeine from the dichloromethane solution with water. In fact, this does not work. Boiling 25 g of tea leaves with 50 mL of dichloromethane gives only 0.05 g of residue after evaporation of the solvent. Subsequent extractions yield even less material. Hot water causes the tea leaves to swell and is obviously a far more efficient extraction solvent. An attempt to sublime caffeine directly from tea leaves is also unsuccessful.

Microscale Procedure

In a 30-mL beaker, place 15 mL of water, 2 g of sodium carbonate, and a wooden boiling stick. Bring the water to a boil on the sand bath, remove the boiling stick, and brew a very concentrated tea solution by immersing a tea bag (2.4 g tea) in the very hot water for 5 minutes. After the tea bag cools enough to handle, and being careful not to break the bag, squeeze as much water from the bag as possible. Again, bring the water to a boil and add a new tea bag to the hot solution. After 5 minutes, remove the tea bag and squeeze out as much water as possible. This can be done easily on a Hirsch funnel. Rinse the bag with a few mL of very hot water, but be sure the total volume of aqueous extract does not exceed 12 mL. Pour the extract into a 15-mL centrifuge tube and cool the solution in ice to below 40°C (the boiling point of dichloromethane).

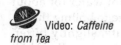
Video: *Caffeine from Tea*

Using three 2-mL portions of dichloromethane, extract the caffeine from the tea. Cork the tube and use a gentle rocking motion to carry out the extraction. Vigorous shaking will produce an intractable emulsion, whereas extremely gentle mixing will fail to extract the caffeine. If you have ready access to a centrifuge, the shaking can be very vigorous because any emulsions formed can be broken fairly well by centrifugation for about 90 seconds. After each extraction, remove the lower organic layer into a reaction tube, leaving any emulsion layer behind. Dry the combined extracts over anhydrous calcium chloride pellets for 5–10 minutes in an Erlenmeyer flask. Add the drying agent in portions with shaking until it no longer clumps together. Transfer the dry solution to a tared 25-mL filter flask, wash the drying agent twice with 2-mL portions of dichloromethane, and evaporate the contents of the flask to dryness (*see* Fig. 7.9 on page 140). The residue will be crude caffeine (determine its weight), which is to be purified by sublimation.

Fit the filter flask with a Pluro stopper or No. 2 neoprene adapter through which is thrust a 15-mL centrifuge tube. Put a pipette bulb on the side arm. Clamp the flask with a large three-prong clamp, fill the centrifuge tube with ice and water, and heat the flask on a hot sand bath (*see* Fig. 7.15 on page 153). Caffeine is reported to sublime at about 170°C. Tilt the filter flask and rotate it in a hot sand bath to drive more caffeine onto the centrifuge tube. Use a heat gun to heat the upper walls of the filter flask. When sublimation ceases, remove the ice water from the centrifuge tube and allow the flask to cool somewhat before removing the centrifuge tube. Scrape the caffeine onto a tared weighing paper, weigh and, using a plastic funnel, transfer it to a small vial or a plastic bag. At the discretion of your instructor, determine the melting point with a sealed capillary. The melting point of caffeine is 238°C. Using the centrifugation technique to separate the extracts, about 30 mg of crude caffeine can be obtained. This will give you 10–15 mg of sublimed material, depending on the caffeine content of the particular tea being used. The isolated caffeine can be used to prepare caffeine salicylate (experiment 9).

Cleaning Up. Discard the tea bags in the nonhazardous solid waste container. Allow the solvent to evaporate from the drying agent and discard in the same container. If local regulations do not allow for the evaporation of solvents in a hood, dispose of the wet sodium sulfate in a special waste container. Place any unused and unrecovered dichloromethane in the chlorinated organic compounds waste container. The apparatus can be cleaned with soap and hot water. Caffeine can be flushed down the drain because it is biodegradable.

 Macroscale Procedure

To an Erlenmeyer flask containing 25 g of tea leaves (or 10 tea bags) and 20 g of sodium carbonate, add 225 mL of vigorously boiling water. Allow the mixture to stand for 7 minutes and then decant into another Erlenmeyer flask. To the hot tea leaves, add another 50 mL of hot water and then immediately decant and combine with the first extract. Very little, if any, additional caffeine is extracted by boiling the tea leaves for any length of time, so it is not necessary to do this. Decantation works nearly as well as vacuum filtration and is much faster.

Cool the aqueous solution to near room temperature and extract it twice with 30-mL portions of dichloromethane. Do not shake the separatory funnel so vigorously as to cause emulsion formation, bearing in mind that if it is not shaken vigorously enough the caffeine will not be extracted into the organic layer. Use a gentle rocking motion of the separatory funnel. Drain off the dichloromethane layer on

CAUTION: Do not breathe the vapors of dichloromethane and, if possible, work with this solvent in the hood.

Balance the centrifuge tubes.

CAUTION: Carry out work with dichloromethane in the hood.

the first extraction; include the emulsion layer on the second extraction. Dry the combined dichloromethane solutions and any emulsion layer with anhydrous calcium chloride pellets. Add sufficient drying agent until it no longer clumps together on the bottom of the flask. Carefully decant or filter the dichloromethane solution into a tared Erlenmeyer or distilling flask. Silicone-impregnated filter paper allows dichloromethane to pass but retains water. Wash the drying agent with a further portion of solvent and evaporate or distill the solvent. A wood applicator stick is better than a boiling chip to promote smooth boiling because it is easily removed once the solvent is gone. The residue of greenish-white crystalline caffeine should weigh about 0.25 g.

Recrystallization of Caffeine

To recrystallize the caffeine, dissolve it in 5 mL of hot acetone, transfer it with a Pasteur pipette to a small Erlenmeyer flask and, while it is hot, add hexanes to the solution until a faint cloudiness appears. Set the flask aside and allow it to cool slowly to room temperature. This mixed-solvent method of recrystallization depends on the fact that caffeine is far more soluble in acetone than hexanes, so a combination of the two solvents can be found where the solution is saturated in caffeine and will appear cloudy as the caffeine starts to precipitate out of the solution. Cool the solution containing the crystals and remove them by vacuum filtration, employing a Hirsch funnel or a very small Büchner funnel. Use a few drops of hexanes to transfer and wash the crystals. If you wish to obtain a second crop of crystals, collect the filtrate in a test tube, concentrate it to the cloud point using an aspirator tube (*see* Fig. 7.11 on page 149), and repeat the recrystallization process.

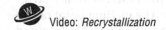
Video: *Recrystallization*

Cleaning Up. The filtrate can be diluted with water and washed down the drain. Any dichloromethane collected goes into the halogenated organic waste container. After the solvent is allowed to evaporate from the drying agent in the hood, the drying agent can be placed in the nonhazardous solid waste container; otherwise it goes in the hazardous waste container. If local regulations do not allow for the evaporation of solvents in a hood, dispose of the wet sodium sulfate in a special waste container. The tea leaves go in the nonhazardous solid waste container.

7. Extraction of Caffeine from Cola Syrup

Coca-Cola was originally flavored with extracts from the leaves of the coca plant and the kola nut. Coca is grown in northern South America; the Indians of Peru and Bolivia have for centuries chewed the leaves to relieve the pangs of hunger and sensitivity to high mountain cold. The cocaine from the leaves causes local anesthesia of the stomach. It has limited use as a local anesthetic for surgery on the eye, nose, and throat. Unfortunately, it is now a widely abused and illicit drug. Kola nuts contain about 3% caffeine as well as a number of other alkaloids. The kola tree is in the same family as the cacao tree from which cocoa and chocolate are obtained. Modern cola drinks do not contain cocaine; however, Coca-Cola contains 46 mg of caffeine per 12-oz serving. The acidic taste of many soft drinks comes from citric, tartaric, phosphoric, and benzoic acids.

Automatic soft drink dispensing machines mix a syrup with carbonated water. In the following experiment, caffeine is extracted from concentrated cola syrup.

Caffeine
mp 238°C

Cocaine

Microscale Procedure

Add 1 mL of concentrated ammonium hydroxide to a mixture of 5 mL of commercial cola syrup and 5 mL of water in a 15-mL centrifuge tube. Add 1 mL of dichloromethane and tip the tube gently back and forth for 5 minutes. Do not shake the mixture as in a normal extraction because an emulsion will form, and the layers will not separate. After the layers have separated as much as possible, remove the clear lower layer, leaving the emulsion behind. Using 1.5 mL of dichloromethane, repeat the extraction in the same way two more times. At the final separation, include the emulsion layer with the dichloromethane. If a centrifuge is available, the mixture can be shaken vigorously, and the emulsion broken by centrifugation for 90 seconds. Combine the extracts in a reaction tube and dry the solution with anhydrous calcium chloride pellets. Add the drying agent with shaking until it no longer clumps together. After 5–10 minutes, remove the solution with a Pasteur pipette and place it in a tared filter flask. Wash off the drying agent with more dichloromethane and evaporate the mixture to dryness. Determine the crude weight of caffeine; then sublime it as described in the preceding experiment.

Macroscale Procedure

Add 10 mL of concentrated ammonium hydroxide to a mixture of 50 mL of commercial cola syrup and 50 mL of water. Place the mixture in a separatory funnel, add 50 mL of dichloromethane, and swirl the mixture and tip the funnel back and forth for at least 5 minutes. Do not shake the solutions together as in a normal extraction because an emulsion will form, and the layers will not separate. An emulsion is made up of droplets of one phase suspended in the other. (Milk is an emulsion.) Separate the layers. Repeat the extraction with a second 50-mL portion of dichloromethane. From your knowledge of the density of dichloromethane and water, you should be able to predict which is the top layer and which is the bottom layer. If in doubt, add a few drops of each layer to water. The aqueous layer will be soluble in the water; the organic layer will not.

Combine the dichloromethane extracts and any emulsion that has formed in a 125-mL Erlenmeyer flask; then add anhydrous calcium chloride pellets to remove water from the solution. Add the drying agent until it no longer clumps together at the bottom of the flask, but swirls freely in solution. Swirl the flask with the drying agent from time to time over a 10-minute period. Carefully decant (pour off) the dichloromethane or remove it by filtration through a fluted filter paper, add about 5 mL more solvent to the drying agent to wash it, and decant this also. Combine the dried dichloromethane solutions in a tared flask and remove the dichloromethane by distillation or evaporation on a steam or sand bath. Remember to add a wood applicator stick to the solution to promote even boiling. Determine the weight of the crude product.

CAUTION: Do not breathe the vapor of dichloromethane. Work with this solvent in the hood.

Chlorinated solvents are toxic, insoluble in water, and expensive and should never be poured down the drain.

Recrystallization of Caffeine

To recrystallize the caffeine, dissolve it in 5 mL of hot acetone, transfer it with a Pasteur pipette to a small Erlenmeyer flask, and, while it is hot, add hexanes to the solution until a faint cloudiness appears. Set the flask aside and allow it to cool slowly to room temperature. This mixed-solvent method of recrystallization depends on the fact that caffeine is far more soluble in acetone than hexanes, so a combination of the two solvents can be found where the solution is saturated in caffeine (the cloud point). Cool the solution containing the crystals and remove them by vacuum filtration, employing a Hirsch funnel or a very small Büchner funnel. Use a few drops of hexanes to transfer and wash the crystals. If you wish to obtain a second crop of crystals, collect the filtrate in a test tube, concentrate it to the cloud point using an aspirator tube (*see* Fig. 7.11 on page 149), and repeat the recrystallization process.

Cleaning Up. Combine all aqueous filtrates and solutions, neutralize them, and flush the resulting solution down the drain. Used dichloromethane should be placed in the halogenated waste container, and the drying agent, once the solvent has evaporated from it, can be placed in the nonhazardous solid waste container. If local regulations do not allow for the evaporation of solvents in a hood, dispose of the wet sodium sulfate in a special waste container. The hexanes-acetone filtrates should be placed in the organic solvents waste container.

Sublimation of Caffeine. Sublimation is a fast and easy way to purify caffeine. Using the apparatus depicted in Figure 7.15 (on page 153), sublime the crude caffeine at atmospheric pressure following the procedure in part 3 of Chapter 6.

8. Isolation of Caffeine from Instant Coffee

Instant coffee, according to manufacturers, contains between 55 mg and 62 mg of caffeine per 6-oz cup, and a cup is presumably made from a teaspoon of the powder, which weighs 1.3 g; so 2 g of the powder should contain 85–95 mg of caffeine. Unlike tea, however, coffee contains other compounds that are soluble in dichloromethane, so obtaining pure caffeine from coffee is not easy. The objective of this experiment is to extract instant coffee with dichloromethane (the easy part), and then to try to devise a procedure for obtaining pure caffeine from the extract.

Photo: *Extraction Procedure*

From TLC analysis (*see* Chapter 8), you may deduce that certain impurities have a high R_f value in hydrocarbons (in which caffeine is insoluble). Consult reference books (see especially the *Merck Index*[2]) to determine the solubility (and lack of solubility) of caffeine in various solvents. You might try trituration (grinding the crude solid with a solvent) to dissolve impurities preferentially. Column chromatography is another possible means of purifying the product. Or you might convert all of it to the salicylate and then regenerate the caffeine from the salicylate. Experiment! Or you can simply use the following procedure.

[2]O'Neill, M. J.; Smith, A.; Heckelman, P. E.; Budavari, S., eds. *The Merck Index*, 13th ed.; Merck and Co., Inc.: Rahway, NJ, 2001.

Procedure

> **IN THIS EXPERIMENT, a very concentrated aqueous solution of coffee is prepared and shaken vigorously with an organic solvent to make an intractable emulsion that can be broken (separated into two layers) by centrifugation. Caffeine is isolated by recrystallization.**

In a 10-mL Erlenmeyer flask, place 2 g of sodium carbonate and 2 g of instant coffee powder. Add 9 mL of boiling water, stir the mixture well, bring it to a boil again with stirring, cool it to room temperature, and then pour it into a 15-mL plastic centrifuge tube fitted with a screw cap. Add 2 mL of dichloromethane, cap the tube, shake it vigorously for 60 seconds; then centrifuge it at high speed for 90 seconds. Remove the clear yellow dichloromethane layer and place it in a 10-mL Erlenmeyer flask. Repeat this process twice more. To the combined extracts, add anhydrous calcium chloride pellets until they no longer clump together and allow the solution to dry for a few minutes; then transfer it to a tared 25-mL filter flask and wash the drying agent with more solvent. Remove the solvent as was done in the tea extraction experiment and determine the weight of the crude caffeine. You should obtain about 60 mg of crude product. Sublimation of this orange powder gives an impure orange sublimate that smells strongly of coffee, so sublimation is not a good way to purify this material.

Caffeine has no odor.

Dissolve a very small quantity of the product in a drop of dichloromethane and perform a TLC analysis of the crude material. Dissolve the remainder of the material in 1 mL of boiling 95% ethanol; then dilute the mixture with 1 mL of *t*-butyl methyl ether, heat to boiling, and allow to cool slowly to room temperature. Long, needlelike crystals should form in the orange solution. Alternatively, recrystallize the product from a 1:1 mixture of hexanes and 2-propanol, using about 2 mL. Cool the mixture in ice for at least 10 minutes and then collect the product on a Hirsch funnel. Complete the transfer with the filtrate and then wash the crystals twice with cold 50/50 ethanol/*t*-butyl methyl ether. The yield of white fluffy needles of caffeine should be more than 30 mg.

Video: *Recrystallization*

Cleaning Up. Allow the solvent to evaporate from the drying agent and discard it in the nonhazardous waste container. If local regulations do not allow for the evaporation of solvents in a hood, dispose of the wet sodium sulfate in a special waste container. Place any unused and unrecovered dichloromethane in the chlorinated organic solvents waste container.

9. Caffeine Salicylate

One way to confirm the identity of an organic compound is to prepare a derivative of it. Caffeine melts and sublimes at 238°C. It is an organic base and can therefore accept a proton from an acid to form a salt. The salt formed when caffeine combines with hydrochloric acid, like many amine salts, does not have a sharp melting point; it merely decomposes when heated. But the salt formed from salicylic acid, even though ionic, has a sharp melting point and can thus be used to help characterize caffeine. Figure 7.17 is the ^{1}H NMR spectrum of caffeine.

Preparation of a derivative of caffeine.

Caffeine   **Salicylic acid**   **Caffeine salicylate**

Procedure

CAUTION: Petroleum ether is very flammable. Extinguish all flames.

Recrystallization from mixed solvents.

Video: *Filtration of Crystals Using the Pasteur Pipette*; Photo: *Drying Crystals Under Vacuum*

The quantities given can be multiplied by 5 or 10, if necessary. To 10 mg of sublimed caffeine in a tared reaction tube, add 7.5 mg of salicylic acid and 0.5 mL of dichloromethane. Heat the mixture to boiling and add petroleum ether (a poor solvent for the product) dropwise until the mixture just turns cloudy, indicating that the solution is saturated. If too much petroleum ether is added, then clarify it by adding a very small quantity of dichloromethane. Insulate the tube to allow it to cool slowly to room temperature; then cool it in ice. The needlelike crystals are isolated by removing the solvent with a Pasteur pipette while the reaction tube is in the ice bath. Evaporate the last traces of solvent under vacuum (Fig. 7.18) and determine the weight of the derivative and its melting point. Caffeine salicylate is reported to melt at 137°C.

Cleaning Up. Place the filtrate in the halogenated organic solvents container.

FIG. 7.17
The ¹H NMR spectrum of caffeine (250 MHz).

FIG. 7.18
The drying of crystals under vacuum in beaker of warm water.

To aspirator

Glass tube

Thermometer adapter

Reaction tube

Beaker of warm water

Crystals to be dried

PPM (δ)

QUESTIONS

1. Suppose a reaction mixture, when diluted with water, afforded 300 mL of an aqueous solution of 30 g of the reaction product malononitrile [$CH_2(CN)_2$], which is to be isolated by extraction with ether. The solubility of malononitrile in ether at room temperature is 20.0 g/100 mL, and in water is 13.3 g/100 mL. What weight of malononitrile would be recovered by extraction with (a) three 100-mL portions of ether and (b) one 300-mL portion of ether? *Suggestion:* For each extraction, let x equal the weight extracted into the ether layer. In part (a), the concentration in the ether layer is $x/100$ and in the water layer is $(30 - x)/300$; the ratio of these quantities is equal to $k = 20/13.3$.

2. Why is it necessary to remove the stopper from a separatory funnel when liquid is being drained from it through the stopcock?

3. The pK_a of *p*-nitrophenol is 7.15. Would you expect this to dissolve in a sodium bicarbonate solution? The pK_a of 2,5-dinitrophenol is 5.15. Will it dissolve in bicarbonate solution?

4. The distribution coefficient, k = concentration in hexanes ÷ concentration in water, between hexanes and water for solute A is 7.5. What weight of A would be removed from a solution of 10 g of A in 100 mL of water by a single extraction with 100 mL of hexanes? What weight of A would be removed by four successive extractions with 25-mL portions of hexanes? How much hexanes would be required to remove 98.5% of A in a single extraction?

5. In experiment 1, how many moles of benzoic acid are present? How many moles of sodium bicarbonate are contained in 1 mL of a 10% aqueous solution? (A 10% solution has 1 g of solute in 9 mL of solvent.) Is the amount of sodium bicarbonate sufficient to react with all of the benzoic acid?

6. To isolate benzoic acid from a bicarbonate solution, it is acidified with concentrated hydrochloric acid, as in experiment 1. What volume of acid is needed to neutralize the bicarbonate? The concentration of hydrochloric acid is expressed in various ways on the inside back cover of this laboratory manual.

7. How many moles of 4-*t*-butylphenol are in the mixture to be separated in experiment 1? How many moles of sodium hydroxide are contained in 1 mL of 5% sodium hydroxide solution? (Assume the density of the solution is 1.0.) What volume of concentrated hydrochloric acid is needed to neutralize this amount of sodium hydroxide solution?

8. Draw a flow sheet to show how you would separate the components of a mixture containing an acid substance, toluic acid, a basic substance, *p*-bromoaniline, and anthracene, a neutral substance.

9. Write equations showing how caffeine could be extracted from an organic solvent and subsequently isolated.

10. Write equations showing how acetaminophen might be extracted from an organic solvent such as an ether, if it were soluble.

11. Write detailed equations showing the mechanism by which aspirin is hydrolyzed in boiling, slightly acidic water.

See *Web Links*

8 CHAPTER

Thin-Layer Chromatography: Analyzing Analgesics and Isolating Lycopene from Tomato Paste

PRELAB EXERCISE: Based on the number and polarity of the functional groups in aspirin, acetaminophen, ibuprofen, and caffeine, whose structures are shown on page 184, predict which of these four compounds has the highest R_f value and which has the lowest.

Chromatography is the separation of two or more compounds or ions caused by their molecular interactions with two phases—one moving and one stationary. These two phases can be a solid and a liquid, a liquid and a liquid, a gas and a solid, or a gas and a liquid. You very likely have seen chromatography carried out on paper towels or coffee filters, which showed various colors denoting the separation of inks and food dyes. In the laboratory, cellulose paper is the stationary or solid phase, and a propanol-water mixture is the mobile or liquid phase. The samples are spotted near one edge of the paper, and this edge is dipped into the liquid phase. The solvent is drawn through the paper by capillary action, and the molecules are separated based on how they interact with the paper. Although there are several different forms of chromatography, the principles are essentially the same.

Thin-layer chromatography (TLC) is a sensitive, fast, simple, and inexpensive analytical technique that you will use repeatedly while carrying out organic experiments. It is a micro technique; as little as 10^{-9} g of material can be detected, although the usual sample size is from 1×10^{-6} g to 1×10^{-8} g. The stationary phase is normally a polar solid adsorbent, and the mobile phase can be a single solvent or a combination of solvents.

TLC requires micrograms of material.

USES OF THIN-LAYER CHROMATOGRAPHY

1. **To determine the number of components in a mixture.** TLC affords a quick and easy method for analyzing such things as a crude reaction mixture, an extract from a plant substance, or the ingredients in a pill. Knowing the

164

number and relative amounts of the components aids in planning further analytical and separation steps.

2. **To determine the identity of two substances.** If two substances spotted on the same TLC plate give spots in identical locations, they *may* be identical. If the spot positions are not the same, the substances cannot be the same. It is possible for two or more closely related but not identical compounds to have the same positions on a TLC plate. Changing the stationary or mobile phase will usually effect their separation.

3. **To monitor the progress of a reaction.** By sampling a reaction at regular intervals, it is possible to watch the reactants disappear and the products appear using TLC. Thus, the optimum time to halt the reaction can be determined, and the effect of changing such variables as temperature, concentrations, and solvents can be followed without having to isolate the product.

4. **To determine the effectiveness of a purification.** The effectiveness of distillation, crystallization, extraction, and other separation and purification methods can be monitored using TLC, with the caveat that a single spot does not guarantee a single substance.

5. **To determine the appropriate conditions for a column chromatographic separation.** In general, TLC is not satisfactory for purifying and isolating macroscopic quantities of material; however, the adsorbents most commonly used for TLC—silica gel and alumina—are also used for column chromatography, which is discussed in Chapter 9. Column chromatography is used to separate and purify up to 1 g of a solid mixture. The correct adsorbent and solvent to use for column chromatography can be rapidly determined by TLC.

6. **To monitor column chromatography.** As column chromatography is carried out, the solvent is collected in a number of small flasks. Unless the desired compound is colored, the various fractions must be analyzed in some way to determine which ones have the desired components of the mixture. TLC is a fast and effective method for doing this.

THE PRINCIPLES OF CHROMATOGRAPHY

To thoroughly understand the process of TLC (and other types of chromatography), we must examine the process at the molecular level. All forms of chromatography involve a dynamic and rapid equilibrium of molecules between the liquid and the stationary phases. For the chromatographic separation of molecules A and B shown in Figure 8.1, there are two states:

1. **Free**—dissolved in the liquid or gaseous mobile phase.
2. **Adsorbed**—sticking to the surface of the solid stationary phase.

Molecules A and B are continuously moving back and forth between the dissolved (free) and adsorbed states, with billions of molecules adsorbing and billions of other molecules desorbing from the solid stationary phase each second. The equilibrium between the free and adsorbed states depends on the relative strength of the attraction of A and B to the liquid phase molecules *versus* the

FIG. 8.1

The mixture of molecules A and B is in a dynamic equilibrium between the free and adsorbed states.

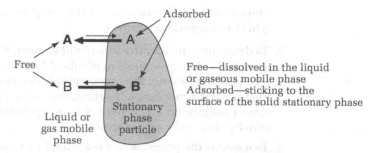

FIG. 8.2

The mixture of molecules A and B is in a dynamic equilibrium between the stationary adsorbent and a *flowing* mobile phase.

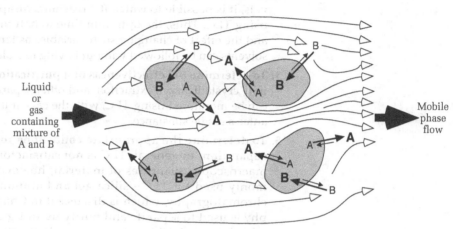

strength of attraction of A and B to the stationary phase structure. As discussed in the introduction to Chapter 3, the strength of these attractive forces depends on the following factors:

- Size, polarity, and hydrogen bonding ability of molecules A and B
- Polarity and hydrogen bonding ability of the stationary phase
- Polarity and hydrogen bonding ability of the mobile phase solvent

Molecules distribute themselves, or *partition*, between the mobile and stationary phases depending on these attractive forces. As implied by the equilibrium arrows in Figure 8.1, the A molecules are less polar and are only weakly attracted to a polar stationary phase, spending most of their time in the mobile phase. In contrast, equilibrium for the more polar B molecules lies in the direction of being adsorbed onto the polar stationary phase. The equilibrium constant *k* (also called the *partition coefficient*) is a measure of the distribution of molecules between the mobile phase and the stationary phase, and is similar to the distribution coefficient for liquid/liquid extraction. This constant changes with structure.

Simply adding a mixture to a combination of a liquid phase and a stationary phase will not separate it into its pure components. For separation to happen, the liquid phase must be mobile and be flowing past the stationary phase, as depicted in Figure 8.2. Because the A molecules spend more time in the mobile phase, they will be carried through the stationary phase and be eluted faster and move farther in a given amount of time. Because the B molecules are adsorbed

FIG. 8.3
A chromatographic separation. Over time, the mobile phase carries the less weakly adsorbed A molecules ahead of the more strongly adsorbed B molecules.

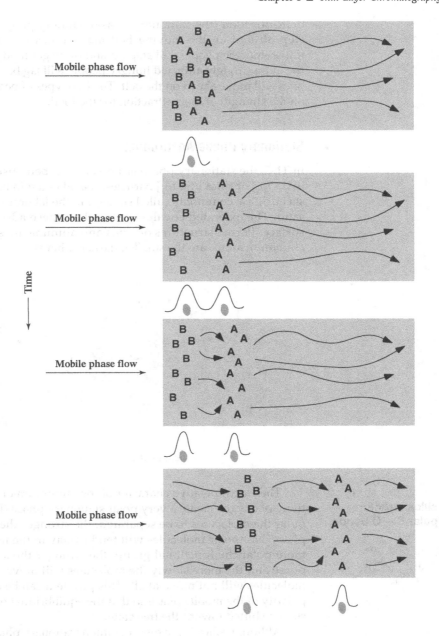

on the stationary phase more than A molecules, the B molecules spend less time in the mobile phase and therefore migrate through the stationary phase more slowly and are eluted later. The B molecules do not migrate as far in the same amount of time. The consequence of this difference is that A is gradually separated from B by moving ahead in the flowing mobile phase as time passes, as shown in Figure 8.3.

A simple analogy may help to illustrate these concepts. Imagine a group of hungry and not-so-hungry people riding a moving sidewalk (the mobile phase in this analogy) that moves beside a long buffet table covered with all sorts of delicious food (the stationary phase). Hungry people, attracted to the food, will step off and on the moving belt many times in order to fill their plates. The not-so-hungry people will step off and on to get food far less often. Consequently, the more strongly attracted hungry people will lag behind, while the not-so-hungry ones will move ahead on the belt. The two types of people are thus separated based on the strength of their attraction for the food.

Stationary Phase Adsorbents

In TLC, the stationary phase is a polar adsorbent, usually finely ground alumina $[(Al_2O_3)_x]$ or silica $[(SiO_2)_x]$ particles, coated as a thin layer on a glass slide or plastic sheet. Silica, commonly called *silica gel* in the laboratory, is simply very pure white sand. The extended covalent network of these adsorbents creates a very polar surface. Partial structures of silica and alumina are shown below. The silicon or aluminum atoms are the smaller, darker spheres:

Silica, $(SiO_2)_x$ Alumina, $(Al_2O_3)_x$

FIG. 8.4
A partial silica structure showing polar Si—O bonds.

The electropositive character of the aluminum or silicon and the electronegativity of oxygen create a very polar stationary phase (Fig. 8.4). Therefore, the more polar the molecules to be separated, the stronger the attraction to the stationary phase. Nonpolar molecules will tend to stay in the mobile phase. In general, the more polar the functional group, the stronger the adsorption on the stationary phase and the more slowly the molecules will move. In an extreme situation, the molecules will not move at all. This problem can be overcome by increasing the polarity of the mobile phase so that the equilibrium between the free and adsorbed state is shifted toward the free state.

Although silica is the most common stationary phase used for TLC, many other types are used, ranging from paper to charcoal, nonpolar to polar, and reverse phase to normal phase. Several different types of stationary phases are listed according to polarity in Table 8.1.

Silica gel and alumina are commonly used in column chromatography for the purification of macroscopic quantities of material (*see* Chapter 9). Of the two, alumina, when anhydrous, is the more active; that is, it will adsorb substances more strongly. It is thus the adsorbent of choice for the separation of relatively nonpolar substrates, such as hydrocarbons, alkyl halides, ethers, aldehydes, and ketones. To separate more polar substrates, such as alcohols, carboxylic acids, and amines, the less active adsorbent, silica gel, is often used.

TABLE 8.1 *Common Stationary Phases Listed by Increasing Polarity*

Polydimethyl siloxane*

Methyl- or Phenylsiloxane*

Cyanopropyl siloxane*

Carbowax [poly(ethyleneglycol)]*

Reverse phase (hydrocarbon-coated silica, e.g., C_{18})

Paper

Cellulose

Starch

Calcium sulfate

Silica (silica gel)

Florisil (magnesium silicate)

Magnesium oxide

Alumina (aluminum oxide; acidic, basic, or neutral)

Activated carbon (charcoal or Norit pellets)

Increasing polarity

*Stationary phase for gas chromatography

Molecular Polarity and Elution Sequence

Elution sequence is the order in which the components of a mixture move during chromatography.

Ethyl acetoacetate

Ethyl pentanoate

Assuming we are using a polar adsorbent, how can we determine how rapidly the compounds in our particular mixture move, that is, their elution sequence? Because the more polar compounds will adsorb more strongly to the polar stationary phase they will move the slowest and the shortest distance on a TLC plate. Non-polar compounds will move rapidly, and will elute first or move the greatest distance on the TLC plate. Table 8.2 lists several common compound classes according to how they move or elute on silica or alumina.

You should be able to look at a molecular structure, identify its functional group(s), and easily determine whether it is more or less polar than another structure with different functional groups. Note that the polarity of a molecule increases as the number of functional groups in that molecule increases. Thus, ethyl acetoacetate, with both ketone and ester groups, is more polar than ethyl pentanoate, which has only an ester group. However, it should be noted that chromatography is not an exact science. The rules discussed here can be used to help predict the order of elution; however, only performing an experiment will give definitive answers.

Mobile Phase Solvent Polarity

The key to a successful chromatographic separation is the mobile phase. You normally use silica gel or alumina as the stationary phase. In extreme situations, very polar substances chromatographed on alumina will not migrate very far from the starting point (i.e., give low R_f values), and nonpolar compounds chromatographed on silica gel will travel with the solvent front (i.e., give high R_f values). These extremes of behavior are markedly affected, however, by the solvents used to carry out the chromatography. A polar solvent will carry along with it polar substrates,

TABLE 8.2 *Elution Order for Some Common Functional Groups with a Silica or Alumina Stationary Phase*

Highest/fastest (elute with nonpolar mobile phase)

Alkane hydrocarbons

Alkyl halides (halocarbons)

Alkenes (olefins)

Dienes

Aromatic hydrocarbons

Ethers

Esters

Ketones

Aldehydes

Amines

Alcohols

Phenols

Carboxylic acids

Sulfonic acids

Lowest/slowest (need polar mobile phase to elute)

(← Increasing polarity of functional group →)

and nonpolar solvents will do the same with nonpolar compounds—another example of the generalization "like dissolves like." You cannot change the polarities of the compounds in your mixture, but by using different solvents, either alone or as mixtures, you can adjust the polarity of the mobile phase and affect the equilibria between the free and adsorbed states. Changing the polarity of the mobile phase can optimize the chromatographic separation of mixtures of compounds with a wide variety of polarities.

Table 8.3 lists, according to increasing polarity, some solvents that are commonly used for both TLC and column chromatography. Because the polarities of benzene, carbon tetrachloride, or chloroform can be matched by other, less toxic solvents, these three solvents are seldom used. Carbon tetrachloride and chloroform are suspected carcinogens and benzene is known to be a carcinogen when exposure is prolonged. In general, the solvents for TLC and column chromatography are characterized by having low boiling points that allow them to be easily evaporated and low viscosities that allow them to migrate rapidly. A solvent more polar than methanol is seldom needed. Often, two solvents are used in a mixture of varying proportions; the polarity of the mixture is a weighted average of the two. Hexane and ether mixtures are often employed.

> **Avoid using benzene, carbon tetrachloride, and chloroform. Benzene is known to be a carcinogen when exposure is prolonged; the others are suspected carcinogens.**

Finding a good solvent system is usually the most critical aspect of TLC. If the mobile phase has not been previously determined, start with a nonpolar solvent such as hexanes and observe the separation. If the mixture's components do not move very far, try adding a polar solvent such as ether or ethyl acetate to the hexanes. Compare the separation to the previous plate. In most cases, a combination of two solvents is the best choice. If the spots stay at the bottom of the plate, add more of the polar solvent. If they run with the solvent front (move to the top), increase the proportion of the nonpolar solvent. Unfortunately, some trial and error is

TABLE 8.3 *Common Mobile Phases Listed by Increasing Polarity*

Increasing polarity ↓

Helium
Nitrogen
Pentanes (petroleum ether)
Hexanes (ligroin)
Cyclohexane
Carbon tetrachloride*
Toluene
Chloroform*
Dichloromethane (methylene chloride)
t-Butyl methyl ether
Diethyl ether
Ethyl acetate
Acetone
2-Propanol
Pyridine
Ethanol
Methanol
Water
Acetic acid

*Suspected carcinogens

usually involved in determining which solvent system is the best. There is a large amount of literature on the solvents and adsorbents used in the separation of a wide variety of substances.

THE SIX STEPS OF THIN-LAYER CHROMATOGRAPHY

The process of thin-layer chromatography (TLC) can be broken down into six main steps: (1) preparing the sample; (2) spotting the TLC plate; (3) picking a solvent; (4) developing the TLC plate; (5) visualizing the TLC plate; (6) calculating R_f values. A detailed description of each of these steps is given in the following sections.

Step 1. Preparing the Sample

Too much sample is a frequent problem. Use a 1% solution of the mixture. Apply very small spots.

You need to dissolve only a few milligrams of material (a 1% solution) because one can detect a few micrograms of compound on a TLC plate. Choose a volatile solvent such as diethyl ether. Even if the material is only partially soluble, you will normally be able to observe the compound because only low concentrations are needed. If the prepared sample is too concentrated, streaking can occur on the plate. Streaking may lead to the overlap of two or more compounds, thus skewing results. See Figure 8.5 for an example of a streaking spot.

FIG. 8.5
A streaking spot.

FIG. 8.7
(a) A spotting capillary.
(b) Soften the glass by heating at the base of the flame as shown and then stretch to a fine capillary.

(a)

(b)

⚠ **CAUTION:** Bunsen burners should be used only in lab areas that are far from flammable organic solvents.

FIG. 8.6
A marked and spotted TLC plate.

Aspirin spot

Acetaminophen spot

Caffeine spot

Ibuprofen spot

Depth of solvent

Pencil line 1 cm from bottom edge

Step 2. Spotting the TLC Plate

The use of commercially available TLC plates, poly(ethylene terephthalate) (Mylar) sheets coated with silica gel using polyacrylic acid as a binder, is highly recommended; these fluoresce under ultraviolet (UV) light.[1] The TLC plates must be handled gently and by the edge, or the 100-mm-thick coating of silica gel can be easily scratched off or contamination of the surface can occur. With a pencil, lightly draw a faint line 1 cm from the end and then three or four short hash marks to guide spotting. Lightly write identifying letters at the top of the plate to keep track of the placement of the compound spots (Fig. 8.6). Note that a pencil is always used to mark TLC plates because the graphite (carbon) is inert. If ink is used to mark the plate, it will chromatograph just as any other organic compound, interfering with the samples and giving flawed results.

Once the sample is prepared, a spotting capillary must be used to add the sample to the plate. Spotting capillaries can be made by drawing out open-end melting point tubes or Pasteur pipette stems in a burner flame (Fig. 8.7).[2] The bore of these capillaries should be so small that once a liquid is drawn into them, it will not flow out to form a drop. Practice spotting just pure solvent onto an unmarked TLC plate. Dip the capillary into the solvent and let a 2–3 cm column of solvent flow into it by capillary action. Do this by holding the capillary vertically over the *coated* side of the plate, and lower the pipette until the tip just touches the adsorbent. Only then will liquid flow onto the plate; quickly withdraw the capillary when the spot is about 1 mm in diameter. The center of the letter *o* on this page is more than 1 mm in diameter. The solvent will evaporate quickly, leaving your mixture behind on the plate. You may have to spot the plate a couple of times in the same place to ensure that sufficient material is present; do not spot too much sample because this will lead to a poor separation. It is extremely important that the spots be as small as possible. If the spot is large, then two or more spots of a sample may overlap on the TLC plate, thus causing erroneous conclusions about the separation and/or the sample's purity or content. Practice placing spots a number of times until you develop good spotting technique. You are now ready to spot the solutions of mixtures as described in Experiments 1 and 2.

[1]Whatman flexible plates for TLC, cat. no. 4410 222 (Fisher cat. no. 05-713-162); cut with scissors to 1" × 3". Unlike student-prepared plates, these coated sheets give very consistent results. A supply of these plates makes it a simple matter to examine most of the reactions in this book for completeness of reaction, purity of product, and side reactions.
[2]Three-inch pieces of old and unusable gas chromatography capillary columns are also effective spotting capillaries.

FIG. 8.8
A fast method for determining the correct solvent for TLC. See the text for the procedure.

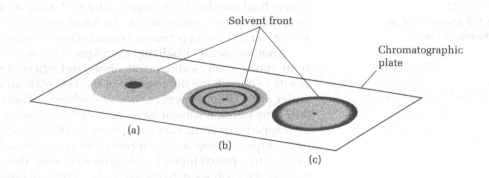

Step 3. Picking a Solvent

One of the most crucial parts of a successful TLC separation is choosing the appropriate mobile phase; see the section "Mobile Phase Polarity" above. Make some spots of the mixture to be separated on a test TLC plate, either a new or a used one. Touch each spot with a different solvent held in a capillary. Referring to Fig. 8.8, note that the mixture did not travel away from the point of origin in Fig. 8.8a, and in Fig. 8.8b, two concentric rings are seen between the origin and the solvent front. This is how a good solvent behaves. In Fig. 8.12c, the mixture traveled with the solvent front.

Step 4. Developing the Plate

Once the dilute solution of the mixture has been spotted on the plate, the next step is the actual chromatographic separation, called *plate development*.

Once a mobile phase has been chosen, the marked and spotted TLC plate is inserted into a 4-oz wide-mouth bottle (Fig. 8.9) or beaker (Fig. 8.10) containing 4 mL of the mobile phase, either a solvent or a solvent mixture. The bottle is lined with filter paper that is wet with solvent to saturate the atmosphere within the container. Use tweezers to place the plate in the development chamber; oils from your fingers can sometimes smear or ruin a TLC plate. Also make sure that the origin spots are not below the solvent level in the chamber. If the spots are submerged in the solvent, they are washed off the plate and lost. The top of the container is put in place and the time noted. (If a beaker is used, the beaker is to be covered with aluminum foil.) The solvent travels up the thin layer by capillary action. If the substance is a pure colored compound, one soon sees a spot traveling either along with the solvent front or, more commonly, at some distance behind the solvent front. Once the solvent has run within a centimeter of the top of the plate, remove the plate with tweezers. Immediately, before the solvent evaporates, use a pencil to draw a line across the plate where the solvent front can be seen. The proper location of this solvent front line is needed for R_f calculations.

Step 5. Visualizing the Results

If you are fortunate enough to be separating organic molecules that are colored, such as dyes, inks, or indicators, then visualizing the separated spots is easy. However, because most organic compounds are colorless, this is rarely the case.

For most compounds, a UV light works well for observing the separated spots. TLC plates normally contain a fluorescent indicator that makes them glow green under UV light of wavelength 254 nm. Compounds that adsorb UV light at this wavelength will quench the green fluorescence, yielding dark purple or bluish spots on the plate.

FIG. 8.9
Using a wide-mouth bottle to develop a TLC plate.

FIG. 8.10
Using a foil-covered beaker to develop a TLC plate.

FIG. 8.11
A UV lamp used to visualize spots.

⚠
Never look into a UV lamp.

Simply hold the plate by its edges under a UV lamp as shown in Figure 8.11, and the compound spots become visible to the naked eye. Lightly circle the spots with a pencil so that you will have a permanent record of their location for later calculations.

Another useful visualizing technique is to use an iodine (I_2) chamber. Certain compounds, such as alkanes, alcohols, and ethers, do not absorb UV light sufficiently to quench the fluorescence of the TLC plate and therefore will not show up under a UV lamp. However, they will adsorb iodine vapors and can be detected (after any residual solvent has evaporated) by placing the plate for a few minutes in a capped 4-oz bottle containing some crystals of iodine. Iodine vapor is adsorbed by the organic compound to form brown spots. These brown spots should be outlined with a pencil immediately after removing the plate from the iodine bottle because they will soon disappear as the iodine sublimes away; a brief return to the iodine chamber will regenerate the spots. Using both the UV lamp and iodine vapor visualization methods will ensure the location of all spots on the TLC plate.

Many specialized spray reagents, also known as TLC stains, have also been developed to give specific colors for certain types of compounds. A detailed listing of different TLC stains that help visualize certain compounds with specific functional groups can be found in *The Chemist's Companion: A Handbook of Practical Data, Techniques, and References*,[3] a valuable classic reference book that contains copious amounts of helpful information.

Step 6. Calculating R_f Values

R_f is the ratio of the distance the spot travels from the origin to the distance the solvent travels.

In addition to qualitative results, TLC can also provide a chromatographic parameter known as an R_f value. The R_f value is the retention factor expressed as a decimal fraction. The R_f value is the ratio of the distance the spot travels from the point of origin to the distance the solvent travels. The R_f value can be calculated as follows:

$$R_f = \frac{\text{distance spot travels}}{\text{distance solvent travels}}$$

This number should be calculated for each spot observed on a TLC plate. Figure 8.12 shows a diagram of a typical TLC plate and how the distances are

FIG. 8.12
A developed TLC plate with spots visualized and R_f values determined.

Solvent front

$R_f = \dfrac{A}{C}$ for Substance A

Substance B

C

B

Substance A

A

Starting spot, < 1 mm dia.

1 cm

Depth of solvent

[3]Gordon, A. J., Richard A. Ford, The *Chemist's Companion: A Handbook of Practical Data, Techniques, and References*. John Wiley & Sons, Inc.: New York, 1972.

TABLE 8.4 *Chromatography Terms and Their Definitions with Examples*

Chromatography Term	Definition	Examples
Mixture	A collection of different compounds	Aspirin, ibuprofen, caffeine, and fluorene/fluorenone
Stationary phase	A fixed material that can adsorb compounds	Alumina, silica gel, and silicone gum, et al.
Mobile phase	A moving liquid or gas that dissolves compounds and carries them along	Hexane, CH_2Cl_2, and ethyl acetate (TLC and column chromatography) et al.; helium gas (gas chromatography)
Adsorption	The strength of attraction between the compounds and the stationary phase	London forces, hydrogen bonds, and dipole-dipole attractive forces
Separation	A measure of the elution or migration rate of compounds	R_f (TLC); elution volume (column chromatography); retention time (gas chromatography)

measured to calculate the R_f value. The best separations are usually achieved when the R_f values fall between 0.3 and 0.7.

If two spots travel the same distance or have the same R_f value, then it might be concluded that the two components are the same molecule. Just as many organic molecules have the same melting point and color, many can have the same R_f value, so identical R_f values do not necessarily mean identical compounds. For comparisons of R_f values to be valid, TLC plates must be run under the exact same conditions for the stationary phase, mobile phase, and temperature. Even then, additional information such as a mixed melting point or an IR spectrum should be obtained before concluding that two substances are identical.

COMPARISON OF DIFFERENT TYPES OF CHROMATOGRAPHY

Table 8.4 summarizes the terminology used in chromatography and how these apply to different types of chromatography. All of the chromatographic types involve the same principles but vary in the nature of the stationary phase and the mobile phase, and the measure of separation.

EXPERIMENTS

1. ANALGESICS

Analgesics are substances that relieve pain. The most common of these is aspirin, a component of more than 100 nonprescription drugs. In Chapter 41, the history of this most popular drug is discussed. In this experiment, analgesic tablets will be analyzed by TLC to determine which analgesics they contain and whether they contain caffeine, which is often added to counteract the sedative effects of the analgesic.

In addition to aspirin and caffeine, the most common components of the currently used analgesics are acetaminophen and ibuprofen. In addition to one or more of these substances, each tablet contains a binder—often starch, microcrystalline cellulose, or silica gel. And to counteract the acidic properties of aspirin, an inorganic buffering agent is added to some analgesics. An inspection of analgesic labels will reveal that most cold remedies and decongestants contain both aspirin and caffeine in addition to the primary ingredient.

Aspirin
Acetylsalicylic acid

Acetaminophen
4-Acetamidophenol

Ibuprofen
2-(4-Isobutylphenyl)propionic acid

Caffeine

To identify an unknown by TLC, the usual strategy is to run chromatograms of known substances (the standards) and the unknown at the same time. If the unknown has one or more spots that correspond to spots with the same R_f values as the standards, then those substances are probably present.

Proprietary drugs that contain one or more of the common analgesics and sometimes caffeine are sold under some of the following brand names: Bayer Aspirin, Anacin, Datril, Advil, Excedrin, Extra Strength Excedrin, Tylenol, and Vanquish. Note that ibuprofen has a chiral carbon atom. The *S*-(+)-enantiomer is more effective than the other.

Procedure

Before proceeding, practice the TLC spotting technique described earlier. Following that procedure, draw a light pencil line about 1 cm from the end of a chromatographic plate. On this line, spot aspirin, acetaminophen, ibuprofen, and caffeine, which are available as reference standards. Use a separate capillary for each standard (or rinse the capillary carefully before reusing). Make each spot as small as possible, preferably less than 0.5 mm in diameter. Examine the plate under UV light to see that enough of each compound has been applied; if not, add more. On a separate plate, run the unknown and one or more of the standards.

Because of the insoluble binder, not all of the unknown will dissolve.

The unknown sample is prepared by crushing a part of a tablet, adding this powder to a test tube or small vial along with an appropriate amount of ethanol, and then mixing the suspension. Not all of the crushed tablet will dissolve, but enough will go into solution to spot the plate. The binder—starch or silica—will not dissolve. Weigh out only part of the tablet to try to prepare a 1% solution of the unknown. Typically, ibuprofen tablets contain 200 mg of the active ingredient, aspirin tablets contain 325 mg, and acetaminophen tablets contain 500 mg.

To the developing jar or beaker (*see* Fig. 8.9 or Fig. 8.10 on page 173), add 4 mL of the mobile phase, a mixture of 95% ethyl acetate and 5% acetic acid. Insert the spotted TLC plates with tweezers. After the solvent has risen nearly to the top of the plate, remove the plate from the developing chamber, mark the solvent front with a pencil, and allow the solvent to dry. Examine the plate under UV light to see the components as dark spots against a bright green-blue background. Outline the spots with a pencil. The spots can also be visualized by putting the plate in an iodine chamber made by placing a few crystals of iodine in the bottom of a capped 4-oz jar. Calculate the R_f values for the spots and identify the components in the unknown.

Cleaning Up. Solvents should be placed in the organic solvents waste container; dry, used chromatographic plates can be discarded in the nonhazardous solid waste container.

2. PLANT PIGMENTS

The botanist Michael Tswett discovered the technique of chromatography and applied it, as the name implies, to colored plant pigments. The leaves of plants contain, in addition to chlorophyll-a and chlorophyll-b, other pigments that are revealed in the fall when the leaves die and the chlorophyll rapidly decomposes. Among the most abundant of the other pigments are the carotenoids, which include the carotenes and their oxygenated homologs, the xanthophylls. The bright orange beta-carotene is the most important of these because it is transformed in the liver to vitamin A, which is required for night vision.

Chlorophyll-a

β-Carotene ($C_{40}H_{56}$)
mp 183°C, λ_{max}^{hexane} 451 nm

FIG. 8.13

An energy-minimized, space-filling model of lycopene. The molecule is flat, but steric hindrance of the methyl groups causes the molecule to bend into an S shape.

3'-Dehydrolutein (a xanthophyll)

Butter Yellow (carcinogenic)

Lycopene (C$_{40}$H$_{56}$)
MW 536.85
mp 173°C, λ_{max}^{hexane} 475 nm

Lycopene from tomato paste and Gr beta-carotene from strained carrots.

Isoprene

As an interesting variation, try extracting lycopene from commercial ketchup.

Cows eat fresh, green grass that contains carotene, but they do not metabolize the carotene entirely, so it ends up in their milk. Butter made from this milk is therefore yellow. In the winter, the silage that cows eat does not contain carotene because that compound readily undergoes air oxidation, and the butter made at that time is white. For some time, an azo dye called Butter Yellow was added to winter butter to give it the accustomed color, but the dye was found to be a carcinogen. Now winter butter is colored with synthetic carotene, as is all margarine.

Lycopene (Fig. 8.13), the red pigment of the tomato, is a C$_{40}$-carotenoid made up of eight isoprene units. (Gr beta-Carotene, the yellow pigment of the carrot, is an isomer of lycopene in which the double bonds at C$_1$—C$_2$ and C'$_1$—C'$_2$ are replaced by bonds extending from C$_1$ to C$_6$ and from C'$_1$ to C'$_6$ to form rings. The chromophore in each case is a system of 11 *all-trans* conjugated double bonds; the closing of the two rings causes Gr beta-carotene to absorb at shorter wavelengths than lycopene does, shifting its color from red to yellow.

In 1911, Richard Willstätter and Heinrich R. Escher isolated 20 mg of lycopene per kilogram of fresh tomatoes, which contain about 96% water.[4] They then found a more convenient source in commercial tomato paste: the seeds and skin were eliminated, and the water content was reduced by evaporation in vacuum to a content of 26% solids. From this they isolated 150 mg of lycopene per kilogram of paste. The expected yield in the following experiment is 0.075 mg, which is not enough to weigh on the usual lab balance.

A jar of strained carrots sold as baby food serves as a convenient source of beta-carotene. The German investigators isolated 1 g of Gr beta-carotene per kilogram of dried, shredded carrots of unstated water content.

[4]Willstätter, R.; Escher, H. R. *Z Physiol. Chem.* **1911**, *64*, 47–61.

The following procedure calls for the dehydration of tomato or carrot paste with ethanol and extraction with dichloromethane, an efficient solvent for lipids.

Experimental Considerations

CAUTION: Do not breathe the vapors of dichloromethane. Carry out the extraction in the hood.

Carotenoids are very sensitive to light-catalyzed air oxidation. Perform this experiment as rapidly as possible; keep the solutions as cool and dark as possible. This extraction produces a mixture of products that can be analyzed by both TLC and column chromatography (*see* Chapter 9). If enough material for TLC only is desired, use one-tenth the quantities of starting material and solvents employed in the following procedure. This extraction can also be carried out with hexane if the ventilation is not adequate enough to use dichloromethane. However, hexane is more prone to form emulsions than the chlorinated solvent.

Procedure

> IN THIS EXPERIMENT, some tomato or carrot paste is treated with acetone, which will remove water and lipids but not the highly colored carotenoid hydrocarbons. The carotenoids are extracted by dichloromethane and analyzed by TLC.

A 5-g sample of fresh tomato or carrot paste (baby food) is transferred to the bottom of a 25 × 150 mm test tube, followed by 10 mL of acetone. The mixture is stirred and shaken before being filtered on a Hirsch funnel. Scrape as much of the material from the tube as possible and press it dry on the funnel. Let the tube drain thoroughly. Place the filtrate in a 125-mL Erlenmeyer flask.

Return the solid residue to the test tube, shake it with a 10-mL portion of dichloromethane, and again filter the material on a Hirsch funnel. Add the filtrate to the 125-mL flask. Repeat this process two more times and then pour the combined filtrates into a separatory funnel. Add water and a sodium chloride solution (which aids in the breaking of emulsions) and shake the funnel gently. This aqueous extraction will remove the acetone and any water-soluble components from the mixture, leaving the hydrocarbon carotenoids in the dichloromethane. Dry the colored organic layer over anhydrous calcium chloride and filter the solution into a dry flask. Remove about 0.5 mL of this solution and store it under nitrogen in the dark until it can be analyzed by TLC (the carotenoids are very susceptible to air oxidation). Evaporate the remainder of the dichloromethane solution to dryness under a stream of nitrogen or under vacuum on a rotary evaporator. This material can be used for column chromatography (*see* Chapter 9). If it is to be stored, fill the flask with nitrogen and store it in a dark place.

Air can be used for the evaporation, but nitrogen is better because these hydrocarbons air oxidize with great rapidity.

Thin-Layer Chromatography

Many spots may be seen. There are two common carotene and chlorophyll isomers and four xanthophyll isomers.

Spot the mixture on a TLC plate about 1 cm from the bottom and 8 mm from the edge. Make one spot concentrated by repeatedly touching the plate in the exact same location, but ensure that the spot is as small as possible, certainly less than 1 mm in diameter. The other spot can be of lower concentration. Develop the plate with an 80:20 hexane-acetone mixture. With other plates, you could try cyclohexane and toluene as eluents and also hexane-ethanol mixtures of various compositions.

The container in which the chromatography is carried out should be lined with filter paper that is wet with the solvent so that the atmosphere in the container will be saturated with the solvent vapor. After elution is completed, remove the TLC plate and mark the solvent front with a pencil and outline the colored spots. Examine the plate under UV light. Also place the plate in an iodine chamber to visualize the spots.

Cleaning Up. The aqueous saline filtrate containing acetone can be flushed down the drain. Recovered and unused dichloromethane should be placed in the halogenated organic waste container; the solvents used for TLC should be placed in the organic solvents waste container. If local regulations allow, evaporate any residual solvent from the drying agents in the hood and place the dried solid in the nonhazardous waste container. Otherwise, place the wet drying agent in a waste container designated for this purpose. Used plant material and dry TLC plates can be discarded in the nonhazardous waste container.

Procedure

In a small mortar, grind 2 g of green or brightly colored fall leaves (do not use ivy or waxy leaves) with 10 mL of ethanol, pour off the ethanol (which serves to break up and dehydrate the plant cells), and grind the leaves successively with three 1-mL portions of dichloromethane that are decanted or withdrawn with a Pasteur pipette and placed in a test tube. The pigments of interest are extracted by the dichloromethane. Alternatively, place 0.5 g of carrot paste (baby food) or tomato paste in a test tube, stir and shake the paste with 3 mL of ethanol until the paste has a somewhat dry or fluffy appearance, remove the ethanol, and extract the dehydrated paste with three 1-mL portions of dichloromethane. Stir and shake the plant material with the solvent to extract as much of the pigments as possible.

Fill the tube containing the dichloromethane extract from leaves or vegetable paste with a saturated sodium chloride solution and shake the mixture. Remove the aqueous layer; add anhydrous calcium chloride pellets to the dichloromethane solution until the drying agent no longer clumps together. Shake the mixture with the drying agent for about 5 minutes and then withdraw the solvent with a Pasteur pipette and place it in a test tube. Add to the solvent a few pieces of Dri-Rite to complete the drying process. Gently stir the mixture for about 5 minutes, transfer the solvent to a test tube, wash off the drying agent with more solvent, and then evaporate the combined dichloromethane solutions under a stream of nitrogen while warming the tube in your hand or in a beaker of warm water. Carry out this evaporation in the hood.

These hydrocarbons air oxidize with great rapidity.

Immediately cork the tube filled with nitrogen and then add 1 or 2 drops of dichloromethane to dissolve the pigments for TLC analysis. Carry out the analysis without delay by spotting the mixture on a TLC plate about 1 cm from the bottom and 8 mm from the edge. Make one spot concentrated by repeatedly touching the plate, but ensure that the spot is as small as possible—less than 1.0 mm in diameter. The other spot can be of lower concentration. Develop the plate with a 70:30 hexane-acetone mixture. With other plates, try cyclohexane and toluene as eluents and also hexane-ethanol mixtures of various compositions. The container in which the chromatography is carried out should be lined with filter paper that is wet with the solvent so that the atmosphere in the container will be saturated with solvent vapor. After elution is completed, mark the solvent front with a pencil and outline the colored spots. Examine the plate under the UV light. Are any new spots seen? Report colors and R_f values for all of your spots and identify each as lycopene, carotene, chlorophyll, or xanthophyll.

Cleaning Up. The ethanol used for the dehydration of the plant material can be flushed down the drain along with the saturated sodium chloride solution. Recovered and unused dichloromethane should be placed in the halogenated organic waste container. The solvents used for TLC should be placed in the organic solvents waste container. If local regulations allow, evaporate any residual solvent from the drying agents in the hood and place the dried solid in the nonhazardous waste container. Otherwise, place the wet drying agent in a waste container designated for this purpose. Used plant material and dry TLC plates can be discarded in the nonhazardous waste container.

3. FOR FURTHER INVESTIGATION

Many of the pigments in plants are made up of compounds called *anthocyanins.* Grind about 4 g of colored plant tissue (flower petals, blueberries, strawberries, cranberries, apple skins, red cabbage, red or purple grapes, etc.) and a small amount of alumina or fine sand with about 4 mL of a mixture of 99% methanol and 1% hydrochloric acid. Spot the extract on cellulose TLC plates and elute with a solvent mixture of 20% concentrated hydrochloric acid, 40% water, and 4% formic acid. Note the number and color of the spots. Look up the structures of the possible anthocyanins, of which many are glycosides of the aglycones delphinidin, peonidin, malvidin, and cyanidin, among others.

4. COLORLESS COMPOUNDS

You will now apply the thin-layer technique to a group of colorless compounds. The spots can be visualized under UV light if the plates have been coated with a fluorescent indicator; chromatograms can also be developed in a 4-oz bottle containing crystals of iodine. During development, spots will appear rapidly but remember that they also disappear rapidly. Therefore, outline each spot with a pencil immediately on withdrawal of the plate from the iodine chamber. Some suggested solvents are pure cyclohexane, pure toluene, toluene (3 mL) plus dichloromethane (1 mL), or toluene (4.5 mL) plus methanol (1/2 mL).

The compounds for trial are to be selected from the following list (all 1% solutions in toluene; those compounds with an asterisk are fluorescent under UV light):

1. Anthracene*
2. Cholesterol
3. 2,7-Dimethyl-3,5-octadiyne-2,7-diol
4. Diphenylacetylene
5. *trans,trans*-1,4-Diphenyl-1,3-butadiene*
6. *p*-Di-*t*-butylbenzene
7. 1,4-Di-*t*-butyl-2,5-dimethoxybenzene
8. *trans*-Stilbene
9. 1,2,3,4-Tetraphenylnaphthalene*
10. Tetraphenylthiophene
11. *p*-Terphenyl*
12. Triphenylmethanol
13. Triptycene

Except for tetraphenylthiophene, the structures for all of these molecules will be found in this book.

Make your own selections.

It is up to you to make selections and to plan your own experiments. Do as many as time permits. One plan would be to select a pair of compounds that are estimated to be separable and that have R_f values determinable with the same solvent. One can assume that a hydroxyl compound will travel less rapidly with a hydrocarbon solvent than a hydroxyl-free compound; you will therefore know what to expect if the solvent contains a hydroxylic component. An aliphatic solvent should carry along an aromatic compound with aliphatic substituents better than one without such groups. Follow the procedure in Step 3 for picking a solvent.

Preliminary trials on used plates.

Once a solvent is chosen, run a complete chromatogram on the two compounds on a fresh plate. If separation of the two compounds seems feasible, put two spots of one compound on a plate, let the solvent evaporate, and put spots of the second compound over the first ones. Run a chromatogram and see if you can detect two spots in either lane (with colorless compounds, it is advisable not to attempt a three-lane chromatogram until you have acquired considerable practice and skill).

Cleaning Up. Solvents should be placed in the organic solvents waste container, and dry, used chromatographic plates can be discarded in the nonhazardous solid waste container.

DISCUSSION

If you have investigated hydroxylated compounds, you doubtless have found that it is reasonably easy to separate a hydroxylated from a nonhydroxylated compound or a diol from a mono-ol. How, by a simple reaction followed by a thin-layer chromatogram, could you separate cholesterol from triphenylmethanol? Heating a sample of each with acetic anhydride and a trace of pyridine catalyst for 5 minutes on a steam bath, followed by chromatography, should do it.

A first trial of a new reaction leaves questions about what has happened and how much, if any, starting material is present. A comparative chromatogram of the reaction mixture with starting material may tell the story. How crude is a crude reaction product? How many components are present? The thin-layer technique may give the answers to these questions and suggest how best to process the product. A preparative column chromatogram may afford a large number of fractions of eluent (say, 1 to 30). Some fractions probably contain nothing and should be discarded, while others should be combined for evaporation and workup. How can you identify the good and the useless fractions? Take a few used plates and put numbered circles on clean places of each; spot samples of each of the fractions and, without any chromatography, develop the plates with iodine. Negative fractions for discard will be obvious, and the pattern alone of positive fractions may allow you to infer which fractions can be combined. Thin-layer chromatograms of the first and last fractions of each suspected group would then show whether or not your inferences are correct.

FLUORESCENCE

Never look into a UV lamp.

Four of the compounds listed in Experiment 4 are fluorescent under UV light. These compounds give colorless spots that can be picked up on a chromatogram by fluorescence (after removal from the UV-absorbing glass developing bottle). If a UV light source is available, spot the four compounds on a used plate and observe the fluorescence.

Take this opportunity to examine a white shirt or handkerchief under UV light to see if it contains a brightener, that is, a fluorescent white dye or optical bleach. These substances are added to counteract the yellow color that repeated washing gives to cloth. Brighteners of the type of Calcofluor White MR, a sulfonated *trans*-stilbene derivative, are commonly used in detergent formulations for cotton. A substituted coumarin derivative is typical of brighteners used for nylon, acetate, and wool. Detergents normally contain 0.1%–0.2% of optical bleach. The amount of dye on a freshly laundered shirt is approximately 0.01% of the weight of the fabric.

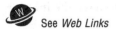
See *Web Links*

THIN-LAYER CHROMATOGRAPHY SUMMARY

1. **Preparing the sample**. Make a 1% solution of the sample in a low-boiling solvent. It is extremely important to make the solution at this concentration. If more sample is needed, it can be applied repeatedly at the same spot.

2. **Spotting the TLC Plate**. Prepare a very fine capillary from a melting point capillary. With a pencil, mark a line 1 cm from the bottom of the plate. Apply the sample on the line and make the spot no more than 1 mm in diameter.

3. **Picking a Solvent**. Apply test spots to a new or used TLC plate. Add a drop of a possible solvent to each spot. Pick the best solvent (Refer to Fig. 8.8).

4. **Developing the Plate**. Place the plate in a covered jar or beaker lined with filter paper. The depth of solvent should be about 0.5 cm. When the solvent rises to within about a cm of the top of the plate, remove it and mark the solvent front with a pencil.

5. **Visualizing the Results**. After the solvent evaporates, observe the plate under a UV light and/or place the plate in a sealed container containing a few crystals of iodine. Circle the developed spots while they are visible.

6. **Calculating the R_f value**. Measure the distance the center of the spot has traveled above the starting line and divide this distance by the distance the solvent front traveled. The result is the R_f value.

QUESTIONS

1. Why might it be very difficult to visualize the separation of *cis*- and *trans*-2-butene by TLC?

2. What error is introduced into the determination of an R_f value if the top is left off the developing chamber?

3. What problem will ensue if the level of the developing liquid is higher than the applied spot in a TLC analysis?

4. In what order (from top to bottom) would you expect to find naphthalene, butyric acid, and phenyl acetate on a silica gel TLC plate developed with dichloromethane?

5. In carrying out an analysis of a mixture, what do you expect to see when the TLC plate has been allowed to remain in the developing chamber too long, so that the solvent front has reached the top of the plate?

6. Arrange the following in order of increasing R_f with TLC: acetic acid, acetaldehyde, 2-octanone, decane, and 1-butanol.

7. What will be the result of applying too much compound to a TLC plate?

8. Why is it necessary to run TLC in a closed container and to have the interior vapor saturated with the solvent?

9. What will be the appearance of a TLC plate if a solvent of too low polarity is used for the development? A solvent of too high polarity?

10. A TLC plate showed two spots with R_f values of 0.25 and 0.26. The plate was removed from the developing chamber, the residual solvent was allowed to evaporate from the plate, and then the plate was returned to the developing chamber. What would you expect to see after the second development was complete?

11. One of the analgesics has a chiral center. Which compound is it? One of the two enantiomers is far more effective at reducing pain than the other.

12. Using a ruler to measure distances, calculate the R_f value for substance B in Figure 8.10.

CHAPTER 9

Column Chromatography: Fluorenone, Cholesteryl Acetate, Acetylferrocene, and Plant Pigments

Column chromatography is one of the most useful methods for the separation and purification of both solids and liquids when carrying out microscale experiments. It becomes expensive and time consuming, however, when more than about 10 g of material must be purified. Column chromatography involves the same chromatographic principles as detailed for TLC in Chapter 8, so be sure that you understand those before doing the experiments in this chapter.

As discussed in Chapter 1, organic chemists obtain new compounds by synthesizing or isolating natural products that have been biosynthesized by microbes, plants, or animals. In most cases, initial reaction products or cell extracts are complex mixtures containing many substances. As you have seen, recrystallization, distillation, liquid/liquid extraction, and sublimation can be used to separate and purify a desired compound from these mixtures. However, these techniques are frequently not adequate for removing impurities that are closely related in structure. In these cases, column chromatography is often used. The broad applicability of this technique becomes obvious if you visit any organic chemistry research lab, where chromatography columns are commonplace.

Three of the five experiments in this chapter involve synthesis and may be your first experience in running an organic reaction. Experiments 1 and 2 involve the synthesis of a ketone. In Experiment 3, an ester of cholesterol is prepared. Experiment 4 demonstrates the separation of colored compounds. Experiment 5 involves the isolation and separation of natural products (plant pigments), which is analogous to Experiment 2 in Chapter 8 but on a larger scale.

185

The most common adsorbents for column chromatography—silica gel and alumina—are the same stationary phases as used in TLC. The sample is dissolved in a small quantity of solvent (the eluent) and applied to the top of the column. The eluent, instead of rising by capillary action up a thin layer, flows down through the column filled with the adsorbent. Just as in TLC, there is an equilibrium established between the solute adsorbed on the silica gel or alumina and the eluting solvent flowing down through the column, with the less strongly absorbed solutes moving ahead and eluting earlier.

Three mutual interactions must be considered in column chromatography: the activity of the stationary adsorbent phase, the polarity of the eluting mobile solvent phase, and the polarity of the compounds in the mixture being chromatographed.

ADDITIONAL PRINCIPLES OF COLUMN CHROMATOGRAPHY

Adsorbents

A large number of adsorbents have been used for column chromatography, including cellulose, sugar, starch, and inorganic carbonates; but most separations employ alumina [$(Al_2O_3)_x$] or silica gel [$(SiO_2)_x$]. Alumina comes in three forms: acidic, neutral, and basic. The neutral form of Brockmann activity grade II or III, 150 mesh, is most commonly employed. The surface area of this alumina is about 150 m^2/g. Alumina as purchased will usually be activity grade I, meaning that it will strongly adsorb solutes. It must be deactivated by adding water, shaking, and allowing the mixture to reach equilibrium over an hour or so. The amount of water needed to achieve certain activities is given in Table 9.1. The activity of the alumina on TLC plates is usually about III. Silica gel for column chromatography, 70–230 mesh, has a surface area of about 500 m^2/g and comes in only one activity.

TABLE 9.1 *Alumina Activity*

Brockmann activity grade	I	II	III	IV	V
Percent by weight of water	0	3	6	10	15

TABLE 9.2 *Elutropic Series for Solvents*

n-Pentane (least polar)

Petroleum ether

Cyclohexane

Hexanes

Carbon disulfide

t-Butyl methyl ether

Dichloromethane

Tetrahydrofuran

Dioxane

Ethyl acetate

2-Propanol

Ethanol

Methanol

Acetic acid (most polar)

Solvents

Solvent systems for use as mobile phases in column chromatography can be determined from TLC, the scientific literature, or experimentally. Normally, a separation will begin with a nonpolar or low-polarity solvent, allowing the compounds to adsorb to the stationary phase; then the polarity of the solvent is *slowly* increased to desorb the compounds and allow them to move with the mobile phase. The polarity of the solvent should be changed gradually. A sudden change in solvent polarity will cause heat evolution as the alumina or silica gel adsorbs the new solvent. This will vaporize the solvent, causing channels to form in the column that severely reduce its separating power.

Several solvents are listed in Table 9.2, arranged in order of increasing polarity (elutropic series), with n-pentane being the least polar. The order shown in the table reflects the ability of these solvents to dislodge a polar substance adsorbed onto either silica gel or alumina, with n-pentane having the lowest solvent power.

As a practical matter, the following sequence of solvents is recommended in an investigation of unknown mixtures: elute first with petroleum ether (pentanes); then hexanes; followed by hexanes containing 1%, 2%, 5%, 10%, 25%, and 50% ether; pure ether; ether and dichloromethane mixtures; followed by dichloromethane and methanol mixtures. Either diethyl ether or *t*-butyl methyl ether can be used, but *t*-butyl methyl ether is recommended. Solvents such as methanol and water are normally not used because they can destroy the integrity of the stationary phase by dissolving some of the silica gel. Some typical solvent combinations are hexanes-dichloromethane, hexanes-ethyl acetate, and hexanes-toluene. An experimentally determined ratio of these solvents can sufficiently separate most compounds.

Compound Mobility

The ease with which different classes of compounds elute from a column is indicated in Table 9.3. Molecules with nonpolar functional groups are least adsorbed and elute first, while more polar or hydrogen-bonding molecules are more strongly adsorbed and elute later. The order is similar to that of the eluting solvents—another application of "like dissolves like."

Sample and Column Size

Chromatography columns can be as thin as a pencil for milligram quantities to as big as a barrel for the industrial-scale separation of kilogram quantities. A microscale column for the chromatography of about 50 mg of material is shown in Figure 9.1; columns with larger diameters, as shown in Figures 9.2 and 9.3, are used for macroscale procedures. The amount of alumina or silica gel used should generally weigh at least 30 times as much as the sample, and the column, when packed, should have a height at least 10 times the diameter. The density of silica gel is 0.4 g/mL, and the density of alumina is 0.9 g/mL, so the optimum size for any column can be calculated.

Packing the Column

Microscale Procedure

Before you pack the column, tare several Erlenmeyer flasks, small beakers, or 20-mL vials to use as receivers. Weigh each one carefully and mark it with a number on the etched circle.

Uniform packing of the chromatography column is critical to the success of this technique. Two acceptable methods for packing a column are dry packing and slurry packing, which normally achieve the best results. Assemble the column as depicted in Figure 9.1. To measure the amount of adsorbent, fill the column one-half to two-thirds full; then pour the powder out into a small beaker or flask. Clamp the column in a vertical position and close the valve. Always grasp the valve with one hand while turning it with the other. Fill the column with a non-polar solvent such as hexanes almost to the top.

Dry Packing Method. This is the simplest method for preparing a microscale column. Slowly add the powdered alumina or silica gel through the funnel while gently tapping the side of the column with a pencil. The solid should "float" to the bottom of the column. Try to pack the column as evenly as possible; cracks, air bubbles, and channels in the powder will lead to a poor separation.

Slurry Packing Method. To slurry pack a column, add about 8 mL of hexanes to the adsorbent in a flask or beaker, stir the mixture to eliminate air bubbles, and

---

Petroleum ether: mostly isometric pentanes.

TABLE 9.3 *Elution Order for Solutes*

Alkanes (first)

Alkenes

Dienes

Aromatic hydrocarbons

Ethers

Esters

Ketones

Aldehydes

Amines

Alcohols

Phenols

Acids (last)

Photo: *Column Chromatography*; Video: *Column Chromatography*

FIG. 9.1
A microscale chromatographic column.

FIG. 9.2
A macroscale chromatographic column.

FIG. 9.3
A chromatographic tube on a ring stand.

Funnel

Glass
column

Alumina

Micro
Büchner
funnel

Polyethylene
frit

10-mL
Erlenmeyer
flask

Solvent

Sand

Alumina or
silica gel

Sand
Glass wool

then (this is the hard part) swirl the mixture to get the adsorbent suspended in the solvent and immediately pour the entire slurry into the funnel. Open the valve, drain some solvent into the flask that had the adsorbent in it and finish transferring the slurry to the column. Place an empty flask under the column and allow the solvent to drain to about 5 mm above the top surface of the adsorbent. Tap the column with a pencil until the packing settles to a minimum height. Try to pack the column as evenly as possible; cracks, air bubbles, and channels in the packed column will lead to a poor separation.

The slurry method normally gives the best column packing, but it is also the more difficult technique to master. Whether the dry packing or slurry packing method is chosen, the most important aspect of packing the column is creating an evenly distributed and packed stationary phase. The slurry method is often used for macroscale separations.

Once the column is loaded with solvent and adsorbent, place a flask under it, open the stopcock (use two hands for the microscale column), and allow the solvent level to drop to the *top* of the packing. Avoid allowing the solvent level to go below the stationary phase (known as letting the column "run dry") because this allows air bubbles and channel formation to occur, which leads to a poor separation.

Macroscale Procedure

Before you pack the column, prepare several small Erlenmeyer flasks to use as receivers by taring (weighing) each one carefully, recording the weight in your laboratory notebook, and marking each with a number on the etched circle.

Dry Packing Method

The column can be prepared using a 50-mL burette such as the one shown in Figure 9.2 or using the less expensive and equally satisfactory chromatographic tube shown in Figure 9.3, in which the flow of solvent is controlled by a screw pinchclamp. Weigh the required amount of silica gel (12.5 g in the first experiment), close the pinchclamp on the tube, and fill about half full with a 90:10 mixture of hexanes and ether. With a wooden dowel or glass rod, push a small plug of glass wool through the liquid to the bottom of the tube, dust in through a funnel enough sand to form a 1-cm layer over the glass wool, and level the surface by tapping the tube. Unclamp the tube. With your right hand, grasp both the top of the tube and the funnel so that the whole assembly can be shaken to dislodge silica gel that may stick to the walls; with your left hand pour in the silica gel slowly (Fig. 9.4) while tapping the column with a rubber stopper fitted on the end of a pencil. If necessary, use a Pasteur pipette full of a 90:10 mixture of hexanes and ether to wash down any silica gel that adheres to the walls of the column above the liquid. When the silica gel has settled, add a little sand to provide a protective layer at the top. Open the pinchclamp, let the solvent level fall until it is just slightly above the upper layer of sand, and then stop the flow.

FIG. 9.4
A useful technique for filling a chromatographic tube with silica gel.

Slurry Packing Method

Alternatively, the silica gel can be added to the column (half-filled with hexanes) by slurrying the silica gel with a 90:10 mixture of hexanes and ether in a beaker. The powder is stirred to suspend it in the solvent and it is immediately poured through a wide-mouth funnel into the chromatographic tube. Rap the column with a rubber stopper to cause the silica gel to settle and to remove bubbles. Add a protective layer of sand to the top. The column is now ready for use.

Cleaning Up. After use, the tube is conveniently emptied by pointing the open end into a beaker, opening the pinchclamp, and applying gentle air pressure to the tip. If the plug of glass wool remains in the tube after the alumina leaves, wet it with acetone and reapply air pressure. Allow the adsorbent to dry in the hood and then dispose of it in the nonhazardous waste container.

Adding the Sample

Dissolve the sample completely in a very minimum volume of dichloromethane (just a few drops) in a small flask or vial. Add to this solution 300 mg of the adsorbent, stir, and evaporate the solvent completely by heating the slurry *very gently* with *constant* stirring to avoid bumping. Remember that dichloromethane boils at 41°C. Pour this dry powder into the funnel of the chromatography column, wash it down onto the column with a few drops of hexane, and then tap the column to remove air bubbles from the layer of adsorbent-solute mixture just added. Open the valve and carefully add new solvent in such a manner that the top surface of the column is not disturbed. A thin layer of fine sand can be added to the column after the sample to avoid disturbance of the column surface when the solvent is being added. Run the solvent down near to the surface several times to apply the sample as a narrow band at the top of the column.

Eluting the Column

Fill the column with solvent, open the stopcock, and continue to add more solvent while collecting 1–3 mL fractions in small previously tared Erlenmeyer flasks. Collecting small fractions is important to the success of your column separation. Fractions that are too small can always be pooled together; however, if the collected fractions are too large, you may get more than one compound in any particular fraction. If this occurs, the only way to attain separation is to redo the chromatography. Column chromatography is a lengthy process, so collecting large fractions is discouraged.

Isolating the Separated Compounds

If the mixture to be separated contains colored compounds, then monitoring the column is very simple. The colored bands will move down the column along with the solvent, and as they approach the end of the column, you can collect the separated colors in individual containers. However, most organic molecules are colorless. In this case, the separation must be monitored by TLC. Spot each fraction on a TLC plate (Fig. 9.5). Four or five fractions can be spotted on a single plate. Before you develop the plate, do a quick examination under UV light to see if there is any compound where you spotted. If not, you can spot the next fraction in that location. Note which fraction is in which lane. Develop the plate and use the observed spot(s) to determine which compound is in each of the collected fractions. Spotting some of the starting material or the product (if available) on the TLC plate as a standard will help in the identification.

The colors of the fractions or the results from analyzing the fractions by TLC will indicate which fractions contain the compound(s) you are interested in isolating. Combine fractions containing the same compound and evaporate the solvent. Recrystallization may be used to further purify a solid product. However, on a milligram scale, there is usually not enough material to do this.

FIG. 9.5
Spot each fraction on a TLC plate. Examine under UV light to see which fractions contain the compound.

OTHER TYPES OF CHROMATOGRAPHY

Flash Chromatography

Relying only on gravity, liquid flow through a column can be quite slow, especially if the column is tightly packed. One method to speed up the process is *flash chromatography*. This method uses a pressure of about 10 psi of air or nitrogen on top of the column to force the mobile phase through the column. Normally, doing this would give a poorer separation. However, it has been found that with a finer mesh of alumina or silica gel, flash chromatography can increase the speed without lowering the quality of the separation. Go to this book's web site for an illustrated set of instructions for packing and using a flash chromatography column.

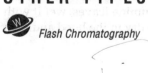

High-performance liquid chromatography.

High-performance liquid chromatography (HPLC) is a high-tech version of column chromatography, which is capable of separating complex mixtures with dozens of components. A high-pressure pump forces solvent at pressures up to 10,000 psi through a stainless steel tube packed tightly with extremely small adsorbent particles. The eluent flows from the column to a detector, such as a tiny UV absorbance cell or a mass spectrometer that is able to detect extremely small amounts of separated components, as little as a picogram (10^{-12} g).

Reverse-phase chromatography.

HPLC is used extensively in biochemistry to separate cellular components such as proteins, lipids, and nucleic acids. Mixtures of these types of compounds can be dissolved only in a predominantly aqueous mobile phase such as methanol-water or acetonitrile-water, and normal silica gel or alumina stationary phases do not work well with high concentrations of water. Rather than polar stationary phases, highly nonpolar ones called *reverse-phase packings* are used. These are manufactured by bonding lots of hydrocarbon molecules to the surfaces of silica gel particles, which convert the particles into highly nonpolar grease balls. With this packing, the order of elution is the reverse of that observed for a normal silica gel phase. On a reverse-phase column, the more nonpolar compounds will adhere to the nonpolar stationary phase more strongly, and the polar compounds will elute first.

Is it possible to separate two enantiomers (optical isomers), both of which have the same intermolecular attractive forces? Chiral stationary phases can be used to separate enantiomers. Giving the stationary phase an asymmetry or handedness allows one enantiomer to be specifically retained on the column. Such columns are quite expensive and are limited to a particular type of separation, but they have led to great achievements in separation science. This separation technique is of great importance in the pharmaceutical industry because the U.S. Food and Drug Administration (FDA) specifies the amounts of impurities, including enantiomers, that can be found in drugs. For example, thalidomide, a drug prescribed as a sedative and an antidepressant in the 1960s, was found to be a potent teratogen that caused birth defects when pregnant women took the drug. It was quickly pulled from the market. Thalidomide has two enantiomers, and further research demonstrated that only one of the enantiomers caused the birth defects.

$$-O-\underset{\underset{CH_3}{|}}{\overset{\overset{CH_3}{|}}{Si}}-(CH_2)_{17}CH_3$$

C_{18} reverse-phase packing

Chiral chromatography

EXPERIMENTS

1. AIR OXIDATION OF FLUORENE TO FLUORENONE

The 9-position of fluorene is unusually reactive for a hydrocarbon. The protons on this carbon atom are acidic by virtue of being doubly benzylic, and, consequently, this carbon can be oxidized by several reagents, including oxygen from the air. Here the oxidation is carried out using a phase-transfer catalyst called methyltricapryl ammonium chloride, commonly known as Stark's catalyst or Aliquat 336. In the presence of this catalyst, the hydroxide is carried into the organic layer, where it can remove one of the acidic fluorene protons, creating a carbanion that can react with oxygen in the air. An intermediate hydroperoxide is formed and loses water to give the ketone.

Sufficiently acidic to be removed by strong base

$$\text{Fluorene} + O_2 \xrightarrow[\substack{10\,M\ \text{NaOH} \\ \text{Toluene} \\ 10\text{–}60\ \text{min}}]{\substack{\text{Methyltricapryl ammonium chloride} \\ \text{(Aliquat 336, Stark's catalyst)}}} \text{Fluorenone} + H_2O$$

Fluorene
mp 114°C
MW 166.22

Methyltricapryl ammonium chloride
(Aliquat 336, Stark's catalyst)

Fluorenone
mp 83°C
MW 180.21

Microscale Procedure

> IN THIS EXPERIMENT, fluorene is oxidized to fluorenone by oxygen from the air in a base-catalyzed reaction involving a phase-transfer catalyst. The reaction is monitored by TLC and stopped when about a 50:50 mixture of product and starting material has formed. The toluene layer is separated and washed with 5% hydrochloric acid and saturated sodium chloride. After drying over calcium chloride, the toluene is removed and the fluorene-fluorenone mixture is separated by microscale column chromatography on alumina, using hexanes as the mobile phase. Fractions are analyzed by TLC; common fractions are pooled and weighed after solvent removal to give pure fluorene and fluorenone.

⚠️
Sodium hydroxide is a strong base and is very corrosive. Wash your hands immediately if contact occurs.

This experiment requires a 50-mL to 125-mL separatory funnel. To a 25-mL Erlenmeyer flask clamped to a ring stand above a magnetic stirrer, add 5 mL of 10 M NaOH and 70 mg of fluorene while stirring with a $\frac{1}{2}$-inch magnetic stirring bar. Add 5 mL of toluene and stir until all of the solid has dissolved. (Observe the color and identify which layer is organic and which is aqueous.) Add approximately 3 drops of Stark's catalyst (Aliquat 336) to the solution. Stir vigorously but without splashing the solution. The reaction can take anywhere from 10 minutes to 30 minutes. Follow the rate of the reaction by TLC. Develop the TLC plate by using 20% dichloromethane in hexanes, and use a UV lamp to visualize the products. Also spot the plate with a 1% fluorene standard. When approximately half of the fluorene has been converted to fluorenone (as evidenced by the fact that the product spot is about the same size and intensity), pour the reaction mixture into a separatory funnel, rinsing the beaker with an additional 3 mL of toluene, which is also added to the separatory funnel.

Separate the organic layer from the aqueous layer. Wash the organic layer in the separatory funnel with 1.5 M hydrochloric acid (three separate times with 5 mL each time) and then saturated sodium chloride (three separate times with 5 mL each time). After each washing, drain the aqueous layer from the separatory funnel into a waste beaker. Dry the remaining toluene layer over anhydrous calcium chloride pellets in a 125-mL Erlenmeyer flask. Add the pellets until they no longer clump together (3–5 scoops). Allow the product to dry for 5–10 minutes before decanting the toluene from the solid calcium chloride and transferring the toluene to a 100-mL tared beaker. Wash the solid calcium chloride with 3 mL of toluene, adding this to the main portion of toluene to complete the transfer of product. The crude mixture of fluorene and fluorenone will be separated by column chromatography in the next lab period. The beaker containing the toluene extract can be allowed to stand in your hood (labeled properly) until the next lab period. The toluene will evaporate in the interim. Alternatively, if you have time, reduce the volume of solvent (~1 mL) by heating gently on a sand bath. Insert a boiling stick if you do this.

Cleaning Up. Carefully dilute the strongly basic aqueous reaction layer 10- to 20-fold with water in a large beaker, add the hydrochloric acid washes, and then neutralize by slowly adding additional hydrochloric acid. Flush this and the sodium chloride washes down the drain with lots of water. If local regulations allow, evaporate any residual solvent from the drying agents in the hood and place the dried solid in the nonhazardous waste container. Otherwise, place the wet drying agent in a waste container designated for this purpose.

Column Chromatography of the Fluorene-Fluorenone Mixture

Figure 9.1 on page 188 shows the typical setup you will use for the chromatographic separation of fluorene and fluorenone, and a general outline of the procedure is given on page 196. It is essential to have at least 10 clean 10-mL Erlenmeyer flasks, reaction tubes, small beakers, test tubes, or vials available to collect the chromatography fractions as they elute. At least two of these should be weighed, with their tare weight recorded. Once you have this done and the column is assembled, you can pack the column with alumina according to the following instructions.

Packing the Column

Set up a sand bath at a heating setting of 50 before you do anything else.

Before you assemble the column, check the small plug that fits into the bottom of the column to make sure that it has a small fritted disk inside. Next, make sure that the plug fits snugly into the glass column and is not easy to pull out. If it is loose, get a new bottom plug from the stockroom. Finish assembling the chromatography column as depicted in Figure 9.1. Be sure to clamp the column securely and vertically.

Grasp the valve with one hand and turn it with the other. Close the valve and fill the column with hexanes to the bottom of the plastic funnel. Weigh out approximately 4.5 g of activity grade III alumina in a small beaker and slowly sprinkle the dry alumina into the hexanes in the column while you tap the column with a pen or pencil. It may be necessary to drain off some of the solvent to keep it from flowing over the top. This amount of alumina should fill the column to a height of about 10 cm. It is extremely important *not* to let the column run dry at any time. This will allow air to enter the column, which will result in uneven bands and poor separation.

After all of the alumina has been added to the column, open the stopcock and continue to tap the column as you allow the solvent to drain slowly until the solvent just barely covers the surface of the alumina, collecting the solvent in an Erlenmeyer flask. Alternatively the slurry packing method (p. 198) can be used.

Adding the Sample

It is important to use a minimum amount of solvent when dissolving the sample. If too much is used, poor separation will result.

The solvent is drained just to the surface of the alumina, which should be perfectly flat. Dissolve the crude mixture of fluorene and fluorenone in 10 drops of dichloromethane and 10 drops of toluene, and add this with a pipette to the surface of the alumina. Be sure to add the sample as a solution; should any sample crystallize, add 1 more drop of dichloromethane. (This is done so that the sample to be added to the column is in the most concentrated solution possible.) Drain some liquid from the column until the dichloromethane-toluene solution just barely covers the surface of the alumina. Then add a few drops of hexanes and drain out some solvent until the liquid just covers the alumina. Repeat until the sample is seen as a narrow band at the top of the column. Carefully add a 4–5 mm layer of sand and then fill the column with hexanes. Alternatively, the sample can be added as a solid adsorbed on 300 mg of alumina (p. 199).

Collect 3-mL fractions in a combination of small vials, 10-mL Erlenmeyer flasks, 13 × 100 mm test tubes, vials, and small beakers. You will probably collect close to ten 3-mL fractions. While the chromatography is running, you will be determining the amount of fluorene or fluorenone in each fraction by TLC. Once you determine which fractions contain which compound, you will combine the "like" fractions and evaporate the solvent.

After you collect each 3-mL fraction in a flask, apply it to a TLC plate by spotting it 2 or 3 times on the plate in the same location. Four or five fractions can be applied and analyzed at the same time using one TLC plate. Allow the solvent to completely evaporate from the spot and examine the plate under a UV lamp to determine if there is any material present, as evidenced by a dark blue spot. The TLC plates can be developed using 20% dichloromethane in hexanes. You will probably collect a few fractions that contain little or no material; these fractions are likely to be the first or the middle of the series.

After spotting and developing each fraction on the TLC plate, combine like fractions and immediately start to boil off the solvent on the sand bath *in the hood* using a boiling stick broken in half. Tilt the flasks and vials on their side as much as possible to allow the heavy vapors to escape. As soon as all the liquid seems to have boiled off, set the flask *on its side* on the bench top in the hood to allow the last traces of heavy solvent vapors to escape. After the flask has cooled to room temperature, if that fraction contains any material, crystals may appear. If an oily, gooey residue is present, you may have to scratch it with a glass stirring rod to induce crystallization. With good organizational effort, you can do the TLC analysis and evaporate off the solvent at about the same rate at which you collect fractions; thus you can follow the progress of the chromatography simply by noting the amount of material in each flask, vial, or test tube. If, after solvent removal and cooling, the flasks are perfectly clean on careful inspection, they can be used to collect subsequent fractions.

If the yellow band has not moved one third of the way down the column after two fractions have been collected, you can speed up the elution by replacing the hexanes solvent at the top of the column with 20% dichloromethane in hexanes. Once the first component has completely eluted, you can speed up the elution of the second component by using 50% dichloromethane in hexanes. Decide when the product has been completely eluted from the column by using visual cues and TLC. Using a few drops of dichloromethane, wash all the fractions that contain fluorene as determined by TLC analysis into a tared container. Do the same for the fluorenone fractions. Evaporate the dichloromethane and obtain dry weights for the product and the recovered fluorene.

Mark all compound spots on all TLC plates with a pencil. Tape your developed TLC plates in your notebook with wide transparent tape. Calculate the theoretical yield and the percent yield of your pure fluorenone both with and without taking into account the amount of fluorene starting material recovered. Calculate the percent recovery of fluorene.

Cleaning Up. When you are done with the column, pour out the excess solvent into the proper waste container, pull out the bottom, and leave the wet column propped in a beaker in your desk hood. The column will dry out by the next lab, and the dry, used alumina can then be easily emptied out into a waste bin.

2. CHROMIUM(VI) OXIDATION OF FLUORENE TO FLUORENONE

The 9-position of fluorene is unusually reactive for a hydrocarbon. The protons on this carbon atom are acidic by virtue of being doubly benzylic, and, consequently, this carbon can be oxidized by several reagents, including elemental oxygen. In this experiment, the very powerful and versatile oxidizing agent chromium(VI), in the form of chromium trioxide, is used to carry out the oxidation. Chromium(VI) in a variety of other forms is used for about a dozen oxidation reactions in this text. The dust of chromium(VI) salts is reported to be a carcinogen, so avoid breathing it.

$$\text{Fluorene} \xrightarrow[\text{CH}_3\text{COOH}]{\text{Na}_2\text{Cr}_2\text{O}_7} \text{Fluorenone}$$

Fluorene
mp 114°C
MW 166.22

Fluorenone
mp 83°C
MW 180.21

 ## Microscale Procedure

IN THIS EXPERIMENT, the hydrocarbon fluorene is oxidized to the ketone fluorenone by sodium dichromate in acetic acid with heating. The mixture is diluted with water, and the crude product is isolated by filtration. then it is dissolved in ether. The ether is dried and evaporated to give a mixture of fluorene and fluorenone, which is separated by column chromatography.

Sodium dichromate is toxic. The dust is corrosive to nasal passages and skin, and is a suspected carcinogen. Hot acetic acid is very corrosive to skin. Handle sodium dichromate and acetic acid in the hood; always wear gloves.

In a reaction tube, dissolve 50 mg of fluorene in 0.25 mL of acetic acid by heating, and add this hot solution to a solution of 0.15 g of sodium dichromate dihydrate in 0.5 mL of acetic acid. Heat the reaction mixture to 80°C for 15 minutes in a hot water bath; then cool it and add 1.5 mL of water. Stir the mixture for 2 minutes; then filter it on a Hirsch funnel. Wash the product well with water and press out as much water as possible. Return the product to the reaction tube, add 2 mL of ether, and add anhydrous calcium chloride pellets until they no longer clump together. Cork and shake the tube, and allow the product to dry for 5–10 minutes before evaporating the ether in another tared reaction tube. Use ether to wash off the drying agent and to complete the transfer of product. Use this ether solution to spot a TLC plate. This crude mixture of fluorene and fluorenone will be separated by column chromatography.

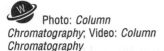 Photo: *Column Chromatography*; Video: *Column Chromatography*

Column Chromatography of the Fluorene-Fluorenone Mixture

Prepare a microscale chromatographic column exactly as described at the beginning of this chapter (*see* Fig. 9.1 on page 188). Use alumina as the adsorbent. Dissolve the crude mixture of fluorene and fluorenone in a mixture of 10 drops of dichloromethane and 10 drops of toluene, and add this to the surface of the alumina. Be sure to add the sample as a solution; should any sample crystallize, add 1 more drop of dichloromethane. Run the hexanes down to the surface of the alumina, add a few drops more of hexanes, and repeat the process until the sample is seen as a narrow band at the top of the column. Carefully add a 3-mm layer of sand, fill the column with hexanes, and collect 5-mL fractions in tared 10-mL Erlenmeyer flasks. Sample each flask for TLC (see Fig. 9.5 on page 190) and evaporate each to dryness. Final drying can be done under vacuum using the technique shown in Figure 9.6. You are to decide when all of the product has been eluted from the column. The TLC plates can be developed using 20% dichloromethane in hexanes. Combine fractions that are identical and determine the melting points of the two substances.

The sample can also be applied to the column using the technique described on page 196.

Cleaning Up. The filtrate probably contains unreacted dichromate. To destroy it, add 3 *M* sulfuric acid until the pH is 1; then complete the reduction by adding solid sodium thiosulfate until the solution becomes cloudy and blue colored. Neutralize with sodium carbonate and then filter the flocculent precipitate of Cr(OH)$_3$ through Celite in a Büchner funnel. If regulations allow, the filtrate can be diluted with water and flushed down the drain; otherwise, it should be disposed of in a designated waste container. The precipitate and Celite should be placed in the heavy metal hazardous waste container.

 ## Macroscale Procedure

In a 250-mL Erlenmeyer flask, dissolve 5.0 g of practical grade fluorene in 25 mL of acetic acid by heating on a steam bath with occasional swirling. In a 125-mL Erlenmeyer flask, dissolve 15 g of sodium dichromate dihydrate in 50 mL of acetic acid by swirling and heating on a hot plate. Adjust the temperature of the dichromate solution to 80°C, transfer the thermometer, and adjust the fluorene–acetic acid solution to 80°C; then, *in the hood*, pour in the dichromate solution. Note the time and the temperature of the solution and heat on a steam bath for 30 minutes. Observe the maximum and final temperature; then cool the solution and add 150 mL of water. Swirl the mixture for a full 2 minutes to coagulate the product and promote rapid filtration. Collect the yellow solid in an 8.5-cm Büchner funnel using vacuum filtration (if filtration is slow, empty the contents of the funnel and flask into a beaker and stir vigorously for a few minutes). Wash the filter cake well with water and then suck the filter cake as dry as possible. Either let the product dry overnight or dry it quickly as follows: Put the moist solid into a 50-mL Erlenmeyer flask, add ether (20 mL) and swirl to dissolve, and add anhydrous calcium chloride (10 g) to scavenge the water. Decant the ethereal solution through a cone of anhydrous calcium chloride in a funnel into a 125-mL Erlenmeyer flask; then rinse the flask and funnel with ether. Evaporate on a steam bath under an aspirator, heat until all the ether is removed, and pour the hot oil into a 50-mL beaker to cool and solidify. Scrape out the yellow solid. The yield should be about 4.0 g.

⚠️

Handle dichromate and acetic acid in the laboratory hood; always wear gloves.

Cleaning Up. Follow the procedure in the immediately preceding microscale experiment for destroying excess dichromate and disposing of reagents and solvents.

One-half hour unattended heating.

FIG. 9.6

Drying a solid by reduced air pressure.

Separation of Fluorene and Fluorenone

Prepare a column of 12.5 g of alumina, run out excess solvent, and pour onto the column a solution of 0.5 g of the fluorene-fluorenone mixture. Elute at first with hexanes and use tared 50-mL flasks as receivers. The yellow color of fluorenone provides one index of the course of the fractionation, and the appearance of solid around the delivery tip provides another. Frequently wash the solid on the tip into the receiver with ether. When you believe that one component has been eluted completely, change to another receiver until you judge that the second component is beginning to appear. Then, when you are sure the second component is being eluted, change to a 1:1 hexanes and ether mixture and continue until the column is exhausted. It is possible to collect practically all of the two components in the two receiving flasks, with only a negligible intermediate fraction. After evaporation of the solvent, evacuate each flask under vacuum (Fig. 9.7) and determine the weight and melting point of the products. A convenient method for evaporating fractions is to use a rotary evaporator (Fig. 9.8).

FIG. 9.7

An aspirator tube in use. A boiling stick may be necessary to promote even boiling.

Aspirator tube

To water aspirator

Clamp here

Tared flask

Boiling stick

Steam in

Outlet to sink

Steam bath (or sand bath)

FIG. 9.8

A rotary evaporator. The rate of evaporation with this apparatus is very fast due to the thin film of liquid spread over the entire inner surface of the rotating flask, which is heated under vacuum. Foaming and bumping are also greatly reduced.

Condenser

To aspirator

Liquid to be evaporated

Condensate

Ice

Cleaning Up. All organic material from this experiment can go in the organic solvents waste container. If local regulations allow, evaporate any residual solvent from the alumina in the hood and place the dried solid in the nonhazardous waste container. Otherwise, place the wet drying agent in a waste container designated for this purpose.

---

3. ACETYLATION OF CHOLESTEROL

Cholesterol is a solid alcohol; the average human body contains about 200 g distributed in the brain, spinal cord, and nerve tissue and, it occasionally clogs the arteries and the gallbladder.

In the following experiment, cholesterol is dissolved in acetic acid and allowed to react with acetic anhydride to form the ester cholesteryl acetate. The reaction does not take place rapidly, and consequently does not go to completion under the conditions of this experiment. Thus, when the reaction is over, both unreacted cholesterol and the product, cholesteryl acetate, are present. Separating these by fractional crystallization would be extremely difficult, but because they differ in polarity (the hydroxyl group of cholesterol is the more strongly adsorbed on alumina), they are easily separated by column chromatography. Both molecules are colorless and hence cannot be detected visually. Each fraction should be sampled by TLC. In that way, not only the presence but also the purity of each fraction can be assessed. It is also possible to put 1 drop of each fraction on a watch glass and evaporate it to see if the fraction contains product. Solid will also appear on the tip of the column while a compound is being eluted.

Microscale Procedure

IN THIS EXPERIMENT, cholesterol is refluxed with acetic acid and acetic anhydride. In the standard procedure, the mixture is diluted with water and extracted with ether, and the ether is dried and evaporated. The resulting mixture of cholesterol and cholesteryl acetate is separated by column chromatography on silica gel, eluting with hexanes and then hexanes and ether mixtures. Cholesteryl acetate comes off first, followed by cholesterol.

Cholesterol + Acetic anhydride → Cholesteryl acetate + CH₃COOH

In a reaction tube, add 0.5 mL of acetic acid to 50 mg of cholesterol. The initial thin slurry may set into a stiff paste of the molecular complex consisting of one molecule of cholesterol and one molecule of acetic acid. Add 0.10 mL of acetic anhydride and a boiling chip, and gently reflux the reaction mixture on a hot sand bath for no more than 30 minutes (*see* Fig. 1.1 on page 5).

While the reaction is taking place, prepare the microscale chromatography column as described previously, using silica gel as the adsorbent. Refer to Figure 9.1 on page 188 and the associated procedure earlier in the chapter. Cool the mixture, add 2 mL of water, and extract the product with three 2-mL portions of ether that are placed in a 15-mL centrifuge tube. Wash the ether extracts in the tube with two 2-mL portions of water and one 2.5-mL portion of 3 *M* sodium hydroxide (these three washes remove the acetic acid) and dry the ether by shaking it with 2.5 mL of saturated sodium chloride solution. Then complete the drying by adding enough anhydrous calcium chloride pellets to the solution so that the drying agent does not clump together.

Shake the ether solution with the drying agent for 10 minutes and then transfer it in portions to a tared reaction tube and evaporate to dryness. Use 1 drop of this ether solution to spot a TLC plate for later analysis. If the crude material weighs more than the theoretical weight, you will know that it is not dry or that it contains acetic acid, which can be detected by its odor. Dissolve this crude cholesteryl acetate in a minimum quantity of ether and apply it to the top of the chromatography column.

To prevent the solution from dribbling from the pipette, use a pipette pump to make the transfer. It also could be applied as a dry powder adsorbed on silica gel, as in Experiment 1. Elute the column with hexanes, collecting two 5-mL fractions in tared 10-mL Erlenmeyer flasks or other suitable containers. Add a boiling stick to each flask and evaporate the solvent under an aspirator tube on a steam bath or a sand bath (*see* Fig. 9.7). If the flask appears empty, it can be used to collect later fractions. Lower the solvent layer to the top of the sand and elute with 15 mL of a 70:30 mixture of hexanes and ether, collecting five 3-mL fractions. Evaporate the solvent under an aspirator tube (Fig. 9.7). The last traces of solvent can be removed using reduced pressure, as shown in Figure 9.6 on page 196. Follow the 70:30 mixture with 10 mL of a 50:50 mixture of hexanes and ether, collecting four 2-mL fractions. Save any flask that has any visible residue. Analyze the original mixture and each fraction by TLC on silica gel plates using a 1:1 mixture of hexanes and ether to develop the plates, and either UV light or iodine vapor to visualize the spots.

Cholesteryl acetate (mp 115°C) and cholesterol (mp 149°C) should appear, respectively, in early and late fractions with a few empty fractions (no residue) in between. If so, combine consecutive fractions of early and late material and determine the weights and melting points. Calculate the percentage of the acetylated material compared to the total recovered and calculate the percentage yield from cholesterol.

Cleaning Up. After neutralization, acetic acid, the aqueous layers, and the saturated sodium chloride layers from the extraction can be flushed down the drain with water. Ether, hexanes, and TLC solvents should be placed in the organic solvents waste container. If local regulations allow, evaporate any residual solvent from the drying agents and the chromatography packing in the hood and place the dried solid in the nonhazardous waste container. Otherwise, place the wet materials in waste containers designated for this purpose.

Macroscale Procedure

FIG. 9.9
A bubbler for adding solvent automatically.

Cover 0.5 g of cholesterol with 5 mL of acetic acid in a small Erlenmeyer flask; swirl and note that the initially thin slurry soon sets to a stiff paste of the molecular compound $C_{27}H_{45}OH \cdot CH_3CO_2H$. Add 1 mL of acetic anhydride and heat the mixture on a steam bath for any convenient period of time from 15 minutes to 1 hour; record the actual heating period. While the reaction takes place, prepare the chromatographic column. Cool the reaction mixture, add 20 mL of water, and extract with two 25-mL portions of ether. Wash the combined ethereal extracts twice with 15-mL portions of water and once with 25 mL of 3 M sodium hydroxide and dry by shaking the ether extracts with 25 mL of saturated sodium chloride solution. Then dry the ether over anhydrous calcium chloride pellets for 10 minutes in an Erlenmeyer flask, filter, and evaporate the ether. Save a few crystals of this material for TLC analysis. Dissolve the crystals in 3–4 mL of ether, transfer the solution with a Pasteur pipette onto a column of 12.5 g of silica gel, and rinse the flask with another small portion of ether.[1] In order to apply the ether solution to the top of the sand and avoid having it coat the interior of the column, pipette the solution down a 6-mm-diameter glass tube that is resting on the top of the sand. Label a series of 50-mL Erlenmeyer flasks as fractions 1 to 10. Open the pinchclamp, run the eluant solution into a 50-mL Erlenmeyer flask, and as soon as the solvent in the column has fallen to the level of the upper layer of sand, fill the column with a part of a measured 125 mL of a 70:30 mixture of hexanes and ether. When about 25 mL of eluant has collected in the flask (fraction 1), change to a fresh flask; add a boiling stone to the first flask and evaporate the solution to dryness on a steam bath under an aspirator tube (*see* Fig. 9.7 on page 197). Evacuation using an aspirator helps to remove last traces of ligroin (*see* Figure 9.6 on page 196). If fraction 1 is negative (no residue), use the flask for collecting further fractions. Continue adding the hexanes and ether mixture until the 125-mL portion is exhausted; then use 100 mL of a 1:1 hexanes and ether mixture. A convenient bubbler (Fig. 9.9) made from a 125-mL Erlenmeyer flask, a short piece of 10-mm-diameter glass tubing, and a cork will

[1]Ideally, the material to be adsorbed is dissolved in hexanes (ligroin), the solvent of lowest elutant power. The present mixture is not soluble enough in hexanes, and so ether is used, but the volume is kept to a minimum.

Carry out the procedure in a laboratory hood.

automatically add solvent. A separatory funnel with a stopper and a partially open stopcock serves the same purpose. Collect and evaporate successive 25-mL fractions of eluant. Save any flask that has any visible solid residue. The ideal method for the removal of solvents involves the use of a rotary evaporator (*see* Fig. 9.8 on page 197). Analyze the original mixture and each fraction by TLC on silica gel plates using a 1:1 mixture of hexanes-ether to develop the plates, and either UV light or iodine vapor to visualize the spots.

Cholesteryl acetate (mp 115°C) and cholesterol (mp 149°C) should appear, respectively, in early and late fractions with a few empty fractions (no residue) in between. If so, combine consecutive fractions of early and of late material, and determine the weights and melting points. Calculate the percentage of the acetylated material compared to the total recovered and compare your result with those of others in your class employing different reaction periods.

Cleaning Up. After neutralization, acetic acid, the aqueous layers, and the saturated sodium chloride layers from the extraction can be flushed down the drain with water. Ether, hexanes, and TLC solvents should be placed in the organic solvents waste container. Hexanes and other solvents from the chromatography go into the organic solvents container. If local regulations allow, evaporate any residual solvent from the drying agents and silica gel in the hood and place the dried solid in the non-hazardous waste container. Otherwise, place the wet drying agent and silica gel in waste containers designated for this purpose.

4. CHROMATOGRAPHY OF A MIXTURE OF FERROCENE AND ACETYLFERROCENE

IN THIS EXPERIMENT, a mixture of two compounds is separated by chromatography on alumina. The first compound to come down the column is ferrocene (a yellow band). The solvent polarity is changed so that acetylferrocene is eluted as an orange band. The solvents are evaporated from the collection flasks and the compounds recrystallized. Both of these compounds are colored (see Chapter 49 for their preparation), so it is easy to follow the progress of the chromatographic separation.

Photo: *Column Chromatography*; Video: *Column Chromatography*

Acetylferrocene is toxic.

Prepare the microscale alumina column exactly as described at the beginning of the chapter. Then add a dry slurry of 90 mg of a 50:50 mixture of acetylferrocene and ferrocene that has been adsorbed onto 300 mg of alumina, following the procedure for preparing and adding the sample given at the beginning of the chapter.

Carefully add hexanes to the column, open the valve (use both hands), and elute the two compounds. The first to be eluted, ferrocene, will be seen as a yellow band. Collect this in a 10-mL flask. Any crystalline material seen at the tip of the valve should be washed into the flask with a drop or two of ether. Without allowing the column to run dry, add a 50:50 mixture of hexanes and ether, and elute the acetylferrocene, which will be seen as an orange band. Collect it in a 10-mL flask. Spot a silica gel TLC plate with these two solutions. Evaporate the solvents from the two flasks and determine the weights of the residues. An easy way to evaporate the solvent is to place it in a tared 25-mL filter flask and heat the flask in your hand under vacuum while swirling the contents (Fig. 9.10).

Ferrocene
MW 186.04
mp 172–174°C

(b)

Acetylferrocene
MW 228.08
mp 85–86°C

FIG. 9.10
Evaporation of a low-boiling liquid under vacuum. Heat is supplied by the hand, the contents of the flask are swirled, and the vacuum is controlled with the thumb.

Recrystallize the products from the minimum quantities of hot hexanes. Isolate the crystals, dry them, and determine their weights and melting points. Calculate the percent recovery of the crude and recrystallized products based on the 45 mg quantity of each in the original mixture.

The TLC plate is eluted with a 30:1 mixture of toluene and absolute ethanol. Do you detect any contamination of one compound by the other?

Cleaning Up. If regulations allow, empty the chromatography column onto a piece of aluminum foil in the hood. After the solvent has evaporated, place the alumina and sand in the nonhazardous waste container. Otherwise, place the wet alumina and sand in a designated waste container. Evaporate the crystallization mother liquor to dryness and place the residue in the hazardous waste container.

---

5. ISOLATION OF LYCOPENE AND β-CAROTENE

Lycopene, the red pigment in tomatoes, is a C_{40}-carotenoid made up of eight five-carbon isoprene units. β-Carotene, the yellow pigment of the carrot, is an isomer of lycopene in which the double bonds at C_1—C_2 and C'_1—C'_2 are replaced by bonds extending from C_1 to C_6 and from C'_1 to C'_6 to form rings. The chromophore in each case is a system of 11 all-trans conjugated double bonds; the closing of the two rings renders β-carotene less highly pigmented than lycopene.

These colored hydrocarbons have been encountered in the TLC experiment (*see* Chapter 8). The isolation procedure described here affords sufficient carotene and lycopene to carry out analytical spectroscopy and some isomerization reactions. It might be of interest if some students isolate carotene from strained carrot baby food while others isolate lycopene from tomato paste.

Lycopene is responsible not only for the red color of tomatoes but also of red grapefruit, watermelon,, and flamingos. If flamingos do not include foods containing lycopene in their diet, they will be white.

Lycopene is the predominant carotenoid in blood plasma. It is not converted into vitamin A as carotene is, but it is a powerful antioxidant and is an efficient scavenger of singlet oxygen.

To aspirator

Isoprene

Lycopene ($C_{40}H_{56}$)
MW 536.85
mp 173°C, λ_{max}^{hexane} 475 nm

β-Carotene ($C_{40}H_{56}$)
mp 183°C, λ_{max}^{hexane} 451 nm

Carotenoids are highly sensitive to photochemical air oxidation; therefore, protect solutions and solids from undue exposure to light and heat and work as rapidly as possible. Do not heat solutions when evaporating solvents and, if possible, flush apparatus with nitrogen to exclude oxygen. Research workers isolate these compounds in dimly lit rooms and/or wrap all containers and chromatographic columns in aluminum foil, and carry out extractions and crystallizations using solvents that have been deoxygenated.

 ## Dehydration and Extraction of Tomato or Carrot Paste

> IN THIS EXPERIMENT, a vegetable paste is stirred with acetone to remove water, but not the coloring matter, from the paste. The mixture is filtered, the yellow filtrate discarded, and the material on the filter squeezed as dry as possible. This solid is then extracted three times with dichloromethane. The solution is dried over calcium chloride and evaporated at room temperature under vacuum to leave the crude carotenoids.

Add 5 g of tomato or carrot paste to a 15-mL centrifuge tube or 25 × 150-mm test tube; then add about 7 mL of acetone and stir the paste for several minutes until it is no longer gummy. This acetone treatment removes most of the water from the cellular mixture. Filter the mixture on a small Büchner funnel. Scrape out the tube with a spatula, let it drain thoroughly, and squeeze out as much liquid as possible from the solid residue in the funnel with a spatula. Discard the yellow filtrate. Then return the solid residue to the centrifuge tube and add 5 mL of dichloromethane to effect extraction. Cap the tube and shake the mixture vigorously. Filter the mixture on a Büchner funnel once more, repeat the extraction and filtration with two or three further 5-mL portions of dichloromethane, clean the tube thoroughly, and place the filtrates in it. Dry the solution over anhydrous calcium chloride pellets, filter the solution into a small flask, and evaporate the solution to dryness with a stream of nitrogen or under vacuum using a rotary evaporator (Fig. 9.8 on page 197) or the apparatus shown in Figure 9.10 on page 201, never heating the sample above 50°C. Determine the weight of the crude material. It will be very small. If the residue is dry, as it should be, add just enough dichloromethane to dissolve the residue. Save 1 drop of this solution to carry out a TLC analysis (using dichloromethane as the eluent on silica gel plates; *see* Chapter 8). Then add 200 mg of alumina to the remaining dichloromethane solution and evaporate the mixture to dryness, again without heat.

Video: *Column Chromatography*; Photo: *Column Chromatography*

 ## Column Chromatography

The crude carotenoid is to be chromatographed on an 8-cm column of basic or neutral alumina, prepared with hexanes as the solvent (see the detailed procedure at the beginning of this chapter). Run out excess solvent or remove it from the top of the chromatography column with a Pasteur pipette. Using the dry sample loading method described at the beginning of this chapter, add the 300 mg of alumina that has the crude carotenoids absorbed on it. Add a few drops of hexanes to wash down the inside of the chromatography column and to consolidate the carotenoid mixture at the top of the column. Elute the column with hexanes, discard the initial colorless eluate, and collect all yellow or orange eluates together. Place a drop of solution on a microscope slide and evaporate the remainder to dryness using a stream of nitrogen or a rotary evaporator (*see* Fig. 9.8 on page 197). Examination of the material spotted on the slide may reveal crystallinity. If you are using tomato paste, a small amount of yellow Gr beta-carotene will come off first, followed by lycopene. Collect the red lycopene separately by eluting with a mixture of 10% acetone in hexane and also evaporate that solution to dryness.

Finally, dissolve the samples obtained by evaporating the solvent in the least possible amount of dichloromethane and carry out TLC of the two products in order to ascertain their purity (*see* Chapter 8, Experiment 2). You may want to combine your purified products with those of several other students, evaporate the solution to dryness, dissolve the residue in deuterochloroform, $CDCl_3$, and determine the ^1H NMR spectrum (*see* Chapter 12). Also obtain an infrared spectrum and a visible spectrum (in hexane).

Note that Gr beta-carotene is in demand as a source of vitamin A and is manufactured by an efficient synthesis. Until very recently no use for lycopene had been found.

Cleaning Up. Place recovered and unused dichloromethane in the halogenated organic waste container; the solvents used for TLC in the organic solvents waste container. If local regulations allow, evaporate any residual solvent from the drying agents in the hood and place the dried solid in the nonhazardous waste container. Otherwise, place the wet drying agent in a waste container designated for this purpose. Used plant material and dry TLC plates can be discarded in the nonhazardous waste container.

For Further Investigation

The carotenoids of any leaf can be isolated in the manner described in this experiment. Grind the leaf material (about 10 g) in a mortar with some sand; then follow the above procedure. Waxy leaves do not work well. The carotenoids are present in the leaf during its entire life span, so a green leaf from a maple tree or euonymus shrub, also known as burning bush, known to turn bright red in the fall, will show lycopene even when the leaf is green. In the fall, the chlorophyll decomposes before the carotenoids, so the leaves appear in a variety of orange and red hues.

It is of interest to investigate the carotenoids of the tomato, of which there are some 80 varieties. The orange-colored tangerine tomato contains an isomer of lycopene. If a hexane solution of the prolycopene from this tomato is treated with a drop of a very dilute solution of iodine in hexane and then exposed to bright light, the solution will turn deep-orange in color, indicating that a *cis*-double bond has isomerized to the *trans* form. The product is, however, still not identical to natural lycopene.

Isomerization

Prepare a hexane solution of either carotene or lycopene, and save a drop for TLC. Treat the solution with a very dilute solution of iodine in hexane, expose the resulting mixture to strong light for a few minutes, and then carry out TLC on the resulting solution. Also compare the visible spectrum before and after isomerization.

Iodine serves as a catalyst for the light-catalyzed isomerization of some of the *trans*-double bonds to an equilibrium mixture containing *cis*-isomers.

QUESTIONS

1. Predict the order of elution of a mixture of triphenylmethanol, biphenyl, benzoic acid, and methyl benzoate from an alumina column.

2. What would be the effect of collecting larger fractions when carrying out the experiments in this chapter?

3. What would have been the result if a large quantity of petroleum ether alone were used as the eluent in either experiments 1 or 2?

4. Once the chromatographic column has been prepared, why is it important to allow the level of the liquid in the column to drop to the level of the alumina before applying the solution of the compound to be separated?

5. A chemist started to carry out column chromatography on a Friday afternoon, reached the point at which the two compounds being separated were about three-fourths of the way down the column, and then returned on Monday to find that the compounds came off the column as a mixture. Speculate the reason for this. The column had not run dry over the weekend.

6. Write a detailed mechanism for the formation of fluorenone from fluorene. Explain the purpose of the phase-transfer catalyst.

7. The primary cause of low yields in the isolation of lycopene is oxidation of the product during the procedure. Once crystalline, it is reasonably stable. Speculate on the primary products formed by photochemical air oxidation of lycopene.

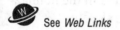

See *Web Links*

CHAPTER 10

Gas Chromatography: Analyzing Alkene Isomers

> **PRELAB EXERCISE:** If the dehydration of 2-methyl-2-butanol occurred on a purely statistical basis, what would be the relative proportions of 2-methyl-1-butene and 2-methyl-2-butene?

Gas chromatography (GC) is a rapid and sensitive method of separating and analyzing mixtures of gaseous or liquid compounds. The information it provides can tell you:

1. if you have successfully synthesized your product;
2. whether your product contains unreacted starting material or other impurities;
3. whether your product is a mixture of isomers; and
4. the relative amounts of different materials or isomers in a mixture.

Gas chromatography is one of several *instrumental* analysis methods used by organic chemists. Unlike the apparatus for thin-layer (TLC) or column chromatography, the apparatus used for gas chromatography—a modern gas chromatograph like that shown in Figure 10.1—costs thousands of dollars and is therefore shared among many users. There are two major reasons for spending this much money for this instrument. First, very complex mixtures containing hundreds of components can be separated. Second, separated components can be detected in very small amounts, 10^{-6} to 10^{-15} g. The chromatogram in Figure 10.2 is a good example of the power of gas chromatography; it shows the separation of 1 mg of crude oil into the hundreds of compounds that are present: alkanes, alkenes, and aromatics, including many isomers. The exceptional sensitivity of GC instruments is the major reason they are often used in environmental and forensic chemistry labs, where the detection of trace amounts is necessary.

Gas chromatography involves the same principles that apply to all forms of chromatography, which were covered in Chapter 8. The mobile phase is a gas, usually helium. The stationary phase is often a fairly nonpolar polymer such as polydimethylsiloxane or poly(ethylene glycol) (Carbowax) that is stable at temperatures as high as 350°C. The most commonly used phase is polydimethyl-siloxane in which 5% of the methyl groups have been replaced by phenyl groups.

There are two types of GC columns:

1. *Packed columns* in which the stationary phase consists of solid particles similar to the alumina or silica gel used in column chromatography, but coated with a nonpolar polymer (e.g., polydimethylsiloxane or Carbowax) and packed into 3–6 mm diameter metal or glass tubes that are 1–3 m long and rolled into a compact coil.

205

FIG. 10.1
A typical modern gas chromatograph with a data acquisition analysis computer.

FIG. 10.2
A chromatogram from the GC analysis of 1 mg of crude petroleum. The larger peaks represent the series of *n*-alkanes from C₅ to >C₃₀. The column was temperature programmed from 40°C to 300°C at 20°C/minutes.

Polydimethylsiloxane

$$\left[\begin{array}{c} CH_3 \\ | \\ Si-O \\ | \\ CH_3 \end{array} \right]_n$$

Polydimethylsiloxane

$$\left[CH_2-CH_2-O \right]_n$$

Carbowax

2. *Capillary columns* are long, thin, flexible quartz tubes with a very thin coating of a nonpolar stationary phase polymer on the inside wall. They can be 15–60 m long with internal diameters of 0.1–0.5 mm. Their successful development came about because of the invention of fiber optics and the discovery that coating the outside of hollow quartz fibers with a polyimide polymer prevented them from being easily scratched and broken.

Packed columns can separate milligram quantities of materials, while capillary columns work best with microgram quantities or less. On the other hand, capillary columns have much better separating power than packed columns.

The GC instrument has the following components (Fig. 10.3). Helium at a pressure of 10–30 psi from a compressed gas cylinder flows through the heated injector port, the column (located in a temperature-controlled oven), and the heated detector at a flow rate of 10–60 mL/minutes for a packed column and about 1 mL/minutes for a capillary column. A microliter syringe is used to inject 1–25 μL of sample

FIG. 10.3
A diagram of a gas chromatograph.

Syringe for
sample injection

Injector

Data acquisition and
analysis system

Detector

Carrier gas (He)

Column

Oven

through a rubber septum into the hot (~250°C) injector, where any liquid compounds are instantly vaporized to the gaseous state. As the vaporized molecules are swept through the column, they interact with the stationary phase and are adsorbed and desorbed many times each second in a dynamic equilibrium. As discussed in Chapter 8, the equilibria between adsorbed and free states depends on each molecule's size (London forces), polarity, and ability to hydrogen bond. Molecules spending more time absorbed to the stationary phase will not be carried through the column as rapidly as those that are weakly bound and free. A molecular view of this differential adsorption and flow is depicted in Figure 10.4.

The separated components pass one after the other into the detector. In column chromatography (*see* Chapter 9), human eyes are the detectors, either seeing colored compounds flow out of the column or visualizing the presence of colorless compounds on a fluorescent TLC plate. Gas chromatographs have electronic detectors that produce a signal voltage proportional to the number of molecules passing through them at any instant in time. A record of this voltage versus time is a gas chromatogram, with peak areas representing the amount of each individual component passing through the detector. Figure 10.5 is the chromatogram produced by the injection of a mixture of two compounds that were separated on the column and detected to produce peaks A and B. The amount of each is proportional to the area under its peak, so we can say that there appears to be about twice as much B as A. If an integrating recorder or computer data acquisition system is used, the exact areas under all peaks are automatically determined and can be used to quantify the amount of each component in a mixture.

Most GC instruments use one of the following types of detectors:

- The *thermal conductivity detector* (TCD) consists of an electrically heated wire or thermistor. The temperature of the sensing element depends on the thermal conductivity of the gas flowing around it. Changes in thermal conductivity, such as when organic molecules displace some of the carrier gas, cause a temperature rise in the element that is sensed as a change in resistance. The TCD is the least sensitive (detecting micrograms per second, 10^{-6} g/s, of material) of the four detectors described here, but it is quite rugged. It will detect all types of molecules, not just those containing C—H bonds, and compounds passing through it are unchanged and can be collected.

FIG. 10.4

The differential adsorption of two compounds in a flowing gas leads to the separation of the compounds over time.

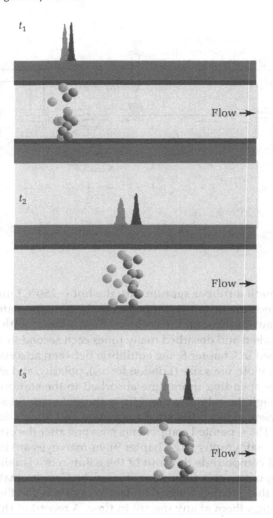

FIG. 10.5

A gas chromatogram of a mixture of two compounds, A and B.

- The *flame ionization detector* (FID) is at least a thousand times more sensitive than the TCD, easily detecting nanograms per second (10^{-9} g/s) of material. The molecules, however, must contain C—H bonds because the sample is actually burned to form ions. These ions carry a tiny current between two electrodes, which is greatly amplified to produce the signal output.

- The *electron capture detector* (ECD) contains a tiny amount of a radioactive substance, such as ^{63}Ni, that emits high-energy electrons (β^- particles).

The sample molecules can capture these electrons, become charged, and carry a current between two electrodes, as in the FID detector. Halocarbons have exceptionally good cross sections for electron capture because of the electronegativity of the halogen atoms, and these types of compounds can be detected at picogram per second (10^{-12} g/s) levels. For this reason, ECD is used to measure levels of chlorocarbon pollutants, such as chloroform, DDT, and dioxin in the environment.

- A *mass spectrometer detector* is the only one of these four detectors that provides information about the structure of the molecules that pass into it. For this reason, combination gas chromatography-mass spectrometry (GC–MS) systems are often used in organic research, forensic science, and environmental analysis in spite of their high cost ($40,000 to $250,000). Sensitivity is at the nanogram to picogram per second level. Chapter 13 discusses mass spectrometry in detail.

The instant you inject your sample into the GC instrument, you normally press a button that starts a clock in the data recorder, either an electronic integrator or a computer data system. Then, as each eluting component produces a peak in the detector, the top of the peak is detected, and the elapsed time since injection, called the *retention time*, is recorded and stored. In Figure 10.5, the retention time of compound A is T_1 and of B is T_2. Which compound is more strongly absorbed by the stationary phase?

One powerful variable in gas chromatography that is not available in TLC or column chromatography is temperature. Because the GC column is in an oven whose temperature is programmable—that is, the temperature can be raised from near room temperature to as high as 350°C at a constant and reproducible rate— we are able to separate much more complex mixtures than if the oven could be set to only one temperature. At room temperature, a mixture containing lower-boiling, weakly adsorbed components (such as ether and dichloromethane) and higher-boiling, strongly adsorbed components (such as butanol and toluene) might take hours to separate because the latter would move significantly more slowly through the column at low temperature. If the column were kept at a high temperature, the higher-boiling compounds would come out in a shorter time, but the lower-boiling ones would not be retained at all and therefore would not be separated. By programming the oven temperature, we can inject such a mixture at a low initial temperature so that weakly adsorbed components are separated. Then, as the temperature slowly rises, the more strongly retained components will move through the column faster and also have reasonable retention times. Temperature programming allows the separation of very complex mixtures containing both low-boiling small molecules and high-boiling large ones, as demonstrated by the GC analysis of crude petroleum in Figure 10.2 on page 206.

Temperature programming

THE GENERAL GC ANALYSIS PROCEDURE

Most GC separations are of gaseous and liquid mixtures. Although some solids will pass through a gas chromatograph at higher temperatures, it is best if all of the samples are distilled or vacuum transferred before injection into the GC instrument to ensure that only volatile compounds are present. If samples contain materials that cannot be vaporized and swept through the GC column, even at high temperatures, these will remain on the column and can ultimately ruin its performance. GC columns are expensive and can cost up to $400 to replace.

The guidelines given here are for GC analysis using a capillary column and an FID detector, which require very dilute solutions to avoid overwhelming the column, even if 90%–95% of the sample is split away so that it does not enter the column, a common practice in capillary chromatography. Samples analyzed with a packed column and a TCD detector can be much more concentrated or even undiluted (neat).

Sample Preparation

There are different ways of preparing a GC sample, depending on whether your product is a solid, a liquid (usually obtained by distillation), or a gaseous mixture; on the type of column (capillary or packed); and on the type of detector (FID, ECD, or TCD) being used.

Solid Samples

Low-melting, sublimable solids can be analyzed at higher column temperatures. Run a GC analysis on solids only if your experimental procedure explicitly says that you can do so. To prepare a solid sample for capillary column analysis, put a *small* crystal of the solid into a small vial and dissolve it in 1 mL of dichloromethane.

Liquid Samples

Dilute solutions of liquid organic mixtures in dichloromethane are the most common form of GC samples. Place 1 or 2 drops of your distilled product into a small vial and add 1 mL of dichloromethane. Because GC columns can be damaged by moisture, it is suggested that enough *anhydrous* sodium sulfate be added to cover the bottom of the vial to a depth of 1–2 mm to ensure that all traces of water are removed. The sodium sulfate can be left in the sample because it usually will not go into the fine needle of the microliter syringe used to inject the sample. Injection of 1 μL of a sample prepared in this manner usually provides strong signals in an FID detector. In special cases, undiluted neat or pure liquids can be injected directly without dilution as noted; for example, the methylbutenes in Experiment 1. Also, if preparative gas chromatography is used to separate and collect the components of a mixture, neat liquids are usually injected.

Gaseous Samples

Gases are normally collected over water, as in Experiment 2. Do not remove the septum-capped collection tube from the beaker of water, but bring it and the beaker of water together to the gas chromatograph. A gas syringe is inserted through the rubber septum and 10–500 μL (depending on the type of the gas chromatograph) of the gas sample is withdrawn and injected into the unit.

Sample Analysis

Make sure that the required gases are flowing and that the instrument has been on at least 1 hour so that all zones, the injector, the oven, and the detector have come to the required temperatures. Enter a temperature program: initial temperature, heating rate (in degrees per minutes), and final temperature, as required by the particular experiment. Fill the microliter syringe with the sample solution, normally 1 μL. A 10-μL capacity syringe with a plunger guide is recommended. Handle this expensive syringe carefully; it has a sharp needle, and the glass barrel is easily dropped and broken. Make sure that there are no bubbles in the syringe barrel when you draw up the sample. If bubbles are present, fill the syringe about halfway and depress the plunger quickly. Draw up the sample again slowly. Repeat as necessary to remove all bubbles. To obtain a quality chromatogram, the needle should be inserted rapidly, the sample should be injected rapidly and the syringe should be removed as soon as the plunger has been depressed and the sample injected. Then quickly press the start analysis button on the gas chromatograph, computer, or integrator to start data acquisition or mark the paper on the pen recorder.

Do not touch the metal injector cap. It is very HOT.

Once all the compounds have eluted and the oven temperature program has finished, the run should be stopped. Plot your chromatogram using the computer or remove the chromatogram chart from the integrator or flat bed recorder. Record the GC analysis parameters: column diameter and length, column packing type, carrier gas and its flow rate, column temperature (initial, final, and heating rate if programmed), detector and injector temperatures, sample injection amount and solvent (if used), signal attenuation, and chart speed; keep these with your gas chromatogram. Write the structures of all identifiable peaks on the chromatogram. If you used dichloromethane to dilute your sample, the largest peak will be due to this substance and will have a short retention time.

Remember that retention times are not constants. If the programmed oven temperature rate is higher or lower than for a prior analysis, then the retention times for all of the peaks will be consistently shorter or consistently longer. Changes in helium flow and the aging of the column also affect retention times. Chemists primarily look for similarities in the pattern of eluting peaks, not for perfect matches in retention times. In general, for simple mixtures chromatographed on nonpolar stationary phases, the retention time order is the same as the order of increasing boiling points. For example, you would expect cyclohexene (bp 83°C) to have a shorter retention time than toluene (bp 110°C). You can often ascertain the identity of a certain peak by adding a small amount of a known standard to the sample and rerunning the GC analysis. The peak corresponding to the standard will increase significantly and can be identified. Often the chromatogram will show a number of small peaks that cannot be assigned to the product, the starting material, or the solvents; these are likely due to byproducts. As long as these impurities are minor, say, less than 10% of the total area (not including the solvent), they can probably be ignored. The ultimate method of identifying every peak is to analyze the sample on a GC–MS instrument (Fig. 10.6).

Cleaning Up. Rinse out the syringe by filling it with dichloromethane and squirting it onto a tissue or paper towel at least four times. Clean and return any sample collection tubes, if used.

Collecting a Sample for an Infrared Spectrum

The small amount of sample analyzed in gas chromatography is an advantage in many cases, but it precludes isolating the separated components. Some specialized chromatographs can separate samples as large as 0.5 mL per injection and automatically collect each fraction in a separate container. At the other extreme, gas chromatographs equipped with FIDs can detect micrograms of substances, such as traces of pesticides in food, or drugs in blood and urine. Clearly, a gas chromatogram gives little information about the chemical nature of the sample being detected. Gas chromatography cannot positively identify most samples, nor can it always detect all substances in a sample. All that a gas chromatogram can truly tell you is that the detector was sensitive to a compound, and it can give you the relative time that a component eluted from a column. However, certain

FIG. 10.6
A combined gas chromatograph/mass spectrometer, fitted with an automatic sample changer.

FIG. 10.7
Some gas chromatographs with packed columns allow the collection of small amounts of separated compounds.

FIG. 10.8
A gas chromatographic collection device. Fill the container with ice or a dry ice–acetone mixture and attach to the outlet port of the gas chromatograph.[1]

Polypropylene cup, fill with ice

1-mm Hole

Polypropylene microscale centrifuge tube, 5.3 × 47 mm

Outlet port of gas chromatograph

preparative chromatographs, like that shown in Figure 10.7, allow the collection of enough sample at the exit port to obtain an infrared spectrum. About 10–15 μL of a mixture (not diluted in solvent) is injected, and as the peak for the compound of interest appears, a 2-mm-diameter glass tube, 3 in. long and packed with glass wool, is inserted into the rubber septum at the exit port. The sample, if it is not too volatile, will condense in the cold glass tube. Subsequently, the sample is washed out with 1 or 2 drops of solvent, and an infrared spectrum is obtained. This process can be repeated to collect enough sample for obtaining an NMR spectrum (*see* Chapter 12), using a few drops of deuterochloroform ($CDCl_3$) to wash out the tube each time. See Figure 10.8 for another collection device.

[1]This apparatus is available from Kimble Kontes (Vineland, NJ).

EXPERIMENTS

1. 2-METHYL-1-BUTENE AND 2-METHYL-2-BUTENE SYNTHESIS BY DEHYDRATION OF AN ALCOHOL[2]

2-Methylcyclohexanol can be used as a substrate if the volatility of the butenes is a problem.

The dilute sulfuric acid–catalyzed dehydration of 2-methyl-2-butanol (*t*-amyl alcohol) proceeds readily to give a mixture of alkenes that can be analyzed by gas chromatography. The mechanism of this reaction involves the intermediate formation of the relatively stable tertiary carbocation, followed by the loss of a proton either from a primary carbon atom to give the terminal olefin, 2-methyl-1-butene, or from a secondary carbon to give 2-methyl-2-butene.

$$CH_3CH_2\overset{\overset{\displaystyle OH}{|}}{\underset{\underset{\displaystyle CH_3}{|}}{C}}CH_3 + H_2SO_4 \underset{\text{fast}}{\rightleftharpoons} CH_3CH_2\overset{\overset{\displaystyle \overset{+}{O}H_2}{|}}{\underset{\underset{\displaystyle CH_3}{|}}{C}}CH_3 + HSO_4^-$$

2-Methyl-2-butanol
bp 102°C
den. 0.805
MW 88.15

$$CH_3CH_2\overset{\overset{\displaystyle \overset{+}{O}H_2}{|}}{\underset{\underset{\displaystyle CH_3}{|}}{C}}CH_3 \underset{\text{slow}}{\rightleftharpoons} CH_3CH_2\overset{+}{\underset{\underset{\displaystyle CH_3}{|}}{C}}CH_3 + H_2O$$

$$CH_3CH_2\overset{+}{C}-CH_2 \rightleftharpoons CH_3CH_2C=CH_2$$
$$\phantom{CH_3CH_2\overset{+}{C}-}\underset{\displaystyle CH_3}{|} \underset{\displaystyle CH_3}{|}$$

2-Methyl-1-butene
bp 31.16°C
den. 0.662
MW 70.14

---

[2]Schimelpfenig, C. W. *J. Chem. Educ.* 1962, *39*, 310.

$$CH_3CH-\overset{+}{C}CH_3 \rightleftharpoons CH_3CH=CCH_3$$

2-Methyl-2-butene
bp 38.57°C
den. 0.662
MW 70.14

2-Methyl-2-butanol can also be dehydrated in high yield using iodine as a catalyst:

$$CH_3CH_2\overset{OH}{\underset{CH_3}{C}}CH_3 \overset{I_2 \text{ (trace)}}{\rightleftharpoons} CH_3CH_2\overset{OI}{\underset{CH_3}{C}}CH_3 \overset{-HOI}{\rightleftharpoons}$$

$$CH_3CH_2\overset{}{\underset{CH_3}{C}}=CH_2 + CH_3CH=\overset{}{\underset{CH_3}{C}}CH_3 + HI + HOI$$

Each step of this E_1 elimination reaction is reversible, and thus the reaction is driven to completion by removing one of the products, the alkene. Often these reactions produce several alkene isomers. The Saytzeff rule states that the more substituted alkene is the more stable, and thus the one formed in larger amount. The *trans*-isomer is more stable than the *cis*-isomer. With this information, it should be possible to deduce which peak on the gas chromatogram corresponds to a given alkene and to predict the ratios of the products.

In analyzing your results from this experiment, consider the fact that the carbocation can lose any of six primary hydrogen atoms but only two secondary hydrogen atoms to give the product olefins.

Microscale Procedure

IN THIS EXPERIMENT, a tertiary alcohol is dehydrated to a mixture of alkenes in a reaction catalyzed by sulfuric acid. The products are collected by simple distillation into an ice-cold vial. Cold aqueous base is added to remove the acid, and the organic layer is dried with calcium chloride. The products are again distilled and then analyzed by gas chromatography.

Into a 5-mL long-necked, round-bottomed flask, place 1 mL of water and then add dropwise with thorough mixing 0.5 mL of concentrated sulfuric acid. Cool the hot solution in an ice bath; then add to the cold solution 1.0 mL (0.80 g) of 2-methyl-2-butanol. Mix the reactants thoroughly, add a boiling stone, and set up the apparatus for simple distillation, as shown in Figure 10.9. Hold the flask in a

FIG. 10.9
An apparatus for the dehydration of 2-methyl-2-butanol. The beaker can be clamped with a large three-prong clamp.

Air condenser

Ice

Receiver vial

Boiling chip

⚠
Handle sulfuric acid with care.

Keep the side arm well down inside the cold vial to avoid losing product.

towel while connecting the apparatus to guard against spills or flask breakage. Cool the receiver (a vial) in ice to avoid losing the highly volatile products. Warm the flask on a sand bath to start the reaction and distill the products over the temperature range 30°C–45°C. After all the products have distilled, the rate of distillation will decrease markedly. Cease distillation at this point. After this, the temperature registered on the thermometer will rise rapidly as water and sulfuric acid begin to distill.

To the distillate, add 0.3 mL *cold* 3 *M* sodium hydroxide solution to neutralize sulfurous acid, mix well, draw off the aqueous layer, and dry the product over anhydrous calcium chloride pellets, adding the drying agent in small quantities until it no longer clumps together. Keep the vial cold. While the product is drying, rinse out the distillation apparatus with water, ethanol, and then a small amount of acetone and dry it thoroughly by drawing air through it using an aspirator. If this is not done carefully, the products will become contaminated with acetone. Carefully transfer the dry mixture of butenes to the distilling apparatus using a Pasteur pipette, add a boiling chip to the now dry products, and distill into a tared, cold receiver. Collect the portion boiling up to 43°C. Weigh the product and calculate the yield, which is normally around 50% on this small scale compared to 84% on a macroscale. Inject a few microliters of product into a gas chromatograph maintained at room temperature (packed column suggestion: 6-mm-diameter × 3-m column packed with 10% SE-30 silicone rubber on Chromosorb-W).

Products are easily lost by evaporation. Store the mixture in a spark-proof refrigerator if GC analysis must be postponed.

For capillary column analysis, inject 1–10 μL of just the gaseous *vapors* above the liquid. Oven temperatures should be as low as room temperature (oven door open) to obtain baseline separation of the methylbutene isomers. In a few minutes, two peaks should appear. Measure the relative areas under the two peaks. From your knowledge of the mechanisms of the dehydration of secondary alcohols, which olefin should predominate? Does this agree with the boiling points? (In general, the compound with the shorter retention time has the lower boiling point.)

Cleaning Up. The residue in the reaction tube should be diluted with water, neutralized with sodium carbonate, and then flushed down the drain.

 Macroscale Procedure

Cool a 100 mL flask containing 18 mL of water in an ice-water bath while slowly pouring in 9 mL of concentrated sulfuric acid. Cool this 1:2 acid mixture further with swirling while slowly pouring in 18 mL (15 g) of 2-methyl-2-butanol. Shake the mixture thoroughly and then mount the flask for fractional distillation over a flask heater, with the arrangement for ice cooling of the distillate seen in Figure 19.2 (on page 337). Cooling is needed because the olefin is volatile. Use a long condenser and an ample stream of cooling water. Heat the flask slowly with an electric flask heater until distillation of the hydrocarbon is complete. If the ice-cooled test tube will not hold 15 mL, be prepared to collect half of the distillate in another ice-cooled test tube. Transfer the distillate to a cool separatory funnel and shake it with about 5 mL of a cold 3 *M* sodium hydroxide solution to remove any traces of sulfurous acid. The aqueous solution sinks to the bottom and is drawn off. Dry the hydrocarbon layer by adding sufficient anhydrous calcium chloride pellets until the drying agent no longer clumps together. After about 5 minutes, remove the drying agent by gravity filtration or careful decantation into a dry 25-mL round-bottomed flask, and distill the dried product through a fractionating column (*see* Fig. 19.2 on page 337), taking the same precautions as before to avoid evaporation losses. Rinse the fractionating column with acetone and dry it with a stream of air to remove water from the first distillation. Collect in a tared bottle the portion boiling at 30°C–43°C. The yield reported in the literature is 84%; the average student yield is about 50%. Analyze the sample by injecting a few microliters of product into a gas chromatograph maintained at room temperature and equipped with a 6-mm-diameter × 3-m column packed with 10% SE-30 silicone rubber on Chromosorb-W or a similar inert packing. In a few minutes, two peaks should appear. From your knowledge of the mechanisms of dehydration of secondary alcohols, which olefin should predominate? Does this agree with the boiling points? (In general, the compound with the shorter retention time has the lower boiling point.) Measure the relative areas under the two peaks.

Handle sulfuric acid with care.

Cleaning Up. The pot residue from the reaction is combined with the sodium hydroxide wash and neutralized with sodium carbonate. The pot residue from the distillation of the product is combined with the acetone that was used to wash out the apparatus and placed in the organic solvents waste container. If the calcium chloride pellets are dry, they can be placed in the nonhazardous solid waste container. If they are wet with organic solvents, they must be placed in the hazardous solid waste container for solvent-contaminated drying agents.

2. COMPUTATIONAL CHEMISTRY

The steric energies of the two isomeric butenes produced in Experiment 1 can be calculated using a molecular mechanics program, but the results are not valid because the bonding type is not the same. It is possible to compare the steric energies of *cis*- and *trans*-isomers of an alkene, but not a 1,1-disubstituted alkene with a 1,2-disubstituted alkene.

Compare your yields of the two isomers to their heats of formation, calculated using AM1 or a similar semiempirical calculation as described in Chapter 15. Do the calculated heats of formation correlate with the relative percentages of the isomers? What does this correlation or lack thereof tell you about the mechanism of the reaction?

3. 1-BUTENE AND *cis*- AND *trans*-2-BUTENE SYNTHESIS BY DEHYDRATION OF AN ALCOHOL[3]

2-Butanol
MW 74.12
bp 98°C

1-Butene
MW 56.11
bp −6.3°C

***cis*-2-Butene**
MW 56.11
bp 3.7°C

***trans*-2-Butene**
MW 56.11
bp 0.9°C

IN THIS EXPERIMENT, 2-butanol is dehydrated with sulfuric acid to give a mixture of gaseous alkenes that are collected by the downward displacement of water. The gaseous mixture is analyzed by gas chromatography.

Video: *Butenes from Butanol*; Photo: *Placing a Polyethylene Tube through a Septum*

Bend the polyethylene tubing to shape in hot sand or steam.

In a 10 × 100 mm reaction tube, place 0.10 mL (81 mg) of 2-butanol and 0.05 mL (1 drop) of concentrated sulfuric acid. It is not necessary to measure the quantities of alcohol and acid exactly. Mix the reactants well and add a boiling chip. Stirring the reaction mixture is not necessary because it is homogeneous. Insert a polyethylene tube through a septum (Fig. 10.10), place this septum on the reaction tube, and lead the tubing into the mouth of the distilling column/collection tube, which is also capped with a septum. The distilling column/collection tube is filled with water, the open end capped with a finger, and inverted in a beaker of water and clamped for the collection of butene by the downward displacement of water (Fig. 10.11).

Lower the reaction tube into a hot (~100°C) sand bath and increase the heat slowly to complete the reaction. Collect a few milliliters of the butene mixture and *remove the polyethylene tube from the water bath*. If the polyethylene tube is not removed from the water bath, water will be sucked back into the reaction tube

[3]Helmkamp, G. K.; Johnson, H. W. Jr. *Selected Experiments in Organic Chemistry*, 3rd ed., Freeman: New York, 1983; 99.

FIG. 10.10

To thread a polyethylene tube through a septum, make a hole in the septum with a needle and then push a toothpick through the hole. Push the polyethylene tube firmly onto the toothpick; then pull and push on the toothpick to thread the tubing through the septum. Finally, pull the tube from the toothpick after it has come out the other side of the septum. A blunt syringe needle can also be used instead of a toothpick.

FIG. 10.11

An apparatus for the dehydration of 2-butanol. Butenes are collected by the downward displacement of water.

when it cools. Do not remove the septum-capped collection tube from the beaker of water, but bring it and the beaker of water together to the gas chromatograph. Use about 0.5 mL of the gaseous butene mixture to carry out the GC analysis with a TCD detector, or a smaller amount if an FID detector is used.

Cleaning Up. The residue in the reaction tube may be diluted with water and flushed down the drain.

QUESTIONS

1. Write the structures of the three olefins produced by the dehydration of 3-methyl-3-pentanol.

2. When 2-methylpropene is bubbled into dilute sulfuric acid at room temperature, it appears to dissolve. What new substance has been formed?

3. A student wished to prepare ethylene gas by the dehydration of ethanol at 140°C, using sulfuric acid as the dehydrating agent. A low-boiling liquid was obtained instead of ethylene. What was the liquid, and how might the reaction conditions be changed to give ethylene?

4. What would be the effect on retention time of increasing the carrier gas flow rate?

5. What would be the effect on retention time of raising the column temperature?

6. What would be the effect of raising the temperature or increasing the carrier gas flow rate on the ability to resolve two closely spaced peaks?

7. If you were to use a column one-half the length of the one you actually used, how do you think the retention times of the butenes would be affected? How do you think the separation of the peaks would be affected? How do you think the width of each peak would be affected?

8. From your knowledge of the dehydration of tertiary alcohols, which olefin should predominate in the product of the dehydration of 2-methyl-2-butanol? Why?

9. What is the maximum volume (at standard temperature and pressure, STP) of the butene mixture that could be obtained by the dehydration of 81 mg of 2-butanol?

10. What other gases are in the collection tube besides the three butenes at the end of the reaction in Experiment 3?

11. Using a computational chemistry program (*see* Chapter 15), calculate the steric energies or heats of formation of the three isomeric butenes produced in Experiment 3. Do these energies correlate with the product distributions found? What does a correlation or lack thereof tell you about the mechanism of the reaction?

For Additional Experiments, sign in at this book's premium website at **www.cengage.com/login**.

11 CHAPTER

Infrared Spectroscopy

PRELAB EXERCISE: When an infrared (IR) spectrum is run, it is possible that the chart paper is not properly placed or that the spectrometer is not mechanically adjusted. Describe how you could calibrate an IR spectrum.

The types and molecular environment of functional groups in organic molecules can be identified by infrared (IR) spectroscopy. Like nuclear magnetic resonance (NMR) and ultraviolet (UV) spectroscopy, IR spectroscopy is nondestructive. Moreover, the small quantity of sample needed, the speed with which a spectrum can be obtained, the relatively low cost of the spectrometer, and the wide applicability of the method combine to make IR spectroscopy one of the most common structural elucidation tools used by organic chemists.

IR radiation consists of wavelengths that are longer than those of visible light. It is detected not with the eyes, but by a feeling of warmth on the skin. When absorbed by molecules, radiation of these wavelengths (typically 2.5–5 μm) increases the amplitude of vibrations of the chemical bonds joining atoms.

IR spectra are measured in units of frequency or wavelength. The wavelength is measured in micrometers[1] or microns, μ (1 μm = 1 × 10⁻⁶ m). The positions of absorption bands are measured in frequency units called wavenumbers ν, which are expressed in reciprocal centimeters, cm⁻¹, corresponding to the number of cycles of the wave in each centimeter.

2.5–25 μm equals 4000–400 cm⁻¹. Wavenumber(cm⁻¹) is proportional to frequency (c is the speed of light).

$$\bar{\nu}\,(\text{cm}^{-1}) = \frac{\nu}{c}$$

$$\text{cm}^{-1} = \frac{10{,}000}{\mu\text{m}}$$

Examine the scale carefully.

Unlike UV and NMR spectra, IR spectra are inverted, with the strongest absorptions at the bottom (called "peaks" although they look like valleys), and are not always presented on the same scale. Some spectrometers record the spectra on an ordinate linear in microns, but this compresses the low-wavelength region. Other spectrometers present the spectra on a scale linear in reciprocal centimeters, but linear on two different scales: one between 4000 and 2000 cm⁻¹, which spreads out the low-wavelength region; and the other a smaller one between 2000 and 667 cm⁻¹. Consequently, spectra of the same compound run on two different spectrometers will not always look the same.

---

[1]Although micrometers are known as microns, the micron is not the official SI (International System of Units) unit.

220

IR spectroscopy easily detects:

Hydroxyl groups	—OH
Amines	—NH₂
Nitriles	—C≡N
Nitro groups	—NO₂

IR spectroscopy is especially useful for detecting and distinguishing among all carbonyl-containing compounds:

$$
\begin{array}{l}
\quad\quad\quad O \\
\quad\quad\quad \| \\
Acids \quad\quad -C-OH
\end{array}
$$

$$
\begin{array}{l}
\quad\quad\quad\quad O \\
\quad\quad\quad\quad \| \\
Amides \quad\quad -C-NH_2
\end{array}
$$

$$
\begin{array}{l}
\quad\quad\quad\quad\quad O \quad\quad O \\
\quad\quad\quad\quad\quad \| \quad\quad \| \\
Anhydrides \quad -C-O-C-
\end{array}
$$

$$
\begin{array}{l}
\quad\quad\quad\quad O \\
\quad\quad\quad\quad \| \\
Aldehydes \quad -C-H
\end{array}
$$

$$
\begin{array}{l}
\quad\quad\quad\quad O \\
\quad\quad\quad\quad \| \\
Ketones \quad -C-
\end{array}
$$

$$
\begin{array}{l}
\quad\quad\quad O \\
\quad\quad\quad \| \\
Esters \quad -C-O-
\end{array}
$$

$$
\begin{array}{l}
\quad\quad\quad\quad O \\
\quad\quad\quad\quad \| \\
Lactones \quad -C-O-
\end{array}
$$

To picture the molecular vibrations that interact with IR light, imagine a molecule as being made up of balls (atoms) connected by springs (bonds). The vibration can be described by Hooke's law from classical mechanics, which says that the frequency of a stretching vibration is directly proportional to the strength of the spring (bond) and inversely proportional to the masses connected by the spring. Thus we find that C—H, N—H, and O—H bond-stretching vibrations are high frequency (short wavelength) compared to those of C—C and C—O because of the low mass of hydrogen compared to that of carbon or oxygen. The bonds connecting carbon to bromine and iodine, atoms of large mass, vibrate so slowly that they are beyond the range of most common IR spectrometers. A double bond can be regarded as a stiffer, stronger spring, so we find C=C and C=O vibrations at higher frequencies than C—C and C—O stretching vibrations. And C≡C and C≡N stretch at even higher frequencies than C=C and C=O (but at lower frequencies than C—H, N—H, and O—H). These frequencies are in keeping with the bond strengths of single (~100 kcal/mol), double (~160 kcal/mol), and triple bonds (~220 kcal/mol).

These stretching vibrations are intense and particularly easy to analyze. A nonlinear molecule of n atoms can undergo $3n - 6$ possible modes of vibration, which means cyclohexane with 18 atoms can undergo 48 possible modes of vibration. Each vibrational mode produces a peak in the spectrum because it corresponds to the absorption of energy at a discrete frequency. These many modes of vibration create a complex spectrum that defies simple analysis, but even in very complex molecules, certain functional groups have characteristic frequencies that can easily be recognized. Within these functional groups are the above-mentioned atoms and bonds, C—H, N—H, O—H, C=C, C=O, C≡C, and C≡N. Their absorption frequencies are given in Table 11.1.

When the frequency of IR light is the same as the natural vibrational frequency of an interatomic bond, light will be absorbed by the molecule, and the amplitude of the bond vibration will increase. The intensity of IR absorption bands is proportional to the change in dipole moment that a bond undergoes when it stretches. Thus, the most intense bands (peaks) in an IR spectrum are often from C=O and C—O stretching vibrations, whereas the C≡C stretching band for a symmetrical acetylene is almost nonexistent because the molecule undergoes no net change of dipole moment when it stretches:

TABLE 11.1 *Characteristic IR Absorption Wavenumbers*

Functional Group	Wavenumber (cm⁻¹)
O—H	3600–3400
N—H	3400–3200
C—H	3080–2760
C≡N	2260–2215
C≡C	2150–2100
C=O	1815–1650
C=C	1660–1600
C—O	1200–1050

$$\overset{\mid}{\underset{\mid}{C}}=O \longleftrightarrow \overset{+}{\underset{\mid}{C}}=\overset{-}{O} \qquad H_3C-C\equiv C-CH_3 \longleftrightarrow H_3C-\overset{+}{C}\equiv \overset{-}{C}-CH_3$$

Change in dipole moment   No change in dipole moment

Unlike proton NMR spectroscopy, where the area of the peaks is strictly proportional to the number of hydrogen atoms causing the peaks, the intensities of IR peaks are not proportional to the numbers of atoms causing them. Given the chemical shifts and coupling constants, it is not too difficult to calculate a theoretical NMR spectrum that is an exact match to the experimental one. For larger molecules, the calculation of all possible stretching and bending frequencies (the IR spectrum) requires large amounts of time on a fast computer. Every peak or group of peaks in an NMR spectrum can be assigned to specific hydrogens in a molecule, but the assignment of the majority of peaks in an IR spectrum with absolute certainty is usually not possible. Peaks to the right (longer wavelength) of 1250 cm^{-1} are the result of combinations of vibrations that are characteristic not of individual functional groups but of the molecule as a whole. This part of the spectrum is often referred to as the *fingerprint region* because it is uniquely characteristic of each molecule. Although two organic compounds can have the same melting points or boiling points and can have identical UV and NMR spectra, they cannot have identical IR spectra (except, as usual, for enantiomers). IR spectroscopy is thus the final arbiter in deciding whether two compounds are identical.

The intensity of absorption is proportional to the change in dipole moment.

ANALYSIS OF IR SPECTRA

Only a few simple rules or equations govern IR spectroscopy. Because it is not practical to calculate theoretical spectra, the analysis is done almost entirely by *correlation* with other spectra. In printed form, these comparisons take the form of lengthy discussions, so detailed analysis of a spectrum is best done with a good reference book at hand.

In a modern analytical or research laboratory, a collection of many thousands of spectra is maintained on a computer. When the spectrum of an unknown compound is run, the analyst picks out five or six of the strongest peaks and asks the computer to list all the known compounds that have peaks within a few reciprocal centimeters of the experimental peaks. From the printout of a dozen or so compounds, it is often possible to pinpoint all the functional groups in the molecule being analyzed. There may be a perfect match of all peaks, in which case the unknown will have been identified.

For relatively simple molecules, a computer search is hardly necessary. Much information can be gained about the functional groups in a molecule from relatively few correlations.

To carry out an analysis, (1) pay most attention to the strongest absorptions; (2) pay more attention to peaks to the left (shorter wavelength) of 1250 cm^{-1}; and (3) pay as much attention to the absence of certain peaks as to the presence of others. The absence of characteristic peaks will definitely exclude certain functional groups. Be wary of weak O—H peaks because water is a common contaminant of many samples. Because potassium bromide is hygroscopic, water is often found in the spectra of samples prepared as KBr pellets.

The Step-by-Step Analysis of IR Spectra

IR spectra are analyzed as follows:

1. Is there a peak between 1820 cm^{-1} and 1625 cm^{-1}? If not, go to Step 2.
   (a) Is there a strong, wide O—H peak between 3200 cm^{-1} and 2500 cm^{-1}? If so, the compound is a carboxylic acid (Fig. 11.1, oleic acid). If not . . .
   (b) Is there a medium-to-weak N—H band between 3520 cm^{-1} and 3070 cm^{-1}? If there are two peaks in this region, the compound is a primary amide; if not, it is a secondary amide. If there is no peak in this region . . .
   (c) Are there two strong peaks, one in the region 1870 cm^{-1} to 1800 cm^{-1} and the other in the region 1800 cm^{-1} to 1740 cm^{-1}? If so, an acid anhydride is present. If not . . .
   (d) Is there a peak in the region of 2720 cm^{-1}? If so, is the carbonyl peak in the region 1715 cm^{-1} to 1680 cm^{-1}? If so, the compound is a conjugated aldehyde; if not, it is an isolated aldehyde (Fig. 11.2, benzaldehyde). However, if there is no peak near 2720 cm^{-1} . . .
   (e) Does the strong carbonyl peak fall in the region 1815 cm^{-1} to 1770 cm^{-1} and the compound give a positive Beilstein test? If so, it is an acid halide. If not . . .
   (f) Does the strong carbonyl peak fall in the region 1690 cm^{-1} to 1675 cm^{-1}? If so, the compound is a conjugated ketone. If not . . .

FIG. 11.1
The IR spectrum of oleic acid (thin film).

FIG. 11.2
The IR spectrum of benzaldehyde (thin film).

FIG. 11.3
The IR spectrum of *n*-butyl acetate (thin film).

FIG. 11.4
The IR spectrum of cyclohexanol (thin film).

(g) Does the strong carbonyl peak fall in the region 1670 cm⁻¹ to 1630 cm⁻¹? If so, the compound is a tertiary amide. If not . . .

(h) Does the spectrum have a strong, wide peak in the region 1310 cm⁻¹ to 1100 cm⁻¹? If so, does the carbonyl peak fall in the region 1730 cm⁻¹ to 1715 cm⁻¹? If so, the compound is a conjugated ester; if not, the ester is not conjugated (Fig. 11.3, *n*-butyl acetate). If there is no strong, wide peak in the region 1310 to 1100 cm⁻¹, then . . .

(i) The compound is an ordinary nonconjugated ketone (see for example Fig. 22.8, the IR spectrum of cyclohexanone).

2. If the spectrum lacks a carbonyl peak in the region 1820 cm⁻¹ to 1625 cm⁻¹, does it have a broad band in the region 3650 cm⁻¹ to 3200 cm⁻¹? If so, does it also have a peak at about 1200 cm⁻¹, a C—H stretching peak to the left of 3000 cm⁻¹, and a peak in the region 1600 cm⁻¹ to 1470 cm⁻¹? If so, the compound is a phenol. If the spectrum does not meet these latter three criteria, the compound is an alcohol (Fig. 11.4, cyclohexanol). However, if there is no broad band in the region 3650 cm⁻¹ to 3200 cm⁻¹, then . . .

(a) Is there a broad band in the region 3500 cm⁻¹ to 3300 cm⁻¹, and does the compound smell like an amine, or does it contain nitrogen? If so, are there

FIG. 11.5
The IR spectrum of benzonitrile (thin film).

FIG. 11.6
The IR spectrum of 3-methylpentane (thin film).

two peaks in this region? If so, the compound is a primary amine; if not, it is a secondary amine. However, if there is no broad band in the region 3500 cm⁻¹ to 3300 cm⁻¹, then . . .

(b) Is there a sharp peak of medium-to-weak intensity at 2260 cm⁻¹ to 2100 cm⁻¹? If so, is there also a peak at 3320 cm⁻¹ to 3310 cm⁻¹? If so, then the compound is a terminal acetylene. If not, the compound is most likely a nitrile (Fig. 11.5, benzonitrile), although it might be an asymmetrically substituted acetylene. If there is no sharp peak of medium-to-weak intensity at 2260 cm⁻¹ to 2100 cm⁻¹, then . . .

(c) Are there strong peaks in the region 1600 cm⁻¹ to 1540 cm⁻¹ and 1380 cm⁻¹ to 1300 cm⁻¹? If so, the molecule contains a nitro group. If not . . .

(d) Is there a strong peak in the region 1270 cm⁻¹ to 1060 cm⁻¹? If so, the compound is an ether. If not . . .

(e) The compound is either a tertiary amine (odor?), a halogenated hydrocarbon (Beilstein test?), or just an ordinary hydrocarbon (Fig. 11.6, 3-methylpentane, and Fig. 11.7, *t*-butylbenzene).

Many comments can be added to this bare outline. For example, dilute solutions of alcohols will show a sharp peak at about 3600 cm⁻¹ for a nonhydrogen-bonded O—H in addition to the usual broad hydrogen-bonded O—H peak.

FIG. 11.7
The IR spectrum of *t*-butylbenzene (thin film).

Aromatic hydrogens give peaks just to the left of 3000 cm⁻¹, whereas aliphatic hydrogens appear just to the right of 3000 cm⁻¹. However, NMR spectroscopy is the best method for identifying aromatic hydrogens.

The carbonyl frequencies listed earlier refer to an open chain or an unstrained functional group in a nonconjugated system. If the carbonyl group is conjugated with a double bond or an aromatic ring, the peak will be displaced to the right by 30 cm⁻¹. When the carbonyl group is in a ring smaller than six members or if there is oxygen substitution on the carbon adjacent to an aldehyde or ketone carbonyl, the peak will be moved to the left (refer to the margin notes about the effect of ring size and Table 11.2).

The effect of ring size on the carbonyl frequencies of lactones and esters:

1727 cm⁻¹

1745 cm⁻¹

1740 cm⁻¹

1775 cm⁻¹

1832 cm⁻¹

TABLE 11.2 *Characteristic IR Carbonyl Stretching Peaks (Chloroform Solutions)*

Carbonyl-Containing Compounds	Wavenumber (cm⁻¹)
Aliphatic ketones	1725–1705
Acid chlorides	1815–1785
α,β-Unsaturated ketones	1685–1666
Aryl ketones	1700–1680
Cyclohexanones	1725–1705
β-Diketones	1640–1540

The effect of ring size on carbonyl frequency of ketones:

1705 cm^{-1}

1715 cm^{-1}

1715 cm^{-1}

1745 cm^{-1}

1780 cm^{-1}

1815 cm^{-1}

TABLE 11.2 (*continued*)

	Carbonyl-Containing Compounds	Wavenumber (cm^{-1})
RCH	Aliphatic aldehydes	1740–1720
R—C=C—CH	α,β-Unsaturated aldehydes	1705–1685
Ar CH	Aryl aldehydes	1715–1695
RCOOH	Aliphatic acids	1725–1700
R—C=C—COOH	α,β-Unsatur.ated acids	1700–1680
ArCOOH	Aryl acids	1700–1680
RCOR′	Aliphatic esters	1740
R—C=C—COR′	α,β-Unsaturated esters	1730–1715
Ar COR	Aryl esters	1730–1715
HCOR	Formate esters	1730–1715
CH$_2$=CHOCCH$_3$ C$_6$H$_5$OCCH$_3$	Vinyl and phenyl acetate	1776
R—C—O—C—R	Acyclic anhydrides (two peaks) 1780–1740	1840–1800
RCNH$_2$	Primary amides	1694–1650
RCNHR′	Secondary amides	1700–1670
RCNR′$_2$	Tertiary amides	1670–1630

Methyl groups often give a peak near 1375 cm^{-1}, but NMR is a better method for detecting this group.

The pattern of substitution on an aromatic ring (mono-, *ortho*-, *meta*-, and *para*, di-, tri-, tetra-, and penta-) can be determined from C—H out-of-plane bending vibrations in the region 670–900 cm^{-1}. Much weaker peaks between 1650 cm^{-1} and 2000 cm^{-1} are illustrated in Figure 11.8.

Extensive correlation tables and discussions of characteristic group frequencies can be found in the specialized references listed at the end of this chapter.

THE FOURIER TRANSFORM INFRARED (FTIR) SPECTROMETER

Like their NMR counterparts, Fourier transform IR instruments are computer based, can sum a number of scans to increase the signal-to-noise ratio, and allow enormous flexibility in the ways spectra can be analyzed and displayed because they are digitally oriented. In addition, they are faster and more accurate than double-beam analog spectrometers.

A schematic diagram of a single-beam FTIR spectrometer is given in Figure 11.9. IR radiation goes to a Michelson interferometer in which half the light beam passes through a partially coated mirror to a fixed mirror, and half goes to a moving mirror. The combined beams pass through the sample and are then focused on the detector. The motion of the mirror gives a signal that varies sinusoidally. Depending on the mirror position, the different frequencies of light either reinforce or cancel each other, resulting in an interferogram. The mirror, the only moving part of the spectrometer, thus affects the light frequencies that encode the very high optical frequencies, transforming them to low-frequency signals that change as the mirror moves back and forth. The Fourier transform converts the digitized signal into a signal that is a function of frequency—creating a spectrum.

FIG. 11.9

The optical path diagram of an FTIR spectrometer.

Like Fourier transform NMR spectroscopy, all IR frequencies are sampled simultaneously instead of being scanned successively, so a spectrum is obtained in seconds. Because there is no slit to sort out the wavelengths, high resolution is possible without losing signal strength. Extremely small samples or very dilute solutions can be examined because it is easy to sum hundreds of scans in the computer. It is even possible to take a spectrum of an object seen under a microscope. The spectrum of one compound can be subtracted from, say, a binary mixture spectrum to reveal the nature of the other component. Data can be smoothed, added, resized, and so on because of the digital nature of the output from the spectrometer.

EXPERIMENTAL CONSIDERATIONS

The sample, solvents, and equipment must be dry.

Glass, quartz, and plastics are opaque to IR radiation and absorb it. Therefore, sample holders must be made of other transparent materials. Metal halide salts such as sodium or silver chloride, calcium or barium fluoride, and potassium bromide are transparent to IR radiation; these are prepared as large polished crystals for use in cell holders, with NaCl and KBr being the most common. They are fragile and are easily attacked by moisture, so they must be handled gently by the edges and kept away from moisture and aqueous solutions. IR spectra can be determined on neat (undiluted) liquids, on solutions with an appropriate solvent, and on solids using mulls (a finely ground solid suspended in oil) and KBr pellets, and by diffuse reflectance of the solid mixed with KBr. All IR cells or KBr powder must be stored in a desiccator when not in use.

THE SPECTRA OF NEAT LIQUIDS

To run a spectrum of a neat (free of water!) liquid, remove a demountable cell (Fig. 11.10) from the desiccator, place a drop of the liquid between the salt plates, press the plates together gently to remove any air bubbles, and add the top rubber gasket and metal top plate. Next, put on all four of the nuts and *gently* tighten them to apply an even pressure to the top plate. Place the cell in the sample compartment (nearest the front of the spectrometer) and run the spectrum.

Although running a spectrum on a neat liquid is convenient and results in no extraneous bands to interpret, it is not possible to control the path length of the light through the liquid in a demountable cell. A low-viscosity liquid when squeezed between the salt plates may be so thin that the short path length gives peaks that are too weak. A viscous liquid, on the other hand, may give peaks that are too intense. A properly run spectrum will have the most intense peak with a transmittance of about 10%.

A fast, simple alternative: Place a drop of the compound on a round salt plate, add a top plate, and mount the two on the holder pictured in Figure 11.11.

Another demountable cell is pictured in Figure 11.11. The plates are thin wafers of silver chloride, which is transparent to IR radiation. This cell has advantages over the salt cell in that the silver chloride disks are more resistant to breakage than NaCl plates, less expensive, and not affected by water. Because silver chloride is photosensitive, the wafers must be stored in a dark place to prevent them from turning black. Because one side of each wafer is recessed, the thickness of the sample can be varied according to the manner in which the cell is assembled. In general, the spectra of pure liquids are run as the thinnest possible films. Most of the spectra in this chapter have been obtained in this way. The disks are cleaned by

FIG. 11.10

An exploded view of a demountable salt cell for analyzing the IR spectra of neat liquids. The salt plates are fragile and expensive. Do not touch the surfaces. Use only dry solvents and samples.

Solvents: CHCl₃, CS₂, CCl₄

⚠ Chloroform, carbon tetrachloride, and carbon disulfide are toxic. The first two are carcinogens. Use a laboratory hood to minimize exposure to vapors.

Three drops are needed to fill the cell.

FIG. 11.11

A demountable silver chloride or sodium chloride cell.

Thin film of liquid to be analyzed

Cross-section of wafers or disks

O-rings

AgCl (or NaCl) disks

rinsing them with an organic solvent such as acetone or ethanol, and wiping dry with an absorbent paper towel.

A very simple cell consists of two circular NaCl disks (1-in. diameter × 3/16-in. thick, 25 mm × 4 mm). The sample, 1 drop of a pure liquid or solution, is applied to the center of a disk with a polyethylene pipette (to avoid scratching the NaCl disk). The other disk is added, the sample is squeezed to a thin film, and the two disks are placed on the V-shaped holder shown in Figure 11.11.

THE SPECTRA OF SOLUTIONS

The most widely applicable method of running the spectra of solutions involves dissolving an amount of the liquid or solid sample in an appropriate solvent to give a 10% solution. Just as in NMR spectroscopy, the best solvents to use are carbon disulfide and carbon tetrachloride. Because these compounds are not polar enough to dissolve many substances, chloroform is used as a compromise when the sample refuses to dissolve. Unlike NMR solvents, no solvent suitable in IR spectroscopy is entirely free of absorption bands in the frequency range of interest (Figs. 11.12, 11.13, and 11.14). In chloroform, for instance, no light passes through the cell between 650 cm⁻¹ and 800 cm⁻¹. As can be seen from the figures, spectra obtained using carbon disulfide and chloroform cover the entire IR frequency range. Carbon tetrachloride would appear to be a good choice because it has few interfering peaks, but it is a poor solvent for polar compounds. In practice, a background spectrum is run with the same solvent in the same cell used to run the sample solution, and the data system subtracts the solvent peaks in background spectrum from the solution spectrum to yield an IR spectrum of the sample only.

Three large drops of solution will fill the usual sealed IR cell (Fig. 11.15). A 10% solution of a liquid sample can be approximated by diluting 1 drop of the liquid sample with 9 drops of the solvent. Because weights are more difficult to estimate, solid samples should be weighed to obtain a 10% solution.

FIG. 11.12
The IR spectrum of chloroform (thin film).

FIG. 11.13
The IR spectrum of carbon disulfide (thin film).

FIG. 11.14
The IR spectrum of carbon tetrachloride (thin film).

FIG. 11.15
A sealed IR sample cell.

Hypodermic syringe port

Top plate

NaCl plates

Lead gasket 0.1 mm thick

Bottom plate

FIG. 11.16
Flushing an IR sample cell. The solvent used to dissolve the sample is used in this process.

NaCl

The solvent and the sample must be dry. Do not touch or breathe on NaCl plates. Cells are very expensive.

Dispose of waste solvents in the container provided.

First, obtain a background spectrum of the solvent. The IR cell is filled by inclining it slightly and placing about 3 drops of the solvent in the lower hypodermic port with a capillary dropper. The cell must be completely dry because the new sample will not enter if the cell contains solvent. The liquid can be seen rising between the salt plates by looking into the cell's window. In the most common sealed cell, the salt plates are spaced 0.1 mm apart. Be sure that the cell is filled past the top of the window and that no air bubbles are present. Then place a Teflon stopper lightly but firmly in the hypodermic port. Be particularly careful not to spill any of the sample on the outside of the cell windows. Place the cell in the instrument cell holder and acquire a background spectrum. Blow dry nitrogen or draw dry air through the cell to remove the solvent and dry the cell, fill with the sample solution prepared above, and acquire the spectrum.

After running the sample, force clean solvent through the cell using a syringe attached to the top port of the cell (Fig. 11.16). Dry using dry nitrogen or air, and store in a desiccator.

Cleaning Up. Discard halogenated liquids in the halogenated organic waste container. Other solutions should be placed in the organic solvents waste container.

MULLS

The sample must be finely ground.

Solids insoluble in the usual solvents can be run as mulls. In preparing a mull, the sample is ground to a particle size less than that of the wavelength of light going through the sample (2.5 μm) to avoid scattering light. About 15–20 mg of the sample is ground for 3–10 minutes in an agate mortar until it is spread over the entire inner surface of the mortar and has a caked and glassy appearance. Then to make a mull, add 1 or 2 drops of paraffin oil (Nujol; Fig. 11.17) and grind the sample for 2–5 more minutes. The mull, which should have the consistency of thin margarine, is transferred to the bottom salt plate of a demountable cell (*see* Fig. 11.10 on

FIG. 11.17
The IR spectrum of Nujol (paraffin oil).

page 230) using a rubber policeman, the top plate is added and rotated back and forth to distribute the sample evenly to eliminate all air pockets, and the spectrum is run. Because the bands from Nujol obscure certain frequency regions, running another mull using Fluorolube as the mulling agent will allow the entire IR spectral region to be covered. If the sample has not been ground sufficiently fine, there will be marked loss of transmittance at the short-wavelength end of the spectrum. After running the spectrum, the salt plates are wiped clean with a cloth saturated with an appropriate solvent.

A fast, simple alternative: Grind a few milligrams of the solid with 1 drop of tetrachloroethylene between two round salt plates. Mount on the holder as shown in Figure 11.11 on page 230.

POTASSIUM BROMIDE DISK

The spectrum of a solid sample can also be run by incorporating the sample in a potassium bromide (KBr) disk. This procedure needs only one disk to cover the entire spectral range because KBr is completely transparent to IR radiation. Although very little sample is required, making the disk calls for special equipment and time to prepare it. Because KBr is hygroscopic, water is a problem.

Into a stainless steel capsule containing a ball bearing are weighed 1.5–2 mg of the compound and 200 mg of spectroscopic-grade KBr (previously dried and stored in a desiccator). The capsule is shaken for 2 minutes on a Wig-L-Bug (the device used by dentists to mix silver amalgam). The sample is evenly distributed over the face of a 13-mm stainless steel die and subjected to a pressure of 14,000–16,000 psi for 3–6 minutes while under vacuum in a hydraulic press. A transparent disk is produced, which is removed from the die with tweezers and placed in a holder like that shown in Figure 11.11 on page 230 prior to running the spectrum.

DIFFUSE REFLECTANCE

Reasonable IR spectra of solids can be obtained without pressing a KBr pellet if the IR instrument is equipped with diffuse reflectance optics. A mixture of the sample and KBr is put in a small sample cup, and this is placed in the diffuse

FIG. 11.18
A simplified diagram of a diffuse reflectance system.

reflectance optics system (Fig. 11.18). When the IR beam enters the sample, it can either be reflected off the surface of a particle or be transmitted through a particle. The IR beam that passes through a particle can either reflect off the next particle or be transmitted through the next particle. This transmission-reflectance event can occur many times in the sample, which increases the path length. Finally, any scattered IR energy that is not absorbed by the sample is collected by a spherical mirror that is focused onto a detector. A background spectrum of only pure KBr should be run before the sample to subtract out any absorbance that is not from the sample.

Weigh out 0.160–0.170 g of KBr quickly (KBr readily absorbs atmospheric moisture) and place it in a vial. Weigh out between 4 mg and 7 mg of the solid sample to be analyzed and add this to the vial. Mix and transfer the mixture into a small, dry mortar and pestle. Grind for 1–2 minutes until a fine powder is obtained. Transfer to weighing paper and then to the cup of the diffuse reflectance sample holder. Place the holder in the reflectance attachment and acquire the spectrum.

GAS PHASE IR SPECTROSCOPY: THE WILLIAMSON GAS PHASE IR CELL

In the past, it was difficult to obtain the IR spectra of gases. A commercial gas cell costs hundreds of dollars; the cell must be evacuated, and the dry gas carefully introduced—not a routine process. But we have found that a uniquely simple gas phase IR cell can be assembled at virtually no cost from a 105° microscale connecting adapter.[2]

To make the Williamson gas phase IR cell, attach a thin piece of polyethylene film from, for example, a sandwich bag to each end of the adapter with a small rubber band, fine wire, or thread. Place a loose wad of cotton in the side arm and mount the IR cell in the beam of the spectrometer (Fig. 11.19 and Fig. 11.20).

The adapter can be supported on a V-block as shown in Figure 11.20 or, temporarily, on a block of modeling clay. Be sure the beam, usually indicated by a red laser, strikes both ends of the cell. Run a background spectrum on the cell. The spectrum of polyethylene (Fig. 11.21) is very simple, so interfering bands will be few. This spectrum is automatically subtracted when you put a sample in the cell and run a spectrum.

FIG. 11.19
The Williamson Gas Phase IR Cell utilizing the 105° connecting adapter from the microscale kit that accompanies this text.

[2]The microscale connecting adapter is a available from Kimble Kontes (catalog no. 748001-1000).

FIG. 11.20
The Williamson Gas Phase IR Cell mounted in a cell holder.

FIG. 11.21
The IR spectrum of polyethylene film.

2926 cm^{-1} 2852 cm^{-1} 1463 cm^{-1} 720 cm^{-1}

Wavenumber (cm^{-1})

A more permanent cell can be constructed by attaching two thin plates of silver chloride to the ends of the adapter with epoxy glue. These silver chloride plates can be made in the press used for making KBr discs, or they can be purchased.[3]

Obtaining a Spectrum

To run a gas phase spectrum, remove the cell from the spectrometer and spray a very short burst of a gas from an aerosol can onto the cotton. The nonvolatile components of the spray will stick to the cotton, and the propellant gas will diffuse into the cell. Run the spectrum in the usual way. The concentration of the gas is about

[3]The silver chloride disks can be purchased from Fisher Scientific (catalog no. 14-385-860).

the same as a thin film of liquid run between salt plates. If the concentration of the gas is too high, remove the cell from the spectrometer, remove the cotton, and "pour out" half the invisible gas by holding the cell in a vertical position.

You may be fortunate in having in your school's library a copy of Volume 3 of *The Aldrich Library of FT-IR Spectra: Vapor Phase* or an online database of IR spectra in your IR instrument data system. Either resource contains hundreds of reference spectra that will help you analyze the IR spectra of propellants in aerosol cans, and any other gases you may encounter. Otherwise, you may want to compare your spectra to the few in this text and available on the web site for this text, and assemble your own library of gas phase spectra. It is possible to make approximate calculations of IR vibrational frequencies using a semi-empirical calculation at the AM1 level (*see* Chapter 15).

Throughout the remainder of this book, representative IR spectra of starting materials and products are presented, and the important bands in each spectrum are identified.

FOR FURTHER INVESTIGATION

The Gas Phase IR Spectra of Aerosol Propellants

Acquire gas phase spectra from a number of substances that come from aerosol cans. Some cans will be labeled with the name of the propellant gas; others will not. Analyze the spectra, bearing in mind that the gas will be a small molecule such as carbon dioxide (Fig. 11.22), methane (Fig. 11.23), nitrous oxide (Fig. 11.24), propane, butane, isobutane, or a fluorocarbon such as 1,1,1,2-tetrafluoroethane. A very old aerosol can may contain an illegal chlorofluorocarbon, now outlawed because these substances destroy the ozone layer. Some examples of aerosol cans include hairsprays, lubricants (WD-40, Teflon), Freeze-It, inhalants for asthma, cigarette lighters, butane torches, and natural gas from the lab.

FIG. 11.22
The IR spectrum of carbon dioxide (gas phase).

FIG. 11.23
The IR spectrum of methane (gas phase).

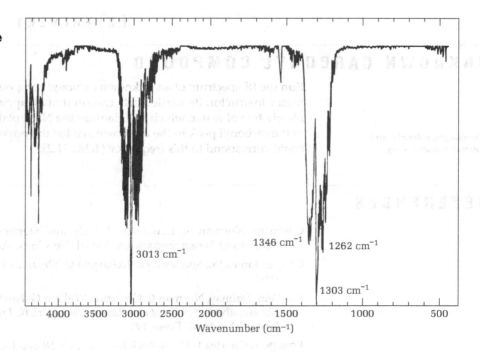

FIG. 11.24
The IR spectrum of nitrous oxide (gas phase).

Other Gas Phase Spectral Research

You can deliberately generate hydrogen chloride (or deuterium chloride) and sulfur dioxide, and then analyze the gas that is evolved from a thionyl chloride reaction. Can you detect carbon monoxide in automobile exhaust? How about marsh gas that you see bubbling out of ponds? With perhaps dozens of scans, can you record the spectra of vanillin being exuded over vanilla beans, eugenol vapor over cloves, anisaldehyde over anise seeds? What is the nature of the volatile components of chili peppers, orange peel, nail polish, and nail polish remover? Could you use this method to determine if someone has been drinking alcohol?

EXPERIMENT

UNKNOWN CARBONYL COMPOUND

The sample, solvents, and apparatus must be dry.

Run the IR spectrum of an unknown carbonyl compound obtained from your laboratory instructor. Be particularly careful that all apparatus and solvents are completely free of water, which will damage the NaCl plates. Determine the frequency of the carbonyl peak in the unknown *and* list the possible types of compounds that could correspond to this frequency (Table 11.2).

REFERENCES

Colthrup, Norman B., Lawrence H. Daly, and Stephen E. Wiberley, *Introduction to Infrared and Raman Spectroscopy*, 3rd ed. New York: Academic Press, 1990.

Cooper, James W., *Spectroscopic Techniques for Organic Chemists*. New York: John Wiley, 1980.

Lin-Vein, Daimay, Norman B. Colthrup, William G. Fateley, and Jeannette G. Grasselli, *The Handbook of Infrared and Raman Characteristic Frequencies of Organic Molecules*. Boston: Academic Press, 1991.

Pouchert, Charles J. *The Aldrich Library of FT-IR Spectra*, 2nd ed. Milwaukee: Aldrich Chemical Co., 1997.

Roeges, Noel P. G, *A Guide to the Complete Interpretation of Infrared Spectra of Organic Structures*. New York: John Wiley, 1994.

Silverstein, Robert M., Francis X. Webster, and David Kiemle, *Spectrometric Identification of Organic Compounds*, 7th ed.[4] New York: Wiley, 2005.

Pretsch, Ernö, Philippe Bühlmann, and Martin Badertscher, *Structure Determination of Organic Compounds: Tables of Spectral Data*, 4th ed. Berlin: Springer, 2009.

[4]This book includes IR, UV, and NMR spectra.

17 CHAPTER

Nucleophilic Substitution Reactions of Alkyl Halides

PRELAB EXERCISE: Predict the outcomes of the two sets of experiments to be carried out with the 11 halides used in this chapter.

The alkyl halides, R—X (where X = Cl, Br, I, and sometimes F), play a central role in organic synthesis. These can easily be prepared from, among others, alcohols, alkenes, and, industrially, alkanes. In turn, they are the starting materials for the synthesis of a large number of new functional groups. The syntheses are often carried out by nucleophilic substitution reactions in which the halide is replaced by another group such as cyano, hydroxyl, ether, ester, alkyl—the list is long. As a consequence of the importance of this substitution reaction, it has been studied carefully by employing reactions such as the two used in this chapter. Some of the questions that can be asked are as follows:

- How does the structure of the alkyl part of the alkyl halide affect the reaction?
- What is the effect of changing the . . .
  nature of the halide?
  nature of the solvent?
  relative concentrations of the reactants?
  temperature of the reaction?
  nature of the nucleophile?

In this chapter, we explore the answers to some of these questions.

In free radical reactions, the covalent bond undergoes homolysis when it breaks:

$$R{:}\ddot{\underset{\cdot\cdot}{C}}l{:} \longrightarrow R{\cdot} + {\cdot}\ddot{\underset{\cdot\cdot}{C}}l{:}$$

318

A carbocation is planar and has an empty *p*-orbital.

Order of carbocation stability

Nucleophilic substitution

One step

Two steps

Reaction kinetics

whereas in ionic reactions, it undergoes heterolysis:

$$R{:}\ddot{C}\ddot{l}{:} \longrightarrow R^+ + {:}\ddot{C}\ddot{l}{:}^-$$

A carbocation is often formed as a reactive intermediate in these reactions. This carbocation is sp^2 hybridized and trigonal-planar in structure with a vacant *p*-orbital. Much experimental evidence of the type obtained in this chapter indicates that the order of stability of carbocations is:

$$\underset{\underset{R}{|}}{\overset{\overset{R}{|}}{R-C^+}} > \underset{\underset{H}{|}}{\overset{\overset{R}{|}}{R-C^+}} > \underset{\underset{H}{|}}{\overset{\overset{H}{|}}{R-C^+}} > \underset{\underset{H}{|}}{\overset{\overset{H}{|}}{H-C^+}}$$

The alkyl (R) groups stabilize the positive charge of the carbocation by displacing or releasing electrons toward the positive charge. As the number of alkyl groups attached to the carbocation increases, the stabilization increases.

Many organic reactions occur when a nucleophile (a species with an unshared pair of electrons) reacts with an alkyl halide to replace the halogen with the nucleophile.

$$Nu{:}^- + R{:}\ddot{X}{:} \longrightarrow Nu{:}R + {:}\ddot{X}{:}^-$$

This substitution reaction can occur in one smooth step:

$$Nu{:}^- + R{:}\ddot{X}{:} \longrightarrow \left[\overset{\delta-}{Nu} \cdots R \cdots \overset{\delta-}{\ddot{X}}{:} \right] \longrightarrow Nu{:}R + {:}\ddot{X}{:}^-$$

or it can occur in two discrete steps:

$$R{:}\ddot{X}{:} \longrightarrow R^+ + {:}\ddot{X}{:}^-$$
$$Nu{:}^- + R^+ \longrightarrow Nu{:}R$$

depending primarily on the structure of the R group. The nucleophile (Nu:⁻) can be a substance with a full negative charge, such as $:\ddot{I}{:}^-$ or $H{:}\ddot{O}{:}^-$, or an uncharged molecule with an unshared pair of electrons such as exists on the oxygen atom in water, $H—\ddot{O}—H$. Not all of the halides, $:\ddot{X}{:}^-$, depart with equal ease in nucleophilic substitution reactions. In this chapter, we investigate the ease with which the different halogens leave in one of the substitution reactions.

To distinguish between the reaction that occurs as one smooth step and the reaction that occurs as two discrete steps, it is necessary to study the kinetics of the reaction. If the reaction were carried out with several different concentrations of $R{:}\ddot{X}{:}^-$ and Nu:⁻, we could determine if the reaction is bimolecular or unimolecular.

In the case of the smooth, one-step reaction, the nucleophile must collide with the alkyl halide. The kinetics of the reaction:

$$Nu:^- + R:\overset{..}{\underset{..}{X}}: \longrightarrow \left[\overset{\delta-}{Nu} \cdots R \cdots \overset{\delta-}{\underset{..}{X}}: \right] \longrightarrow Nu:R + :\overset{..}{\underset{..}{X}}:^-$$

$$Rate = k\left[Nu:^- \right]\left[R:\overset{..}{\underset{..}{X}}: \right]$$

are found to depend on the concentration of both the nucleophile and the halide. Such a reaction is said to be a bimolecular nucleophilic substitution reaction, S_N2. If the reaction occurs as a two-step process,

$$R:\overset{..}{\underset{..}{X}}: \xrightarrow{\text{slow}} R^+ + :\overset{..}{\underset{..}{X}}:^-$$

$$Nu:^- + R^+ \xrightarrow{\text{fast}} Nu:R$$

$$Rate = k\left[R:\overset{..}{\underset{..}{X}}: \right]$$

the rate of the first step, the slow step, depends only on the concentration of the halide, and it is said to be a unimolecular nucleophilic substitution reaction, S_N1.

The S_N1 reaction proceeds through a planar carbocation. Even if the starting material were chiral, the product would be a 50:50 mixture of enantiomers because the planar intermediate can form a bond with the nucleophile on either face.

Racemization: S_N1

Chiral alkyl chloride   Planar carbocation   Enantiomers

Inversion: S_N2   The S_N2 reaction occurs with inversion of configuration to give a product of the opposite chirality from the starting material.

Order of S_N2 reactivity   The order of reactivity for *simple* alkyl halides in the S_N2 reaction is:

$$CH_3-X > R-CH_2-X > R-\underset{\underset{R}{|}}{CH}-X > R-\underset{\underset{R}{|}}{\overset{\overset{R}{|}}{C}}-X$$

Steric hindrance toward S$_N$2

The tertiary halide is in parentheses because it usually does not react by an S$_N$2 mechanism. The primary factor in this order of reactivity is steric hindrance, that is, the ease with which the nucleophile can come within bonding distance of the alkyl halide; 2,2-dimethyl-1-bromopropane, even though it is a primary halide, reacts 100,000 times slower than ethyl bromide (CH$_3$CH$_2$Br) because of steric hindrance that prevents attack on the bromine atom in the dimethyl compound.

$$
\begin{array}{c}
CH_3 \\
| \\
CH_3-C-CH_2-Br \qquad\qquad CH_3CH_2Br \\
| \\
CH_3
\end{array}
$$

Rate = 1   Rate = 100,000

The allyl carbocation

The primary factor in S$_N$1 reactivity is the relative stability of the carbocation that is formed. For simple alkyl halides, this means that only tertiary halides react by this mechanism. The tertiary halide must be able to form a planar carbocation. Only slightly less reactive are the allyl carbocations, which derive their great stability from the delocalization of the charge on the carbon by resonance.

$$CH_2{=}CH{-}CH_2{-}\ddot{B}r\!: \longrightarrow CH_2{=}CH{-}\overset{+}{C}H_2 \longleftrightarrow \overset{+}{C}H_2{-}CH{=}CH_2 + :\ddot{B}r:^-$$

Solvent effects

The nature of the solvent has a large effect on the rates of S$_N$2 reactions. In a solvent with a hydrogen atom attached to an electronegative atom such as oxygen, the protic solvent forms hydrogen bonds to the nucleophile. These solvent molecules get in the way during an S$_N$2 reaction.

$$
\begin{array}{c}
\ddot{O}{-}H \\
| \\
H \\
| \\
H\ddot{O} \\
\ddot{O}{-}H{-}{-}{-}:\ddot{C}l:{-}{-}{-}H{-}\ddot{O} \\
HH \\
| \\
H \\
| \\
\ddot{O} \\
H
\end{array}
$$

Aprotic: no ionizable protons

If the solvent is polar and aprotic, solvation of the nucleophile cannot occur, and the S$_N$2 reaction can occur up to a million times faster. Some common polar, aprotic solvents are N,N-dimethylformamide and dimethylsulfoxide:

$$
\begin{array}{cc}
\begin{array}{c}
CH_3 \qquad O \\
\backslash \quad \quad \parallel \\
N{-}C \\
/ \qquad \backslash \\
CH_3 \qquad H
\end{array}
&
\begin{array}{c}
O \\
\parallel \\
CH_3{-}S{-}CH_3
\end{array}
\end{array}
$$

N,N-Dimethylformamide   **Dimethylsulfoxide**

In the S$_N$1 reaction, a polar protic solvent such as water stabilizes the transition state more than it does the reactants, lowering the energy of activation for the reaction and thus increasing the rate, relative to the rate in a nonpolar solvent. Acetic acid, ethanol, and acetone are relatively nonpolar solvents and have lower dielectric constants than the polar solvents water, dimethylsulfoxide, and N,N-dimethylformamide. The rate of S_N1 and S_N2 reactions depends on the nature of the leaving group, the best leaving groups being the ones that form stable ions. Among the halogens, we find that the iodide ion (I^-) is the best leaving group as well as the best nucleophile in the S_N2 reaction.

The leaving group

Vinylic and aryl halides

do not normally react by S_N1 reactions because the resulting carbocations

are relatively difficult to form. For S_N2 reactions, electrons in the nearby double bonds repel the nucleophile, which is either an ion or a polarized neutral species.

The rates of both S_N1 and S_N2 reactions depend on the temperature of the reaction. As the temperature increases, the kinetic energy of the molecules increases, leading to a greater rate of reaction. The rate of many organic reactions will approximately double when the temperature increases about 10°C. This information is summarized in Table 17.1.

Temperature dependence

TABLE 17.1 *Summary of S_N1 and S_N2 Reactions*

	Unimolecular Nucleophilic Substitution (S_N1)	*Second-Order Nucleophilic Substitution (S_N2)*
Kinetics	First order	Second order
Mechanism	Two steps; unimolecular in the rate-determining step *via* a carbocation	One-step, bimolecular
Stereochemistry	Racemization predominates	Inversion of configuration
Reactivity of structure	3° > 2° > 1° > CH$_3$ > vinyl	3° < 2° < 1° < CH$_3$
Rearrangements	May occur	No rearrangements because no carbocation intermediate
Effect of leaving group	—I > —Br > —Cl >> —F	—I > —Br > —Cl >> —F
Effect of nucleophile	Not important because it is not in the rate-determining step	$I^- > Br^- > Cl^- > F^-$
Concentration of nucleophile	S_N1 is favored by low concentration	S_N2 is favored by high concentration
Solvent polarity	High, favors S_N1	Low, favors S_N2

EXPERIMENTS

In the experiments that follow, 11 representative alkyl halides are treated with sodium iodide in acetone and with an ethanolic solution of silver nitrate.

---

1. SODIUM IODIDE IN ACETONE

Organic halides that can react by an S_N2 mechanism give a precipitate of NaX with sodium iodide in acetone.

Acetone, with a dielectric constant of 21, is a relatively nonpolar solvent that will readily dissolve sodium iodide. The iodide ion is an excellent nucleophile, and the nonpolar solvent (acetone) favors the S_N2 reaction; it does not favor ionization of the alkyl halide. The extent of reaction can be observed because sodium bromide and sodium chloride are not soluble in acetone, and precipitate from solution if a reaction occurs.

$$Na^+I^- + R\!-\!Cl \longrightarrow R\!-\!I + NaCl\downarrow$$

$$Na^+I^- + R\!-\!Br \longrightarrow R\!-\!I + NaBr\downarrow$$

---

2. ETHANOLIC SILVER NITRATE SOLUTION

Organic halides that can react by an S_N1 mechanism give a precipitate of AgX with an ethanolic silver nitrate solution.

When an alkyl halide is treated with an ethanolic solution of silver nitrate, the silver ion coordinates with an electron pair of the halogen. This weakens the carbon-halogen bond because a molecule of insoluble silver halide is formed, thus promoting an S_N1 reaction of the alkyl halide. The solvent, ethanol, favors ionization of the halide, and the nitrate ion is a very poor nucleophile, so alkyl nitrates do not form by an S_N2 reaction.

$$R\!-\!\ddot{X}\!: \underset{}{\overset{Ag^+}{\rightleftharpoons}} \overset{\delta^+}{R} \overset{\ddots}{X} \overset{\delta^+}{Ag} \longrightarrow R^+ + AgX\downarrow$$

On the basis of the foregoing discussion, tertiary halides would be expected to react with silver nitrate most rapidly, and primary halides least rapidly. The R^+ ion can react with the solvent to give either an alkene or an ether.

MICROSCALE PROCEDURE

Label 11 small containers (reaction tubes, 3-mL centrifuge tubes, 10 × 75-mm test tubes, or 1-mL vials), and place 0.1 mL or 100 mg of each of the following halides in the tubes.

$CH_3CH_2CH_2CH_2Cl$

1-Chlorobutane
bp 77–78°C

$CH_3CH_2CH_2CH_2Br$

1-Bromobutane
bp 100–104°C

$$CH_3CH_2\overset{\overset{\displaystyle Cl}{|}}{C}HCH_3$$

2-Chlorobutane
bp 68–70°C

$$CH_3\!-\!\overset{\overset{\displaystyle CH_3}{|}}{\underset{\underset{\displaystyle CH_3}{|}}{C}}\!-\!Cl$$

2-Chloro-2-methylpropane
bp 51–52°C

Br

Bromobenzene
bp 156°C

CH₃CH=CHCH₂Cl

1-Chloro-2-butene mixture
of *cis* and *trans* **isomers**
bp 63.5°C (*cis*)
bp 68°C (*trans*)

CH₃
|
CH₃CHCH₂Cl

1-Chloro-2-methylpropane
bp 68–69°C

Br
|
CH₃CH₂CHCH₃

2-Bromobutane
bp 91°C

CH₃
|
H₃C—C—Br
|
CH₃

2-Bromo-2-methylpropane
bp 71–73°C

Once all of the halides have been placed into labeled tubes or vials, arrange them into the following groupings:

> Group 1: 1-bromobutane, 2-bromobutane, 2-bromo-2-methylpropane, and bromobenzene
>
> Group 2: 1-chlorobutane, 2-chloro-2-methylpropane, 1-chloro-2-butene
>
> Group 3: 1-bromobutane, 2-bromobutane, 1-chlorobutane, 2-chlorobutane

When you perform experiments on these halides, be sure to do them in the order in which they appear in their group lists in order to observe trends and make conclusions about the reactivity of each halide within its respective group.

To each tube of each group, rapidly add 1 mL of an 18% solution of sodium iodide in acetone, stopper each tube, mix the contents thoroughly, and note the time. Note the time of first appearance of any precipitate. If no reaction occurs within about 5 minutes, place those tubes in a 50°C water bath and watch for any reaction over the next 5 or 6 minutes.

Empty the tubes, rinse them with ethanol, place the same amount of each of the alkyl halides in each tube as in the first part of the experiment and organize them by the groupings described above. Add 1 mL of 1% ethanolic silver nitrate solution to each tube, mix the contents well, and note the time of addition as well as the time of appearance of the first traces of any precipitate. If a precipitate does not appear in 5 minutes, heat the tubes containing these unreactive halides in a 50°C water bath for 5 to 6 minutes and watch for any reaction.

To test the effect of solvent on the rate of S$_N$1 reactivity, compare the time needed for a precipitate to appear when 2-chlorobutane is treated with a 1% ethanolic silver nitrate solution, and when treated with 1% silver nitrate in a mixture of 50% ethanol and 50% water.

In your analysis of the results from these experiments, consider the following for both S$_N$1 and S$_N$2 conditions:

• the nature of the leaving group (Cl vs. Br) in the 1-halobutanes

• the effect of structure, that is, compare simple primary, secondary, and tertiary halides, unhindered primary vs. hindered primary halides, a simple tertiary halide vs. a complex tertiary halide, and an allylic halide vs. a tertiary halide

- the effect of solvent polarity on the S_N1 reaction
- the effect of temperature on the reaction

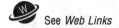
See *Web Links*

Cleaning Up. Because all of the test solutions contain halogenated material, all test solutions and washes as well as unused starting materials should be placed in the halogenated organic waste container.

QUESTIONS

1. What would be the effect of carrying out the sodium iodide in acetone reaction with the alkyl halides using an iodide solution half as concentrated?

2. The addition of sodium or potassium iodide catalyzes many S_N2 reactions of alkyl chlorides or bromides. Explain.

3. In S_N1 reactions, the intermediate carbocations can eliminate a proton to yield alkenes or react with the solvent to yield ethers. Draw the structures of the byproducts of this type that would be derived from the reaction of the carbocation derived from 2-bromo-2-methylbutane in ethanol.

Alkenes from Alcohols: Cyclohexene from Cyclohexanol

OH

H_3PO_4 → + H_2O

Cyclohexanol
mp 25°C, bp 161°C
den. 0.96, MW 100.16

Cyclohexene
bp 83°C
den. 0.81, MW 82.14

The dehydration of cyclohexanol to cyclohexene can be accomplished by pyrolysis of the cyclic secondary alcohol with an acid catalyst at a moderate temperature, or by distillation over alumina or silica gel. The procedure selected for these experiments involves catalysis by phosphoric acid; sulfuric acid is not more efficient, causes charring, and gives rise to sulfur dioxide. When a mixture of cyclohexanol and phosphoric acid is heated in a flask equipped with a fractionating column, the formation of water soon becomes evident. On further heating, the water and the cyclohexene that form distill together by the principle of steam distillation, and any higher-boiling cyclohexanol that may volatilize is returned to the flask. However, after dehydration is complete and the bulk of the product has distilled, the fractionating column remains saturated with a water-cyclohexene mixture that merely refluxes and does not distill. Hence, for the recovery of otherwise lost reaction product, a chaser solvent is added, and distillation is continued. A suitable chaser solvent is the water-immiscible, aromatic solvent toluene (bp 110°C); as it steam distills, it carries over the more volatile cyclohexene. When the total water-insoluble layer is separated, dried, and redistilled through the dried column, the chaser again drives the cyclohexene from the column; the difference in boiling points is such that a sharp separation is possible. The holdup in a metal sponge-packed column is so great (about 1.0 mL) that if a chaser solvent is not used in the procedure to free it from the column, the yield will be much lower.

The mechanism of this reaction involves initial rapid protonation of the hydroxyl group by the phosphoric acid:

This is followed by loss of water to give the unstable secondary carbocation, which quickly loses a proton to water to give the alkene:

EXPERIMENTS

1. THE PREPARATION OF CYCLOHEXENE

IN THIS EXPERIMENT, cyclohexanol undergoes acid-catalyzed dehydration to give cyclohexene. The product is distilled from the reaction flask along with the water generated. Toluene is used as a chaser solvent. The distillate is washed with salt solution, dried, and fractionally distilled.

Handle phosphoric acid with care because it is corrosive to tissue.

Introduce 2.0 g of cyclohexanol followed by 0.5 mL of 85% phosphoric acid and a boiling chip into a 5-mL round-bottomed, long-necked flask. Add a copper sponge to the neck of the flask and shake to mix the layers. Heat will evolve. Use the arrangement for fractional distillation as shown in Figure 19.1. Note that the bulb of the thermometer must be completely below the side arm of the distilling head. Wrap the fractionating column and distilling head with glass wool or cotton. (Refer to the fractional distillation experiments in Chapter 5 for details of this technique.)

Use a black Viton connector.

Heat the mixture gently on a sand bath and then distill until the residue in the flask has a volume of about 0.5 mL to 1.0 mL, and very little distillate is being formed; note the temperature range. Let the assembly cool slightly after removing it from the sand, remove the thermometer briefly, and add 2 mL of toluene (the chaser solvent) into the top of the column using a Pasteur pipette. Note the amount of the upper layer in the boiling flask and distill again until the volume of

Using a chaser solvent

FIG. 19.1
The apparatus for synthesizing cyclohexene from cyclohexanol. The column is packed with a copper sponge.

Vial

30-mL
Beaker

Ice

Copper sponge

Hot sand bath

⚠
Cyclohexene is extremely flammable; keep away from an open flame.

this layer has been reduced by about half. Transfer the contents of the vial into a reaction tube and rinse out the vial with a little toluene. Use toluene for rinsing in subsequent operations. Wash the mixture with an equal volume of saturated sodium chloride solution, remove the aqueous layer, and then add sufficient anhydrous calcium chloride to the reaction tube so that it does not clump together. Shake the solution with the drying agent and let it dry for at least 5 minutes.

While this is taking place, clean the distilling apparatus first with water, then ethanol, and finally a little acetone. It is absolutely essential that the apparatus be completely dry; otherwise, the product will become contaminated with whatever solvent remains in the apparatus. Before starting the distillation, note the barometric pressure and determine the reading expected given that the boiling point is 83°C at 1 atm. Transfer the dry cyclohexene solution to the distilling flask, add a boiling chip, and distill the product. At the moment the temperature starts to rise above the plateau at which the product distills, stop the distillation to avoid contamination of the cyclohexene with toluene. A typical yield of this volatile alkene is about 1 g. Report your yield in grams and your percentage yield. Run an infrared (IR) spectrum and interpret it for purity. Look for peaks due to starting material and toluene. Gas chromatography is especially useful in the analysis of this compound because the expected impurities differ markedly in their boiling points from the product.

Cleaning Up. The aqueous solutions (pot residues and washes) should be diluted with water and neutralized before flushing down the drain. The ethanol wash and sodium chloride solution also can be flushed down the drain, whereas the acetone wash and all toluene-containing solutions should be placed in the organic solvents waste container. Once dried and free of solvent, the calcium chloride can be placed in the nonhazardous solid waste container, if local regulations permit. Otherwise, the wet drying agent should be placed in the designated waste container.

2. THE PREPARATION OF CYCLOHEXENE

Handle phosphoric acid with care because it is corrosive to tissue.

Introduce 20.0 g of cyclohexanol (technical grade), 5 mL of 85% phosphoric acid, and a boiling stone into a 100-mL round-bottomed flask and shake to mix the layers. Note the evolution of heat. Use the typical arrangement for fractional distillation as shown in Figure 5.11 (on page 102), but modified by the use of a bent adapter delivering into an ice-cooled test tube in a 125-mL Erlenmeyer receiver, as shown in Figure 19.2.

FIG. 19.2
Fractionation into an ice-cooled receiver.

Keck clamp

Keck clamp

Water out

Crushed ice

Water in

Note the initial effect of heating the mixture, and then distill until the residue in the flask has a volume of 5-10 mL and very little distillate is being formed; note the temperature range. Then let the assembly cool slightly, remove the thermometer briefly, and pour 20 mL of toluene (the chaser solvent) into the top of the column through a long-stemmed funnel. Note the amount of the upper layer in the boiling flask and distill again until the volume of the layer has been reduced by about half. Pour the contents of the test tube into a small separatory funnel and rinse with a little chaser solvent; use this solvent for rinsing in subsequent operations.

Using a chaser solvent

Wash the mixture with an equal volume of saturated sodium chloride solution, separate the water layer, run the upper layer into a clean flask, and add 5 g of anhydrous calcium chloride (10 × 75-mm test tube-full) to dry it. Before the final distillation, note the barometric pressure, apply any necessary thermometer corrections, and determine the reading expected for a boiling point of 83°C. Dry the boiling flask, column, and condenser; decant the dried liquid into the flask through a stemless funnel plugged with a bit of cotton; and fractionally distill, with all precautions against evaporation losses. The ring of condensate should rise very slowly as it approaches the top of the fractionating column so that the thermometer can record the true boiling point soon after distillation begins. Record both the corrected boiling point of the bulk of the cyclohexene fraction and the temperature range, which should be no more than 2°C. If the cyclohexene has been dried thoroughly, it will be clear and colorless; if wet, it will be cloudy. A typical student yield is 13.2 g. Report your yield in grams and your percent yield.

⚠

Cyclohexene is extremely flammable; keep away from open flame.

Cleaning Up. The aqueous solutions (pot residues and washes) should be diluted with water and neutralized before flushing down the drain with a large excess of water. The ethanol wash and sodium chloride solution can also be flushed down the drain; the acetone wash and all toluene-containing solutions should be placed in the organic solvents waste container. The calcium chloride should be placed in the contaminated drying agents waste container or, if local regulations allow, once free of solvent, the calcium chloride can be placed in the nonhazardous solid waste container.

🌐 For Additional Experiments, sign in at this book's premium website at **www.cengage.com/login.**

QUESTIONS

1. Assign the peaks in the ^1H NMR spectrum of cyclohexene (Fig. 19.3) to specific groups of protons on the molecule.

2. Which product(s) would be obtained by the dehydration of 2-heptanol? of 2-methyl-l-cyclohexanol?

3. Mixing cyclohexanol with phosphoric acid is an exothermic process, whereas the production of cyclohexene is endothermic. Referring to the two chemical reactions on page 335, construct an energy diagram showing the course of this reaction. Label the diagram with the starting alcohol, the oxonium ion (the protonated alcohol), the carbocation, and the product.

4. Is it reasonable that the ^1H spectrum of cyclohexene (Fig. 19.3) should closely resemble the ^{13}C spectrum (Fig. 19.4)? Compare these spectra with the spectrum of cyclohexanol (Fig. 19.5).

FIG. 19.3
The ¹H NMR spectrum of cyclohexene (250 MHz).

FIG. 19.4
The ¹³C NMR spectrum of cyclohexene.

FIG. 19.5
The ¹³C NMR spectrum of cyclohexanol.

MULTIPLES OF ELEMENTS' WEIGHTS

C	12.0112	C_{41}	492.457	H_{31}	31.2471	O_6	95.9964	I	126.904	P	30.9738
C_2	24.0223	C_{42}	504.468	H_{32}	32.2550	O_7	111.996	I_2	253.809	P_2	61.9476
C_3	36.0335	C_{43}	516.479	H_{33}	33.2630	O_8	127.995	I_3	380.713	P_3	92.9214
C_4	48.0446	C_{44}	528.491	H_{34}	34.2710	O_9	143.995			P_4	123.895
C_5	60.0557	C_{45}	540.502	H_{35}	35.2790	O_{10}	159.994	OCH_3	31.0345	P_5	154.869
C_6	72.0669	C_{46}	552.513	H_{36}	36.2869			$(OCH_3)_2$	62.0689	P_6	185.843
C_7	84.0780	C_{47}	564.524	H_{37}	37.2949	N	14.0067	$(OCH_3)_3$	93.1034		
C_8	96.0892	C_{48}	576.535	H_{38}	38.3029	N_2	28.0134	$(OCH_3)_4$	124.138	Na	22.9898
C_9	108.100	C_{49}	588.546	H_{39}	39.3108	N_3	42.0201	$(OCH_3)_5$	155.172	Na_2	45.9796
C_{10}	120.111	C_{50}	600.558	H_{40}	40.3188	N_4	56.0268	$(OCH_3)_6$	186.207	Na_3	68.9694
						N_5	70.0335	$(OCH_3)_7$	217.241		
C_{11}	132.123	H	1.00797	H_{41}	41.3268	N_6	84.0402	$(OCH_3)_8$	248.276	K	39.102
C_{12}	144.134	H_2	2.01594	H_{42}	42.3347			$(OCH_3)_9$	279.31	K_2	78.204
C_{13}	156.145	H_3	3.02391	H_{43}	43.3427	S	32.064	$(OCH_3)_{10}$	310.345	K_3	117.306
C_{14}	168.156	H_4	4.03188	H_{44}	44.3507	S_2	64.128				
C_{15}	180.167	H_5	5.03985	H_{45}	45.3587	S_3	96.192	OC_2H_5	45.0616	Ag	107.868
C_{16}	192.178	H_6	6.04782	H_{46}	46.3666	S_4	128.256	$(OC_2H_5)_2$	90.1231	Ag_2	215.736
C_{17}	204.190	H_7	7.05579	H_{47}	47.3746	S_5	160.320	$(OC_2H_5)_3$	135.185		
C_{18}	216.201	H_8	8.06376	H_{48}	48.3826	S_6	192.384	$(OC_2H_5)_4$	180.246	Cu	63.546
C_{19}	228.212	H_9	9.07173	H_{49}	49.3905			$(OC_2H_5)_5$	225.308	Cu_2	127.092
C_{20}	240.223	H_{10}	10.0797	H_{50}	50.3985			$(OC_2H_5)_6$	270.369	Cr	51.996
						F	18.9984	$(OC_2H_5)_7$	315.431	Hg	200.59
C_{21}	252.234	H_{11}	11.0877	H_{51}	51.4065	F_2	37.9968	$(OC_2H_5)_8$	360.492	Pb	207.19
C_{22}	264.245	H_{12}	12.0956	H_{52}	52.4144	F_3	56.9952			Pt	195.09
C_{23}	276.256	H_{13}	13.1036	H_{53}	53.4224	F_4	75.9936	$OCOCH_3$	59.045	Pt_2	390.18
C_{24}	288.268	H_{14}	14.1116	H_{54}	54.4304	F_5	94.992	$(OCOCH_3)_2$	118.090	Se	78.96
C_{25}	300.279	H_{15}	15.1196	H_{55}	55.4384	F_6	113.99	$(OCOCH_3)_3$	177.135	Th	204.37
C_{26}	312.290	H_{16}	16.1275	H_{56}	56.4463	F_7	132.989	$(OCOCH_3)_4$	236.180		
C_{27}	324.301	H_{17}	17.1355	H_{57}	57.4543	F_8	151.987	$(OCOCH_3)_5$	295.225		
C_{28}	336.312	H_{18}	18.1435	H_{58}	58.4623	F_9	170.986	$(OCOCH_3)_6$	354.270		
C_{29}	348.323	H_{19}	19.1514	H_{59}	59.4702	F_{10}	189.984	$(OCOCH_3)_7$	413.315		
C_{30}	360.334	H_{20}	20.1594	H_{60}	60.4782			$(OCOCH_3)_8$	472.360		
				H_{61}	61.4862	Cl	35.453	$(OCOCH_3)_9$	531.405		
C_{31}	372.346	H_{21}	21.1674	H_{62}	62.4941	Cl_2	70.906	$(OCOCH_3)_{10}$	590.450		
C_{32}	384.357	H_{22}	22.1753	H_{63}	63.5021	Cl_3	106.359				
C_{33}	396.368	H_{23}	23.1833	H_{64}	64.5101	Cl_4	141.812	(H_2O)	9.00767		
C_{34}	408.379	H_{24}	24.1913	H_{65}	65.5181	Cl_5	177.265	H_2O	18.0153		
C_{35}	420.390	H_{25}	25.1993					$(H_2O)_1$	27.0230		
C_{36}	432.401	H_{26}	26.2072	O	15.9994	Br	79.904	$(H_2O)_2$	36.0307		
C_{37}	444.413	H_{27}	27.2152	O_2	31.9988	Br_2	159.808	$(H_2O)_3$	54.0460		
C_{38}	456.424	H_{28}	28.2232	O_3	47.9982	Br_3	239.712	$(H_2O)_4$	72.0614		
C_{39}	468.435	H_{29}	29.2311	O_4	63.9976	Br_4	319.616	$(H_2O)_5$	90.0767		
C_{40}	480.446	H_{30}	30.2391	O_5	79.9970	Br_5	399.52	$(H_2O)_6$	108.092		

BUFFER SOLUTIONS (0.2 M, except as indicated)

pH	Components	pH	Components
0.1	1 M Hydrochloric acid	8.0	11.8 g Boric acid + 9.1 g Borax
1.1	0.1 M Hydrochloric acid		($Na_2B_4O_7 \cdot 10H_2O$) per L
2.2	15.0 g D-Tartaric acid per L (0.1 M solution)	9.0	6.2 g Boric acid + 38.1 g Borax per L
3.9	40.8 g Potassium acid phthalate per L	10.0	6.5 g $NaHCO_3$ + 13.2 g Na_2CO_3 per L
5.0	14.0 g KH-Phthalate + 2.7 g $NaHCO_3$ per L	11.0	11.4 g Na_2HPO_4 + 19.7 g Na_3PO_4 per L
	(heat to expel carbon dioxide, then cool)	12.0	24.6 g Na_3PO_4 per L (0.15 M solution)
6.0	23.2 g KH_2PO_4 + 4.3 g Na_2HPO_4 (anhyd., Merck) per L	13.0	4.1 g Sodium hydroxide pellets per L (0.1 M)
7.0	9.1 g KH_2PO_4 + 18.9 g Na_2HPO_4 per L	14.0	41.3 g Sodium hydroxide pellets per L (1 M)

ATOMIC WEIGHTS

Aluminum	Al	26.9815	Molybdenum	Mo	95.94
Antimony	Sb	121.75	Nickel	Ni	58.71
Arsenic	As	74.9216	Nitrogen	N	14.0067
Barium	Ba	137.34	Osmium	Os	190.2
Beryllium	Be	9.0122	Oxygen	O	15.9994
Bismuth	Bi	208.980	Palladium	Pd	106.4
Boron	B	10.811	Phosphorus	P	30.9738
Bromine	Br	79.904	Platinum	Pt	195.09
Cadmium	Cd	112.40	Potassium	K	39.102
Calcium	Ca	40.08	Praseodymium	Pr	140.907
Carbon	C	12.01115	Rhodium	Rh	102.9055
Cerium	Ce	140.12	Ruthenium	Ru	101.07
Cesium	Cs	132.905	Selenium	Se	78.96
Chlorine	Cl	35.453	Silicon	Si	28.086
Chromium	Cr	51.996	Silver	Ag	107.868
Cobalt	Co	58.9332	Sodium	Na	22.9898
Copper	Cu	63.546	Strontium	Sr	87.62
Europium	Eu	151.96	Sulfur	S	32.064
Fluorine	F	18.9984	Tantalum	Ta	180.948
Gold	Au	196.967	Tellurium	Te	127.60
Hydrogen	H	1.00797	Thallium	Tl	204.37
Iodine	I	126.9044	Thorium	Th	232.038
Iridium	Ir	192.22	Tin	Sn	118.69
Iron	Fe	55.847	Titanium	Ti	47.90
Lead	Pb	207.19	Tungsten	W	183.85
Lithium	Li	6.939	Vanadium	V	50.942
Magnesium	Mg	24.312	Ytterbium	Yb	173.04
Manganese	Mn	54.9380	Zinc	Zn	65.37
Mercury	Hg	200.59	Zirconium	Zr	91.22

ACIDS AND BASES

	Sp. Gr.	% by Wt	Moles per L	Grams per 100 mL
Hydrochloric acid, concd	1.19	37	12.0	44.0
3 *M* (124.3 mL concd. acid diluted to 500 mL)	1.05	10.8	3.0	10.9
Constant boiling (252 mL concd. acid + 200 mL water, bp 110°)	1.10	22.2	6.1	22.2
10% (100 mL concd. acid + 321 mL water)	1.05	10	2.9	10.5
5% (50 mL concd. acid + 380.5 mL water)	1.03	5	1.4	5.2
1 *M* (41.5 mL concd. acid diluted to 500 mL)	1.02	3.6	1	3.6
Hydrobromic acid, constant-boiling (bp 126°)	1.49	47.5	8.8	70.7
Hydriodic acid, constant-boiling (bp 126°)	1.7	57	7.6	97
Sulfuric acid, concd	1.84	96	18	177
1.5 *M* (41.7 mL concd. acid diluted to 500 mL)	1.09	14.1	1.5	14.7
10% (25 mL concd. acid + 398 mL water)	1.07	10	1.1	10.7
0.5 *M* (13.9 mL concd. acid diluted to 500 mL)	1.03	4.7	0.5	4.9
Nitric acid, concd	1.42	71	16	101
Sodium hydroxide, 3 *M* solution	1.12	11	3.0	12.0
10% solution	1:11	10	2.8	11.1
Ammonia solution, concd	0.90	28.4	15	25.6
Acetic acid, glacial	1.05	100.0	17.5	105
Sodium bicarbonate	1.03	4	0.5	4.2
Saturated solution	1.05	8	1	8.3
Sodium chloride, saturated solution	1.20	26	5.3	31.1

Grams of sodium carbonate required to neutralize 1 mL of concd. acid:

0.636 g	1 mL HCl
0.848 g	1 mL HNO_3
1.91 g	1 mL H_2SO_4
0.928 g	1 mL CH_3COOH

CENTIMETER RULER